Reading the *Analects* Today

SUNY series, Translating China

Roger T. Ames and Paul J. D'Ambrosio, editors

Reading the *Analects* Today

LI ZEHOU

Translated by

MAIJA BELL SAMEI

SUNY
PRESS

Cover: *Conversation in a Thatched Hut*, late 1200s. China, Southern Song dynasty. Cleveland Museum of Art. www.clevelandart.org

Published by State University of New York Press, Albany

Printed in the United States of America

This translation is based on the 2015 Zhonghua shuju edition of Li Zehou's *Lunyu jindu* 論語今讀. Translation and publication has been made possible with the permission and support of Deng Liping and the Foundation for Li Zehou Scholarship and Research.

EU GPSR Authorised Representative:
Logos Europe, 9 rue Nicolas Poussin, 17000, La Rochelle, France
contact@logoseurope.eu

For information, contact State University of New York Press, Albany, NY
www.sunypress.edu

Library of Congress Cataloging-in-Publication Data

Names: Li, Zehou, author. | Samei, Maija Bell, 1965– translator.
Title: Reading the *Analects* today / Li Zehou ; translated by Maija Bell Samei.
Description: Albany : State University of New York Press, [2025] | Series: SUNY series, translating China | Includes bibliographical references and index.
Identifiers: LCCN 2024049762 | ISBN 9798855802801 (hardcover : alk. paper) | ISBN 9798855802818 (ebook) | ISBN 9798855802795 (pbk. : alk. paper)
Subjects: LCSH: Confucius. Lun yu. | Philosophy, Confucian.
Classification: LCC PL2471.Z6 L45313 2025 | DDC 181/.112—dc23/eng/20250131
LC record available at https://lccn.loc.gov/2024049762

Contents

Translator's Preface

I will not attempt here a complete scholarly introduction to Li Zehou's *Reading the Analects Today* (論語今讀) or to his stature as a contemporary Chinese philosopher.[1] Since my translation of *The Chinese Aesthetic Tradition* was published in 2010, a number of other major works by Li Zehou have appeared in excellent English translations, introduced by scholars of Chinese thought much better acquainted with Li Zehou's larger work and significance than I. In addition, many more scholarly articles and books have since appeared, including the compendium *Li Zehou and Confucian Philosophy*, edited by Roger Ames and Jinhua Jia (2018), and Jana S. Rosker's *Following His Own Path: Li Zehou and Contemporary Chinese Philosophy* (2019). Michael Nylan has a useful section on Li Zehou (and specifically his *Reading the Analects Today*) in her fine 2014 editor's introduction to Simon Leys's translation of the *Analects*.[2] Instead, in this preface I wish to briefly explain a few aspects of the approach I have taken in translating this work.

First, it is important to note that this is a translation of Li Zehou's own modern translation of the *Analects* of Confucius and his commentary on it, which is particularly directed toward how the *Analects* can be helpful to life in contemporary China, while also addressing premodern, modern, and contemporary philosophical debates about Confucius. **This is not a new scholarly English translation of the *Analects*.** I have not returned to the original manuscripts or commentaries, except in order to understand or annotate Li's own use of them. As such, it should not be considered to compete in any sense with the excellent recent translations by Simon Leys, Roger Ames and Henry Rosemont, or Edward Slingerland, let alone with an elegant classic translation like that of Arthur Waley. In rendering Li's translations, I have attempted to balance faithfulness to his particular renderings with considerations of readability, and in general I have not been able to retain very much of the poetic character of the original classical Chinese. Instead, the translation reflects the vernacular register of Li's modern Chinese translation.

Secondly, Li's original includes the original passages from the *Analects*, his modern Chinese translation, followed by a Notes section drawn from traditional and modern commentaries, and finally his own Comments. For the most part, and with the prior permission of the author, I have not translated the Notes unless they are specifically referred to or commented on in Li Zehou's Comments. This was primarily a practical consideration: translating the Notes would require a deeper familiarity with the traditional commentarial literature than I possess and would have taken a great deal more time. My rationale is that Li Zehou's views on the *Analects* are valuable to the audience of this book for his perspective on the role of Confucius in Chinese thought over the centuries and for his views of the philosopher vis-à-vis Western philosophy and contemporary social realities today. Li Zehou is not primarily known as an expert on the *Analects*. Those who are interested in the reasons for his particular translations of passages are probably well placed to consult those Notes in Li Zehou's original Chinese version. Where translated, the Notes retain the lack of quotation marks in these sections of Li's original.

On a related note, like many important scholarly Chinese works Li's original contains very few complete references or footnotes. For example, Li nowhere notes which edition of the *Analects* he has used as the source for the original text of the *Analects*. I have tried to fill out citations where possible and have provided sources for quotes when I could find them and dates for historical figures, but in general I did not think it necessary or practicable to bring the work completely up to the standard expected of an American scholarly publication. What is important here, again, is to make Li Zehou's opinions and arguments available to an English-speaking audience.

Finally, a brief note about gender-inclusive language. It could be argued that the Chinese character used in modern Chinese for "he," *ta* 他, is actually gender neutral, due to the fact that it bears the "human" radical as opposed to a "male" radical (while the female pronoun "she," *ta* 她, bears a "female" radical). (And indeed, in ancient times *ta* 他 was used to refer to either men or women.) In my English translation I have attempted to use gender-neutral or -inclusive language where possible as appropriate to the context, but in some passages of the translation

I have retained the gendered "he" to reflect the social realities of the times, since the real or hypothetical rulers, ministers, or nobility under discussion (whether by Confucius, his disciples, or Zhu Xi or other commentators) would with very few exceptions all have been male.

I would like to thank Deng Liping and the Foundation for Li Zehou Scholarship and Research for a generous grant underwriting the translation; Yingmiao Liu and Paul Shao for their invaluable assistance with difficult passages; and Jeanne Haizhen Allen for her careful check of the translation. The mistakes that I am certain careful readers will discover are of course my own. My family and friends provided tremendous support and encouragement over six years of work, as well as the quiet and privacy I needed to continue working after the worldwide COVID-19 pandemic struck in 2020.

It is most unfortunate that Li Zehou passed away in 2021 before I was able to complete this translation. I hope he would have been gratified to see his work *Reading the Analects Today* become available to the English-speaking world.

Maija Bell Samei
Chapel Hill, North Carolina, 2024

Author's Prefaces

LI ZEHOU

2014

I first began to draft *Reading the Analects Today* in 1989, and it took the shape of a book in 1994–1996. It was published in 1998 by Hong Kong's Tiandi Tushu Gongsi, then followed editions and reprintings by Yunchen in Taibei, Anhui Wenyi, Tianjin Sheke, Sanlian Shudian, and Jiangsu Wenyi. All of these editions were subtitled "A Preliminary Draft," demonstrating my lack of complete satisfaction with the book and my intention to supplement and revise it. As time passed (now over twenty years), I have had many distractions, while my powers have daily decreased, and although each edition has been revised in a few places, these have been fragmentary and not worth speaking of. I originally intended to undertake a major revision using works like *Kongzi jiyu* and *Kongzi jiayu*, along with the unearthed bamboo and silk manuscripts, and all the various studies, translations, and annotations of the *Analects* that have appeared in recent years (especially the translations), but this has proved difficult and in the end came to nothing. Therefore, for this edition I have eliminated the words "preliminary draft" from the title, for even though I might sigh over this for a lifetime, there is nothing I can do about it.

For this new edition I have added two appendices. For one I have made use of a good part of the *Index to the Analects* by Yao Junzhou 幺峻洲, published by Qilu Shushe in 2005. This index is very useful and convenient for finding the location of any passage of the *Analects*, and I hope it will be of use to readers and scholars.[1] The second is an essay I published in 1980 entitled "A New Evaluation of Confucius."[2] Thirty-five years later, this old work still appears to be worth reading, and I include it here in order not to forget the obstacles, difficulties, twists, and turns that I met with in trying to publish it at the time. Furthermore, it relates to the origins of this book, and how I was attempting to reaffirm tradition at the height of anti-traditionalism, rather than simply joining today's fashion for "Confucian religion" and "national learning" (*guoxue* 國學).

In addition, this new edition adds quite a number of bolded sections, as an aid to people's attention as they read it in this busy and fast-paced era. As a means of advertising, could this be useful? It is impossible to know.

The years of my life draw to a close, and I am already in my twilight years. I do not have a lot of time left, and must overcome my fears. As such, I turn to the words of the sages to see if there are things to learn for the sake of self-cultivation and improving my own writing [so that] I may have no cause for shame before Heaven or Earth.

Boulder, Colorado, Winter 2014

2018

Since this book was published in 1998, there have been numerous editions and printings, in each of which there have been small corrections and additions, and this time is no exception. In each case there may have been several tens of such corrections, which although they are scattered, could not be left unaddressed. Therefore when citing or reading the book, please regard this new edition as the standard.

June 2018

Introduction

Why This Book?

In the afterword to my *A History of Classical Chinese Thought* (中國古代思想史論 *Zhongguo gudai sixiang shi lun*), I noted that "in this book I have discussed many Confucian[1] thinkers, while actually my interests may tend to lie more in the direction of Daoism, neo-Daoism, and Chan Buddhism. This book is but an outline; I would very much like to do a detailed analysis of some of the questions raised here, such as the development of Song-Ming Neo-Confucianism."[2] Ten years later, these two interests remain to be pursued, and it is doubtful whether I will have time to do so in this life. Time speeds by, I have accomplished little, and now find myself in the sunset of my years. Yet I do have some time remaining. Why then would I not choose one of these more interesting tasks, and instead choose to translate and create a commentary on the *Analects*, which has already been translated, annotated, and commented upon by countless others? Am I not just frying up a pan full of stale rice? Perhaps it would be best first to answer this question, both to myself and to my concerned readers. Thus I begin by asking, "Why this book?"

I first set out to begin this book in the autumn of 1989, and worked on it off and on until I finally completed it in the spring of 1994. This was by no means a work undertaken on a whim, at the spur of the moment, nor was the work an excuse to hide myself from certain objective circumstances. Quite the opposite. Even though the *Analects* is far from my favorite book, it is where we find the very "heart and soul" of Chinese culture. Today I believe that Confucianism (by which I mean primarily the teachings of Confucius in the *Analects*) was an irreplaceable and unmatched player in shaping the Han people's "cultural-psychological formation" (*wenhua xinli jiegou* 文化心理結構). Confucianism was the entrance requirement and required curriculum for any who wished to serve at court or sought public office under the dynasties that spanned the two thousand years from the Han to the Qing, so that it became the basis and foundation for the thought and action of scholar-officials and intellectuals. Furthermore, by way of these scholar-officials and intellectuals at all levels, along with the texts they compiled and edited—from the early *Classic of Filial Piety* (孝經) and the primer *Jijiupian* 急就篇 (a few of its passages), through the *Three Character Classic* (三字經), the *Thousand Character Classic* (千字文), and the Ming dynasty primer *Zeng guang xian wen* 增廣賢文; along with all kinds of ledgers of merits and demerits and such, including of course the rules and regulations found in the various "family regulations," "clan lessons," "village requirements," "village norms," and so on—by way of these, Confucianism (meaning, again, Confucius and the teachings of the *Analects*) became the guiding norm for the speech, actions, and ideology of the entire society in both public and private life. Whether among the literate or illiterate, the emperor and his officials or ordinary commoners, consciously or unconsciously the logic, principles, teachings, and thought promulgated and passed on in the *Analects* over many generations has indelibly penetrated Chinese political and religious systems, social customs, and psychological habits, and has influenced people's thought, speech, and behavior for over two thousand years. Confucianism does not represent only elite culture or the Great Tradition, but is also closely tied to popular culture and the lesser tradition. It has created a very important characteristic of Chinese tradition, namely, that elite and popular culture, the Great Tradition and lesser traditions, interpenetrate and interrelate with one another. Though there is a difference between them, or even an opposition, this never widens into a gulf. In this respect, Confucianism and the *Analects* play a role similar to that of the Bible in Western Christianity.

China does not have a religion like Christianity or Islam. Many intellectuals and scholar-officials, if they have to choose between belief and disbelief in an anthropomorphic god, would tend to choose Confucius's attitude of "respecting the gods and spirits while keeping at a distance from them" (*Analects* 6.22), or "when sacrificing to the gods, it seems as if they are present" (3.12). Among the common people, a kind of pluralistic and superficial faith and worship has been expressed. Its object, whether Lord Guan, Mazu, Guanyin, the Jade Emperor, and so on, not only varies according to individual and geographic location, but also changes constantly. Most of these religious practices are oriented toward obtaining good luck and avoiding misfortune, fending off disaster and healing diseases. They have a very worldly focus. The important thing to note is that even in these pluralistic and superficial popular religious practices, there is little emphasis on miracles or preaching. Most of them are oriented toward teaching the Confucian order of relationships and moral concepts.

I remember once taking a taxi in Taipei. The taxi driver was very eagerly sharing with me his faith in Buddha and expressly showed me the Buddhist scripture he studied. I read over it carefully and found that the great majority of its contents were Confucian family principles, like filiality toward parents, affection between brothers, caring for extended family, living in harmony with one's neighbors, uprightness, loyalty, sincerity, and so on. There was little truly Buddhist content. On another occasion in Taiwan, I had the occasion to meet the extremely influential Buddhist teacher Cheng Yen (證嚴法師). She is known for advocating that terminally ill people die at home among family, instead of in the hospital in the hands of strangers and surrounded by doctors and nurses. I found this surprising, since what this demonstrates seems so clearly to be a family-centered, intensely Confucian notion of human relations, while Buddhism is supposedly based upon a disillusionment with and lack of recognition of the relationships of the "dusty world." This reminded me that although throughout Chinese history there has been intense struggle between the three major schools of thought (Confucianism, Buddhism, and Daoism), even leading to the persecutions of Buddhism known as the Three Disasters of Wu during the Six Dynasties and Tang periods, in actual fact such occurrences were rare. To the contrary, the view that the "Three Faiths are One" always represented the cultural mainstream. The three great sages, Confucius, Laozi, and Sakyamuni, have co-existed peacefully and carried on friendly relations, as can be seen equally in the paintings of Song dynasty literati from close to a thousand years ago and in the temples of popular worship in China today. The fact that China has never seen true religious war is an anomaly on the stage of world cultural history. I believe the reason for this lies largely with the inclusivity of Confucianism. Confucianism does not emphasize the miraculous or mysterious, nor does it promulgate a religious faith. In the context of "Three Faiths are One," Confucianism has seamlessly entered the other faiths and transformed itself into their key content and essential components. The reason it has been able to do so is that Confucianism itself originally and fundamentally was far more than aphorisms governing how to conduct oneself in society or ordinary common sense; rather, it had the religious character of addressing "ultimate concerns." It is firmly situated within the quest for the meaning of human life, and encompasses an understanding of, quest for, and realization of the "realm of heaven and earth" that transcends morality and ethics. For this reason, this quality and function of Confucianism can become the basis for people's (individual) life and pursuits as well as their spiritual conversion. It is a quasi-religion that has no anthropomorphic deity, nor any interest in spirits or miracles.

At the same time, Confucianism is quasi-philosophy. It has no emphasis on systematic thought or logical construction. Confucius rarely engaged in abstract thought or "pure" ethics. When he spoke of "humaneness" (*ren* 仁) or "ritual" (*li* 禮), he was extremely concrete. In the *Analects*, **one rarely finds questions about "what is," but rather questions (and especially Confucius's answers to questions) about "how to." And yet in these very practical answers and teachings there is deep rational thought.** They constitute the pursuit, exposition, and discovery of reason and rational categories. For example, the statement "If you would be at ease, then do so" (*Analects* 17.21) is a demonstration of adherence to ethical behavior and traditional ritual systems. "Time and the seasons are just like this! They keep flowing on, day and night" (*Analects* 9.17) is a grasping for or pursuit of the meaning of human life. And "If I am not to be with people, then with whom shall I be?" (*Analects* 18.6) is a firm affirmation of human subjectivity.[3] None of these statements contain anything like Plato's pursuit of the ideal or Hegelian logical constructs, and yet they are still just as characterized by philosophic rationality, while also being full of poetic emotional content. They are the Chinese philosophy of pragmatic reason.

It is precisely because Confucius relies on rationality and philosophy rather than on miracles or faith to persuade and teach people that Confucius is not to be compared with Jesus, nor the *Analects* to the Bible. Similarly, Confucius is no Plato, nor the *Analects* Plato's *Republic*; the *Analects* is not speculative, but rather seeks to be applicable to, and indeed is already firmly grounded in, the broadest direct application to real human life.

I believe that these non-religious, non-philosophical, or perhaps quasi-religious and quasi-philosophical characteristics of Confucius and the *Analects* are really their key and should be the starting point of their study. However, in current Chinese scholarly circles there are few who emphasize or pay adequate attention to this point. Because Confucius cannot command wind and rain or rise from the dead, and makes himself neither Lord nor the son of God, the vast majority of scholars emphasize only his significance as a thinker or philosopher. Although Mou Zongsan (牟宗三 1909–1995) emphasized Confucianism's religious character, because he ignored the real-life effects that religion should exert and its popular manifestations, he turns the religious character of Confucianism into pure scholarly theory, abstruse mystical argument, and high-minded sermonizing, all of which are difficult for the common person to understand and completely divorced from the life of the common people and real society. This completely misses the character and function of the religious quality of Confucianism. In his philosophy, Mou Zongsan spoke of "transcendence and immanence," forcing the Western notion of two worlds (this and the hereafter) to fit over the "this-worldly" Chinese tradition, at great loss to the fundamental meaning of Confucianism, so that in the end his view was not very different from the arguments of those who regard Confucianism as pure philosophy.[4] Thus it is that for the past century, Confucius and the *Analects* have become a plaything among experts in the history of philosophy. Ordering, grouping, analyzing, and unifying its concepts, categories, and arguments to produce one volume after another of major or minor works, whether laudatory, critical, or "critically carrying on the legacy"—this has passed for an adequate treatment of Confucius, Confucianism, and the *Analects*.

I have some doubts about the adequacy of this approach. I believe there is an entirely different task to be undertaken regarding Confucianism and the *Analects*, namely, the task of first deconstructing then reconstructing this "quasi-religious, quasi-philosophical" cultural spirit.

The first step is deconstruction. There are two aspects of this deconstruction: first, the actual (religious) aspect, and secondly, the theoretical (philosophical) aspect. Of course, these two aspects are woven together in a very complex manner.

For example, the Han Confucians, represented by Dong Zhongshu (董仲舒 179–104 BC), constructed an elaborate universal cosmology, encompassing religion, ethics, and politics, out of yin and yang, the Five Elements, and the mutual resonance or responsiveness between Heaven and humanity. This was philosophy, but not *just* philosophy; religion, but not *just* religion. It lacked a living and active, omnipresent and anthropomorphic god that continually intervenes in human affairs. But the mutual resonance between Heaven and humanity, yinyang and

Five Elements theory, did constitute a conceptual system and pattern of consciousness that governed, controlled, and ordered the entire politico-religious system, from "modeling the official system after Heaven" (*guan zhi xiang tian* 官制象天)[5] to medicine and divination. Its legacy continues to influence people's activities and psyche to this day.

For another example, consider how Song Neo-Confucianism as represented by Zhu Xi (朱熹 1130–1200) constructed an ontology centered on the heart-mind and nature and having "Heavenly Principle and human desire" (*tian li ren yu* 天理人欲) at its core. This is of course philosophy, but again, not *just* philosophy. It denies any anthropomorphic deity, yes, but itself constituted later traditional society's incontrovertible pattern of consciousness and legal order, manifest as a moral law that united religion, ethics, and government. Again, this system governed, controlled, and ordered the limits of human behavior, and conceptual thought, and still does even today. This is why Song Neo-Confucianism was always the object of "anti-feudal" attacks in the modern period.

These systems, Qin-Han Confucianism with its framework based on yinyang and Five Elements theory and Song Neo-Confucianism with its framework centering on the heart-mind and nature as substance, are the two major developments in Confucianism after Confucius, Mencius, and Xunzi. They constitute the second and third periods of development of Confucianism. Their religious and philosophical influence continues to be felt to this day and is worth exploring further.

Because of the complete melding and interconnectedness of the religious and philosophical qualities of Confucianism, it does not rely upon the activity of an anthropomorphic god to govern people's spiritual or physical actions, but rather does so through a pattern of consciousness and a governmental/religious system constructed on the basis of the ethical (human) = natural (Heavenly) order. One of the characteristics of this system is the melding together of religious and social morality to create a Chinese-style "unity of church and state," which is then elevated as a faith to the level of a cosmological (yinyang and Five Elements) or ontological (theory of mind-nature) philosophy. By "church" or "religion" here I mean both the cultural teaching and education of humankind and its religious faith. For this reason, the first task of our deconstruction should be to separate the ethics and morality of individual inner faith, cultivation, and emotion that make up the individual (private religious morality) from that of external social behaviors, regulations, and systems (public social morality). We must deconstruct the ethical and political mishmash of "From the Son of Heaven to ordinary people, all, without exception, should regard cultivating the person as the root,"[6] and "If your own conduct is correct, you will be able to accomplish things without giving any orders; if your conduct is not correct, you may give orders but no one will obey them" (*Analects* 13.6). Emotions and faith, rational thought, the establishment of systems, and so on—each of these has its own level, position, and significance. In order to assign and clearly stipulate the position of each, we must start from the original Confucianism (of the earliest period), to see how each of the teachings of Confucians, starting with Confucius himself, apply to and have value for which of these aspects. This may go a long way toward understanding and dispelling the "unity of church and state" or "state religion" of traditional and present-day China.

For example, this deconstruction would point out the roots of early Confucianism in shamanism and ritual, and how in this prehistoric ritual context, the religious and socio-political expectations of the clan leader's character and personality would have intermingled. This early thought system is characterized by the unity and intermixing of the language of moralistic dictates, religion, government, and ethics. As I argued above, this system encompasses two distinct elements, religious morality and social morality. The former (religious morality) developed from Confucius and Mencius through the Song into the quasi-religious pursuits within the individual that constitute the mutual complementarity of Confucianism and Daoism (and to a lesser extent Buddhism) that Neo-Confucians so strongly advocated and delighted in elaborating upon. The latter (social morality) developed from Confucius and Xunzi, incorporating strands of Daoism, Legalism, and yinyang theory into the full set of Confucian-Legalist ethico-political rules and principles that dominated Chinese history for two thousand years. The former deals with "inner sageliness," the latter with "outer kingship." Both aspects are of crucial importance. The two, on the one hand, go their separate ways, while on the other hand they are constantly in a state of mutual entanglement. Especially in Song-Ming Neo-Confucianism and in modern-day revolutionary ethics, social morality and public administration is placed in parallel with and drawn into religious morality and ideals of human personality, and subordinated to them. This is the reason for the endless stream of tragedies resulting from "killing people with principle (*li* 理)" or "killing people with revolution," and for the great number of hypocrites and "old Marxist grandmas"[7] we have seen.

Today, it is high time we separated out these two elements or aspects, these two types of morality, within Confucianism, in order to the best of our abilities to disentangle this religio-politico-ethical trinity that could be characterized by Li Yu's lines "Cut, it doesn't break, / Tidied, a mess again" (剪不斷, 理還亂).[8] Only in this way will we be able to begin to discuss Confucianism's "critical legacy" or its "transformative creation" (*zhuanhua xing de chuang zao* 轉化性的創造) on any number of levels. **Religious morality ("inner sageliness") might undergo a process of transformative creation to become the individual pursuit of meaning and the human realm, whether in the form of religion, philosophy, poetry, or the arts. Social morality ("outer kingship") might undergo such a transformative creation to become a Chinese form of the modern governmental system: melding the characteristic relational harmoniousness, communal relationships, social ideals, integration of emotion and reason, emotionalized education, and the preference for mediation in conflict-solving into the structures of modern democratic governmental systems, in order to open up a creative path for the future.**

In sum, we must tease out, clarify, and bring to consciousness Confucianism as "church" (religion). Confucianism as "school" (philosophy) must also be liberated from the various systematizations of "yinyang and Five Elements theory," theories of human nature and the mandate of Heaven (*xingli tianming* 性理天命), and "moralistic metaphysics," and returned to the truly vibrant, concrete, and human appeal of the original Confucianism of the *Analects*. This is what I call "emotion-as-substance" *qing benti* 情本體 (see below).

Secondly, having deconstructed, should we rebuild? Of course, as for the religious aspect it is not necessary to imitate Christianity or Islam by trying to create an anthropomorphic deity. But might it be possible to consider returning to the loose, elastic Confucian "religious" tradition of "Heaven and Earth, country, parents, and teacher" 天地國親師, which does not have an anthropomorphic deity? The inclusivity and openness of this "religion" means that it occupies a broad, free interpretive space. Xunzi remarked that "the noble person regards it as culture, the common people call it the gods."[9] In the formulation, "Heaven and Earth, country, parents, and teacher," none of these is a "god," though all are worthy of reverence, worship, and self-sacrifice. To the common people, this tradition may accommodate the worship of an anthropomorphic deity (God, Buddha, or any number of folk religious figures); but for the "noble person" (the cultivated person), it might be a spiritual solace, a guide for behavior, and source of belonging. The important thing is that "Heaven and Earth, country, parents, and teacher" cannot be revived or restored, but must be deconstructed and built anew. For example, it must be rescued from the traditional governing system (i.e., "the unity of church and state") and from any government system or fantasy that relied on a "good Emperor" or the "unity of ruler and teacher." It is precisely here that we must emphasize the importance of exchanging "ruler" for "country," and that this "country" no longer connotes a particular government or governmental/administrative system, but rather refers more inclusively and broadly to a sort of psychological identification of the unity of history and culture. It is country, not state or government. Thus it is that **"Heaven and Earth, country, parents, and teacher" can take on a sort of moral and supermoral emotional identification and become a spiritual home for Chinese people that encompasses their views of nature, the universe, home and native land; the relationships of children and parents, husband and wife, siblings, friends, classmates, teachers, and elders; as well as the cultural tradition as a whole.** It no longer bears any political character or any function for social morality, but rather has quasi-religious content and function.

The notion of "Heaven and Earth, country, parents, and teacher," can be directly traced back to Xunzi, but its basic spirit is of course from the *Analects*. **As Cheng Yi 程頤 (1033–1107) remarked regarding this quasi-religious character of the *Analects*, "As for reading the *Analects*, if one is a certain type of person before reading it, and then remains that type of person after reading it, it is as though one has never read it." In other words, reading the *Analects* should have a "transformative quality," rather than simply being a matter of accruing knowledge.** When Qian Mu 錢穆 (1895–1990) emphasized that reading the *Analects* is a matter of learning to act rightly (literally, how to "be human" [*zuo ren* 做人]), he was squarely within this tradition. All of these statements emphasizing the religious function of Confucianism can become good material with which to rebuild Confucianism's religious quality today. Hegel once derided the *Analects* of Confucius as nothing more than "maxims on how to conduct oneself in society," and this is not far from the truth. However, **these maxims have to do with recognizing the value of humans as ontological beings.** With this recognition, although "mountains are still mountains, rivers still rivers," one's conduct in society will be vastly different. Therefore, these "maxims" are far from having to do with individual gain or loss, but instead become quasi-religious teachings and realizations. It is therefore possible that if we were today to make a selection from the *Analects*, the "Caigentan,"[10] the "Three Character Classic," and so on, and importantly add new interpretation and development, such a text could have a similar function to the Bible, the Buddhist scriptures, or other religious texts in helping to mediate relationships, stabilize society, and aid in personal mental and physical health. Is this not possible? Of course, we cannot do so, nor would it be possible to return to the kind of pedantic and hypocritical self-cultivation that characterized traditional tabulations of "merits and demerits" (*gong guo ge* 功過格), but might there be room for new creative forms? Of course, we should be careful to distinguish such an effort from recent preposterous, chaotic, and vulgar movements like the late Qing "National Essence" 國粹主義 movement and the present-day so-called national studies fever (*guoxue re* 國學熱).

As far as "studies" go, it is probably unnecessary to attempt to rebuild any philosophical systems based on *qi*, reason (*li* 理), or theory of mind-nature (心性 *xinxing*) as substance. The "emotion-as-substance" can adequately stand in for all of these. This is so because the "emotion-as-substance" is precisely non-substantive; the substance, after all, exists between real emotion and emotional reality. It adheres to understanding, recognizing, and realizing true, immediate, and artistically expressed emotions and the "interrelationship between Heaven and humans." It is completely uninterested in establishing or constructing any sort of transcendence in order to control people. What it envisions is simply the possibility of and necessity for the mental and physical health, full development, and self-determination of ordinary people. Because the philosophical aspects of Confucianism are discussed so widely today, I will not waste words on them here (please see my "Zhexue tanxun lu"[11]). All of this is a simple statement of the reasons for undertaking this new "reading" of the *Analects*. I will elaborate on them as appropriate in my Comments sections below.

On the "Translation"[12]

People find it quite surprising that the words of Confucius from 500 BC, meaning the words that were spoken at that time and later put down in writing, are not very difficult for people today to read and understand. This can be said to be a miracle among world cultures. It would be impossible for the vast majority of English speakers to understand English from the eleventh century. This is the main reason why I have always strongly opposed any reform involving romanizing or latinizing Chinese characters. In addition to training Chinese people's intelligence (memory, understanding, and thought), on top of unifying multiple dialects and creating a strong, lasting economic and political entity, and unifying immigrant ethnic groups and especially creating the psychological construct of Chinese culture, Chinese characters have had an immeasurably large effect. Traditionally it was said that when "Cangjie 倉頡 created characters," he made "heaven rain millet, and the ghosts cry at night."[13] It is also usual for the common people in China to "cherish paper bearing written words," and to paste posters with writing on the walls and doorposts. All these demonstrate that Chinese characters occupy a mystical and even sacred position. It is a shame that more research into this aspect has not been done. It is apparent that *Chinese characters originated in the recording of events, as opposed to the recording of speech*, which begs the question of the relationship between these two. But this is a question that falls outside of the scope of this book, and I will leave it aside to discuss at some later point.

If the *Analects* is so easy to understand, why should one need to create a "translation" of it? Furthermore, there are already many such translations in existence; why would it be important to create yet another one? The reason is that although the text is easy to understand, in actual fact it is still a several-thousand-year-old text, and in many places is not very easy for the young people of today or tomorrow to understand in the context of their rapidly changing lives. In addition, classical Chinese is both succinct and ambiguous and must be rephrased or pinned down clearly in the language of today before its meaning can be grasped. Of course, in the process, quite a bit will be lost. For it is precisely the concision and ambiguity of the original text's words and phrases that has allowed it frequently to carry so many meanings. Fortunately, the *Analects* is not written in poetry, and sometimes we may be able to approach or accomplish a definitive explanation of its archaic language. It is true that many translations of the *Analects* exist. The reason for making another one is that each translator brings his or her own understanding to the original text or the book as a whole, and therefore each of the translations is quite different. I have carefully gone over the two most recent translations that I know of, Yang Bojun's *Lunyu yizhu* 論語譯注 [*An Annotated Translation of the "Analects"*] (Beijing) and Qian Mu's

Lunyu xinjie 論語新解 [*A New Explanation of the "Analects"*] (Taipei), and neither of them was entirely to my satisfaction. Therefore I set out to create this new translation and added my own critical commentary.

Although, as I said, the *Analects* can readily be read and understood today, when one tries to translate it, there are many difficulties and problems. Notable among them are the important words, concepts, and categories that occur so frequently in the text, and for which it is so difficult to find good translations. Some, indeed, are untranslatable. These include *junzi* 君子 (noble person), *xiaoren* 小人 (petty person), *ren* 仁 (humaneness), *yi* 義 (justice), *dao* 道 (Way), *jing* 敬 (reverence), *zhuang* 莊 (solemnity), and so on, and so on, none of which has a precise equivalent in contemporary language. One reason for this is that they occur in different contexts in the original text, in each of which they may have similar but not entirely identical content, connotation, and meaning, so that it is not always possible to use the same modern Chinese word to translate each instance.

What then shall we do? The more I thought about this problem, the more I recognized that there was really nothing to be done. We can only, first, attempt in this introduction to give some explanation for this situation so that the reader will be psychologically prepared to encounter these terms. And secondly, we can provide the following concrete explanations.[14]

1. The noble person (*junzi* 君子) and petty person (*xiaoren* 小人)

The terms *junzi* ("noble person") and *xiaoren* ("petty person") have been retained [in the modern Chinese translation]. This is because (1) these words are still used in the present day and are very familiar to readers and (2) they carry different connotations in different passages and sentences. *Junzi* and *xiaoren* are usually used to express judgments about high or low moral standards. They are value judgments: for example, *xiaoren* has a pejorative connotation, and still does to this day. But in Confucius's time or earlier, this may not have been the case. For example, there is a passage in the *Shangshu* 尚書 (*Book of Documents*) that reads, "If one knows the difficulties of farming, then one can know what the *xiaoren* depends upon."[15] In this context, *xiaoren* refers to a commoner or peasant and carries no negative moral judgment. Yu Yue 俞樾 (1821–1907) in his *Qun jing ping yi* 群經平議 (*The Plain Meaning of the Classics*) notes, "When the ancient texts speak of the *junzi* and the *xiaoren*, they are for the most part speaking about the respective position of each, and the Han commentators used the terms this way; later Confucians used the terms specifically to mean a person's character or quality, but this was not the ancient meaning." Clearly, *junzi* originally referred to a person of position, that is, to the *shi* 士 ("intellectual") and the *dafu* 大夫 (a scholar who has served as an official). *Xiaoren*, on the other hand, referred to a commoner or peasant. In the *Analects*, we find such formulations as "like little pebbles thumping around, or like the most ordinary of people" 硜硜然小人哉 (*Analects* 13.20) in a passage on the moral standards of the *shi* ("intellectual"). Thus it is also possible that at the time these were both neutral terms describing social position. But the *Analects* frequently addressed the moral standards and expectations of the *shidaifu* ("scholar-officials"), while placing the *junzi* and the *xiaoren* in opposition, with the *junzi* standing for the person of high moral character and the *xiaoren* standing for a person who lacks these moral qualities. In this way, the terms came to take on positive and negative connotations. These two levels of meaning (the real social position and the value judgment) are frequently joined in the *Analects* in such a way as to be difficult to separate. Globally speaking, the value-based connotation applies to a much greater proportion of uses of the term, but not to all. One must look carefully at the specific circumstance or question, the specific object of the terms. For this reason these two are not translated [into modern Chinese].[16]

Somewhat similar but less prominent is the term *shi* 士 ("intellectual") and related terms. *Shi* may sometimes indicate a concrete social status, and sometimes a value judgment (the norms or standards of the *shi*). I have translated *shi* [into modern Chinese] as "intellectual," and *dafu* 大夫 as "official," that is, an intellectual who has been given an official post.

2. Other Important Terms

The most important and most commonly occurring term in the *Analects*, and at the same time the most difficult to translate, is *ren* 仁 ("humaneness").[17] I have usually translated this term [into modern Chinese] as "kindhearted," "benevolent" or "humane." This is because my reading of the *Analects* emphasizes the psychological emotion-as-substance (*qinggan benti* 情感本體), and the term *ren* in the *Analects* also carries precisely this level of basic meaning. Zhu Xi explained *ren* as "the principle of love, the morality or virtue of the heart-mind" (*ai zhi li, xin zhi de* 愛之理, 心之德). Its basic meaning is very close to "love." This should not present any difficulties.

Li 禮 I have translated as "ritual system," because it for the most part indicates the whole set of unwritten systematized norms of ritual behavior.

Yi 義 has generally been translated as "just," "reasonable," "appropriate," or "obligatory" (required by duty).

Dao 道 has a very broad and vague meaning. In general, it can be judged based on the context to mean "principles," "rules," "path," "truth," "direction," "vocation," and so on. "Having the *dao*" 有道 has been rendered "clean government."

Tianxia 天下 ("all under heaven," i.e., the world) I have allowed to stand, as it continues in use in modern Chinese.

Wen 文 I have translated as ceremony, rite, or literary grace, as appropriate.

Jing 敬 is rendered as "respect" (*gongjing* 恭敬), reverence (*jingwei* 敬畏), earnestness or conscientiousness (*renzhen* 認真), and so on.

The formulation X 君 or X 公 is always rendered "the ruler of the state of X." *Bang* 邦 is rendered "state," although it actually referred to a clan or tribal alliance, which is why *bang* often occurs in connection with *jia* 家 ("home"). The families of those who served as officials under the ruler are thus rendered as either "clan" or "tribe," without making any particular distinction, so that the *san jia* 三家 of Lu are the three great clans (or the three great tribes) of the state of Lu.

3. Other Notes on the Translation

The stock opening phrase, 子曰 *zi yue* ("The Master said") is always rendered "Confucius said." I have used a single name for every reference to one of Confucius's disciples, eschewing the nicknames and variants by which they are called in various parts of the text. The honorific 子 *zi* (meaning "Master") has been retained for Zengzi 曾子 and Youzi 有子, since the text largely took shape in the hands of their disciples. I have not used Confucius's given name, Kong Qiu 孔丘, seeing no need to change the several-thousand-year-old custom of referring to him as Kongzi (meaning "Master Kong" 孔子), which is latinized as Confucius. The formulation *wen ren* 問仁 is always rendered "he asked what humaneness is," while *wen zheng* 問政 is always rendered "he asked how to govern (do government)."

In general, I have avoided adding words or phrases to the translation that are not present in the original, like specifying the king of "a certain country," or "Confucius's students," and so on. When such additions are absolutely necessary, I have relegated them to the Notes and Comments sections. This is a translation, not an interpretive translation or paraphrase. Although the translation may of necessity involve interpretation, I have tried to avoid adding explanatory language into the text of the translation proper, in order to preserve as much as possible of the character of the original text. Furthermore, this book does not emphasize the particular historical content of the text passages. Although the sayings all speak into a particular historical backdrop of circumstances and human affairs, and comment on particular historical subjects, some of these might be uncovered through research, but for the most part they cannot be ascertained with any certainty, as many commentaries and arguments have demonstrated in the past. These historical explanations and annotations are largely irrelevant to this reading. Instead, what I wish to emphasize is the text's lasting value due to its transcendence of any single time or place. This is the true historical (sedimented) character of the *Analects* I want to emphasize. That is why I have not added explanatory language into the translation, and instead have tried to follow carefully the old admonition to not "add words to the classics."

As much as possible, I have attempted to keep the translation as close to the original as possible, including following its grammar and sentence structure, again in order to the best of my ability to preserve the character and style of the original text. At times, however, I have adopted usage or vocabulary from the past few decades, such as "policies," "cadre," "report the situation to a higher level," and so on, in order to approach modern usage as closely as possible.

In a record that dates from a couple of thousand years ago, naturally there will be a good number of mistakes based upon oral transmission. When one adds to this breaks in transmission and fragments of text, it is difficult to avoid the occasional break in logic or place where the meaning of a text is unclear or the spirit of the text is inconsistent. In this reading I have not bent over backward to find an interpretation, nor have I felt the need to innovate in my interpretations; rather, I have been governed by the principle that "what we know we know, what we don't know we don't know." I believe that there are some difficulties in the text that will have to await further archaeological discoveries before they can be explained.

The conversations recorded in the *Analects* follow no particular order or system. To the contrary, they are quite scattered and disorderly. However, if one reads the whole text, one will be left with a quite complete and vivid impression. In it, Confucius comes to life as an ordinary, real-life human being, who speaks and laughs, has desires and emotions, loses his temper, does foolish things, makes mistakes, and has weaknesses. He is nothing like the sanctimonious, scrupulous, perfect person painted by later Confucian commentators. Furthermore, it is not the case that every passage in the *Analects* is of earth-shattering importance or reflects deep thought, as later generations would have it. Confucius's disciples are also real people, each with his own temperament, style, and personality, his own strengths and weaknesses. These come across quite clearly and concretely in the *Analects*, so that readers can experience them directly. The figurative depiction of this group of "sage-philosophers" is quite unusual among early classical texts, including *Mencius* and *Zhuangzi*, and is rare in later texts. As much as possible I have tried to reflect this in the translation, in order to give adequate emphasis to the figurative world of the text, but I have probably not succeeded very well.

On the "Notes" (*zhu* 注)

It is said that there have been over two thousand commentators on the *Analects*. **I divide the twenty chapters of the *Analects* into a total of five hundred passages.** Of these, practically every passage has been the subject of various interpretations. The most recent result of attempts to select and collate these is *Lunyu jishi* 論語集釋 (*Collected Explanations of the "Analects"*) by modern scholar Cheng Shude 程樹德 (1878–1944), which also collects the largest number of commentators (around six hundred). Most of the Notes I have included are taken from his book, which includes He Yan's 何晏 (ca. 195–249) *Lunyu jijie* 論語集解 (*Collected Interpretations of the "Analects"*), based on the corrections in the *Shisan jing zhu shu* 十三經注疏 (*Notes and Commentaries on the Thirteen Classics*) edition. For Zhu Xi's *Lunyu jizhu* 論語集注 (*Collected Commentaries on the "Analects"*), Liu Baonan's 劉寶楠 (1791–1855) *Lunyu zhengyi* 論語正義 (*The True Meaning of the "Analects"*), and Kang Youwei's 康有為 (1858–1927) *Lunyu zhu* 論語注 (*A Commentary on the "Analects"*), I have consulted the commonly available editions of these texts. I have also drawn extensively on Yang Bojun's 楊伯峻 (1909–1992) *Lunyu yizhu* 論語議注 (*A Translation and Commentary on the "Analects"*), as this modern edition is relatively easy to understand. Of all the commentaries, Zhu Xi's collection remains the most clear and concise, and offers a great deal of depth, so it is the most heavily excerpted here. Some of the Notes are included because I have taken a very different interpretation from most commentators, in order to show that I have not fabricated these interpretations or made them up out of thin air. A few others are included for the opposite reason, in order to show other possible readings of the passage. But in every case, I have included only such commentaries as I thought absolutely necessary, and thus not every passage includes Notes. Of the vast sea of later comments on the text, I have been able to include only one in a million. To try to include too many different comments would only confuse things. In sum, then, the standard for inclusion in this Notes section has been the degree to which the commentary is helpful to understanding the original text or helpful to my own argument. I have paid no attention whatsoever to archaeological excavations, historical verification, or disputes among commentators.[18]

The similarities and differences among commentators are great and often quite striking. In the present work, of course, I can do no better than to decide what to accept and reject based upon my own opinion. Any translation, explication, or exposition must be influenced by prejudices or preconceptions, as modern hermeneutics has discussed extensively; this book will obviously be no exception. I do have my own thoughts to add, however, which might be considered "notes," or "annotations"; for clarity's sake, these have been placed in the Comments (*ji* 記) section.

Of course, the teachings, actions, and thought of Confucius are by no means confined to the *Analects*. Many accounts and records can be found in the *Spring and Autumn Annals* (*Chunqiu* 春秋), the *Zuo Commentary* (*Zuozhuan* 左轉), *Book of Rites* (*Liji* 禮記), *Da Dai Liji* (大戴禮記), as well as the works of other great masters, and the *Hanshi waizhuan* (韓詩外傳), *Shuo yuan* (說苑), *Xin xu* (新序), and many so-called forged texts (many of which are not actually forgeries, as modern-day archaeologists are demonstrating more and more). Among these are the accounts in *Collected Sayings of Confucius* (*Kongzi ji yu* 孔子集語) and even *Confucius's Sayings on Family Life* (*Kongzi jia yu* 孔子家語), which focus mostly on policy and less on the heart-mind or nature. Even if only half or fewer than half of these are genuine, omitting the fake would still yield a great many passages that can be regarded as supplementary to or helpful to understanding or corroborating the *Analects*. The work of sifting through these would seemingly be more valuable and fruitful than examining old commentaries, but must remain for later pursuit.

Here an important question arises, **which is to what extent the *Analects* can be regarded as a faithful and dependable account or reflection of the actions and words of Confucius. This question has been extremely controversial.** For example, Kang Youwei, a proponent of the New Text School who emphasized the [importance of] the Gongyang commentary, emphatically believed that because the *Analects* was primarily compiled by the disciples of Zengzi's school, it reflects only a certain aspect of Confucius's thought and not its most major aspect, which is more faithfully transmitted by other schools particularly that of Zizhang (see the Notes to *Analects* 8.3 below). It is true that Zengzi's position in the *Analects* is higher than that of any other disciple other than Yan Hui, and thus higher than Zizhang. For example, he is honored with the honorific suffix *zi* 子 ("Master"), while Zizhang is not. The text is replete with similar distinctions between the two. Song-Ming Neo-Confucians regarded Zengzi as the proper successor to Confucius. Ye Shi 葉適 (1150–1223) disagreed somewhat with this opinion (see his *Xi xue ji yan* 習學記言), so differing from orthodoxy that he was excoriated by "modern Neo-Confucian" (or modern New Confucian) Mou Zongsan. Actually, Kang Youwei started from the viewpoint of modern-day politics in emphasizing "outer kingship" (*wai wang* 外王), which meant giving weight to Zizhang's questions on government and so forth. Kang Youwei saw this as the heart of Confucius's teachings, and in this he was not necessarily mistaken. Mou Zongsan, on the other hand, started from the point of view of morality, heart-mind, and nature, emphasizing "inner sageliness" (*nei sheng* 内聖), scrupulously abiding by the ethical tradition, and reverencing Zengzi, and in this he was not necessarily correct. Regrettably, even if the *Analects* is largely the work of Zengzi's school, and whether or not it constitutes a reliable record or a faithful reflection of Confucius, this text has survived over two thousand years until today. Thus, in the face of the doubt expressed by such scholars as Cui Shu 崔述 (1740–1816) regarding Book 15 and following (excluding Book 19, which records the words and actions of the disciples), as well as many earlier passages,[19] we can do little other than acknowledge the difficulty or near impossibility of determining through the evidence available to us which passages, words, and actions were actually those of Confucius and which were not. (Again, perhaps future archaeological finds will be of some help here.) **What is important is that the *Analects* and our notion of Confucius have been passed down to us today in this form beginning with the *Zhang hou lun* (*The Marquis Zhang "Analects"* 張侯論) in the Han dynasty.**[20] The *Analects* has always existed in the midst of hermeneutics, though people may not have been conscious of this until recently. The crucial thing is thus not what relationship the text bears to the truth about Confucius, nor is it what that "truth" about Confucius actually looks like. Rather, this is the form in which the figure of Confucius has spread and exerted influence in China. Therefore, even if new archaeological finds demonstrate that the image of Confucius we find in the *Analects* does not accord with the historical Confucius, this still will not erase **the important "prototypical" position that the text and Confucius have played in the cultural-psychological formation (*wenhua xinli jiegou* 文化心理結構) of the Chinese people for over two thousand years. The version of Confucius we find in this version of the *Analects is* the real Confucius, the Confucius that is fixed in people's minds—this is indisputable historical fact.** This is exactly why it is important as we sift through all the commentaries and explications to the best of our ability to pay attention to how to make up for this flaw, and allow the figure of Confucius and his thought to both flow from the *Analects* and not be bound by it.

On the "Comments" (*ji* 記)

The Comments section contains my own discussion, notes, and explanations. The length and character of this section varies from passage to passage. Some comments focus narrowly on the passage, some wander into philosophy; some present arguments, some complain; some consider the passage as it stands, some use the passage as an opportunity to expound on my own views. In short, there is quite a mix. This is perhaps appropriate to the style of the *Analects* itself, but it also accords with my own opposition to constructing philosophical systems. Of course, all these comments center on the question of how to read the *Analects* today. The problem with commentaries is that they tend to be too repetitious, talking each little point to death. I have no defense to make against this accusation, and simply plead for the reader's patience with my wordiness.

Cheng Shude in his *Lunyu jishi* evaluates Zhu Xi's annotations, saying, "His annotations of the *Analects* are everywhere stuffed with the word 'Principle' (*li* 理). About *ren* 仁 ('humaneness' or 'benevolence'), he says, 'The virtue of the heart-mind, the principle of love' 心之德, 愛之理. About *li* 禮 ('ritual'), he says, 'The patterns and regulations of the Heavenly Principle; it is like mercury when spilled on the ground, it enters every crevice.' "[21] Cheng also quotes Qing scholar Fang Dongshu 方東樹 (1772–1851), who in *Hanxue shangdui* 漢學商兌 criticized the "ravings" of commentators: "The *Analects* is a book passed along by Confucius's disciples, and does not address the idea of *li* (理 'principle'). It is only with the Song Neo-Confucians that we find the School of Principle made into a big pocket, into which they put everything, large and small. Heaven? That is considered to be the same as Principle. Nature? That is also considered to be the same as Principle. They seek Principle in every single thing. For things that cannot be explained, they believe there must be a corresponding Principle. If there are things that cannot be seen, they must lack this Principle. This is where Song Neo-Confucians get their common appellation, the School of Principle."[22] This is the same idea I have been harping on recently, how philosophers use the construction of knowledge and authoritative structures to govern people, and to exercise control over everything, so that in the end they "kill people with Principle" (Dai Zhen 戴震 1724–1777), or "not only close their mouths so that they cannot speak, but also bind their minds, so that they do not dare imagine" (Tan Sitong 譚司同 1865–1898).

This is not, of course, the tack I wish to take in this book. Instead, I will occasionally point out ways in which we see Confucius as a real person, whose behavior, actions, intentions, and emotions are not unlike those of ordinary people. So-called Confucianism is precisely oriented toward offering advice, discussion, and opinions on various aspects of everyday life and the modern condition. It is concrete, not abstract; ordinary, not abstruse. But to actually think and act this way is not easy. Thus, these opinions and positions and so on are characterized by a high level of idealism and consistency. This is what is meant by "reaching for the height of brilliance, in order to follow the path of the Mean" 極高明而道中庸.[23] The truths of the *Analects* are deep and lofty, but its language and its stories are plain and simple (most are based on everyday, ordinary life). In my Comments section I attempt to maintain the same tone, avoiding difficult, abstruse, or profound language. Whether I have succeeded in communicating deep and lofty truths, I am not sure. There are three points I raise in the Comments that I would like to discuss here.

First, **Confucianism places particular emphasis on the cultivation of the humanistic emotions; it emphasizes the melding and unity of**

the animal nature (desire) with the social nature (reason). I believe that in fact Confucianism regards "emotion" as the foundation, substance, and source of human nature and human life. **This is the heart of what I have called the "cultural-psychological formation," that is, the emotio-rational structure (*qingli jiegou* 情理結構).** It is this emotio-rational structure that distinguishes humans from animals on the one hand, and from machines on the other. The emotio-rational structure of the Chinese people has particular characteristics that are directly related to Confucius, Confucianism, and the *Analects*. This is the same thing I wrote about fifteen years ago in my essay "A New Evaluation of Confucius" (孔子再評價) as the Confucian psychological principle involved in the "construction of humaneness" (*ren de jiegou* 仁的結構). Confucius and Confucianism have always emphasized the "parent-child emotion" (*xiao* 孝 "filiality") as the ultimate basis for hierarchy in human relationships and the root of the human (*ren* 人) and humaneness (*ren* 仁). Confucianism starts from the "Five Relationships" between parent and child, minister and ruler, older brother and younger brother, husband and wife, and between friends, which radiate outward and interweave to create the various social and religious feelings that serve as the locus of the "substance" (*benti* 本體). Its emphasis on an education that cultivates human emotion as the very foundation of society has become an important tradition in Chinese civilization.

Apart from humaneness (*ren* 仁), **many other terms in the *Analects* (*cheng* 誠, *yi* 義, *jing* 敬, *zhuang* 莊, *xin* 信, *zhong* 忠, *shu* 恕, etc.) actually all to various degrees have a similar function in or value for the cultivation of emotion.** For example, the scope of the concepts of *jing* 敬 (reverence), and *zhuang* 莊 (solemnity) originally applied to shamanistic practices relating to the realm of gods and spirits, Heaven and Earth, and the ancestors. The emotional elements of these terms are dense and important. Although the *Analects* and Confucianism have rationalized and secularized these elements, they continue to retain the emotional characteristics of that religious tradition. Thus, **it is worth considering how today to explore, consider, or expound upon the *Analects*, Confucianism, or Confucians from the point of view of the cultivation of humanistic emotions.**

Of all the various commentaries, explanations, or studies of the *Analects*, whether ancient or modern, foreign or Chinese, I most appreciate the following remarks of Qian Mu. On the one hand, he notes that Confucian doctrine has a "wholly unadulterated religious spirit,"[24] while at the same time he brings out and emphasizes its "emotional" character:

> The Song Neo-Confucians spoke of the mind-heart unifying one's nature and emotions. In other words, for all of human life, Chinese Confucian thought most emphasizes the emotional part of this mind-heart, much more than its rational intelligence. We can only say that we use rational intelligence to perfect our nature and emotions; we cannot say that we use our nature and emotions to perfect rational intelligence. When emotions stray from correctness, they flow into desire. China's Confucians greatly emphasized the distinction between desire and emotion. Human life should be based upon emotion, but must not be based upon desire. In their discussions of human life, Confucians advocated the regulation or minimization of desire, even its elimination. But they would never allow for the minimization of emotion, the denial of emotion or its elimination.[25]

I believe this formulation is much more exact and understandable than those of modern New Confucians. However, because Qian Mu was a historian, he never elaborated on this from a philosophical standpoint, nor did he thoroughly follow through on its implications in his *New Explanation of the "Analects" (Lunyu xin jie)*. On the contrary, that work is chock full of seemingly fixed and unchanging traditional moral doctrines that are long since obsolete, and do not at all accord with the above remarks. This is the reason I felt it necessary to make a new translation and new comments on this text.

The second main point I wish to make is that Confucianism places a great emphasis on morality. As mentioned above, it melds government, ethics, and religion together into morality. This is why in later generations ideology, religious fervor, autocracy, clan authority and individual self-cultivation are all melded together into a Chinese-style unity of church and state. Despite having endured a purgation in the onslaught of modern Western thought, this unity has never been dismantled. It became a sort of obstacle to entering modern society, leading to the May Fourth slogan, "Down with Confucianism," and today's "crisis of faith" and "crisis of morality." How to separate out personal religious morality from public social morality, so that they form two separate streams, each to itself, and thereby are able to both oppose and complement each other, one regulative and one constitutive—and to do so from within Confucian doctrine—seems to have become a major topic for today's project of transformative creation. In the *Analects*, Zengzi's questions on *ren* 仁 ("humaneness") can be distinguished from Zizhang's questions on *zheng* 政 ("government") as the two trends of personal and public morality, which anticipate the later strands of "inner sageliness" and "outer kingship" (strongly emphasized by the Gongyang school of the Han, as unfortunately I have not been able to discuss in this book). As I pointed out in my book, *A History of Classical Chinese Thought*, apart from the "inner sageliness" strand represented by Confucius (via Yan Hui and Zengzi), Mencius, the Cheng brothers and Zhu Xi, along with Lu Jiuyuan 陸九淵 (1139–1192) and Wang Yangming, there was the other important "outer kingship" strand of Confucianism, represented by Confucius (via Zigong and Zixia), Xunzi, Dong Zhongshu, He Xiu 何休 (129–182), Wang Tong 王通 (584–617), Chen Liang 陳亮 (1143–1194), Ye Shi, Gu Yanwu 顧炎武 (1613–1682), and Huang Zongxi 黃宗羲 (1610–1695). These days people like to speak highly of Chen Yinke 陳寅恪 (1890–1969), not remembering that Chen long ago said that Chinese philosophy was not as good as Western philosophy, and that "over the two thousand years that the Chinese have been influenced by Confucian philosophy, its deepest and greatest influence is on the administrative system, the law, and public and private life."[26] This aspect or strand of Confucianism is often overlooked or minimized by those who study the history of philosophy or thought (including the "modern New Confucians"). But it is this strand that has been most responsible for maintaining the continued existence of Chinese culture and the Chinese people. To discuss Confucianism or the *Analects* without acknowledging this would be a grave error. I have already addressed this point above in my discussion of the role of Zengzi in the production of the *Analects*. Of course, this point touches on the complex relationship between "inner sageliness" and "outer kingship," religious morality and social morality, and I will elaborate on these questions in my Comments on the various passages.

The third point I wish to make is that Confucius emphasized "knowing one's fate" 知命 or "establishing one's fate" 立命, or in other words, the individual establishment of the self, or the individual subjective quest. "Fate" (*ming* 命) here should not be understood to mean "inevitability" or "determinism," as in many traditional explanations. Quite the opposite: it should be understood to mean randomness; that is, each individual must work hard to understand and grasp the specific random shape of his or her own existence and fate, and in that way can establish him or herself. This is what Confucians meant by "knowing one's fate," or "establishing one's fate." **Only in this way can one realize one's actual supersensory existence in [the context of] one's randomly allotted path or circumstances of life.** In this way, one's sensory life can go beyond animal existence, while remaining distinct from any withered and lifeless moral reason, however abstruse; it is instead the emotion-as-substance that truly melds reason and desire into one. It is the realm of life that can be perceived and grasped in day-to-day life, in moral obligation, or in nature or art, and that constitutes the value, meaning, and source of human life.

Engels, having summed up contemporary philosophy as an epistemology of "the relationship between existence and thought," believed that after each branch of science reached independence, all that was left for philosophy was "dialectics and formal logic." Wittgenstein believed that philosophy was nothing more than language therapy. Heidegger, opposing all metaphysics, felt that philosophy would become the poetry of thought. Today, epistemology has long since become the science of knowledge, and language has become a matter of skill or technique, while dialectics has come to stand for a sort of branch of scientific methodology, and the metaphysical or ontological pursuit of the ultimate reality of the world has long lost its meaning. Where then does this leave philosophy? What is philosophy? This has become a real problem. Richard Rorty, meanwhile, has already proclaimed the "end of philosophy."

Kant in his *A Critique of Pure Reason* said, "The superior position occupied by moral philosophy, above all other spheres for the operations of reason, sufficiently indicates the reason why the ancients always included the idea—and in an especial manner—of moralist in that of philosopher. Even at the present day, we call a man who appears to have the power of self-government, even although his knowledge may be very limited, by the name of philosopher."[27] Does this not bear some similarities with the language of Confucius and the *Analects*? **Philosophy is not epistemological or ontological argument, nor is it skill at fixing [our use of] language; rather it lies in the establishment of the self within life and the world, "using real facts to measure real achievement."** But this establishment is not Kant's moral reason; instead, it contains a greater measure of emotion-as-substance. This is also quite different from the "sin-guilt culture" of Christianity, or the "shame culture" of the Japanese *Yamato-damashii*; rather, it is a manifestation of China's "pragmatic reason" and "culture of delight."[28]

These three points represent what I believe to be the fundamental spirit of the *Analects*. For details, see the Comments on individual passages. In sum, I believe the three important points of this new reading of the *Analects* are the cultivation of the human emotions, understanding and distinguishing between private religious morality and public social morality, and paying attention to and grasping the randomness of individual fate. Perhaps my readers will offer their thoughts on these points.

I would also like to address here an interesting phenomenon. I have, to the best of my ability, translated the *Analects* into modern vernacular, but in my notes and comments I often slip into a classical idiom, with lots of classical constructions. I have not done so on purpose, but my pen has led me along not altogether consciously. Why? I have thought about this. Apart from following the style of writing with which I have to do, and apart from the fact that in classical Chinese it is possible to write more concisely, it is very possible that subconsciously I am opposing the roundabout, vague, and difficult to understand style popular among some young theorists. I call this "piling up neologisms," like the chatter of birds, creating labyrinths out of language in which for people (and the authors) to get lost. One could call it the "inflation" of academic language. In light of this, I think it is preferable to simply "resurrect the intrinsic culture," even to the point of using classical language particles, as this will be closer to everyday language than those tortuous sentences that are so difficult to understand. Of course, this has a bit of the flavor of defying widespread opinion. Perhaps the young theorists who are so on target with the latest trends may rise up en masse against me?

I have subtitled this work as a "preliminary draft." This is not out of false modesty, but because I have every intention of returning to the work and making revisions at a later date, including to this introduction. In this respect, I have great respect for the ancients. Zhu Xi, for example, wrote diligently, churning out essays and books, and making the annotation of the Four Books his life's work, not stopping until his death. This might not seem particularly modern, but these days I prefer to be a bit more conservative. If possible, I would still like to do some more translations, commentaries, and annotations, perhaps of the *Laozi*, the *Book of Changes*, or *The Doctrine of the Mean*. I believe that if these traditional Chinese classics can be made truly accessible to today's readers, this will be of greater value and meaning than writing more of my own essays and books. But this type of task is not easy, and for this reason I beg the reader to freely offer opinions, criticism, and suggestions. In particular for the translation, as despite consulting many sources and carefully weighing each word, there are bound to be places where my translation is not apt or precise, or may even be totally incorrect. I welcome any and all specific suggestions, even about a single character. About the Notes, I welcome suggestions as to what needs to be added or removed. As to the Comments, this is even more the case. I welcome sharp criticism on form and content, whether I have digressed, oversimplified, or repeated myself (although of this I am clearly guilty: the original text is quite repetitious, and I believe repetition can be fruitful). In short, abstract, general, or overall impressions and opinions are useful, but concrete, specific, detailed criticism is more so. In this way, I will be able to consider how to incorporate gradual improvements to the Notes and Comments sections in order to make them more complete.

Finally, I wish to bring up a major article criticizing me that the sensational and wildly popular Mr. Liu Xiaobo wrote a few years ago. In that piece, he remarked that my theories "had a great tendency toward resurrecting Confucius." He concluded, "Confucius died. Li Zehou is old. Traditional Chinese culture is long past needing anyone to carry it on."[29] While the categorical nature of his critique, which brooked no defense, was surprising, I remember that at the time I was so happy that I jumped for joy: after all, I had been mentioned in direct connection with Confucius. What could be more fortuitous? At the time, however, I had no inkling that I would ever write this book. The only thing I thought of at that point was that Liu's conclusion was rather too hasty and presumptuous. It seems there was still plenty of time. Though I was indeed old, there must have been many who were ready to take on the mantle of traditional Chinese culture. When I think back, it feels like yesterday, and yet how the world has changed, like clouds forming dark dogs in the sky. One cannot avoid suffering the vicissitudes of life, but can only reflect on them with a sigh.

Colorado Springs, Colorado, February 1994

The *Analects*

A Record of Conversations with Confucius in Twenty Books, or Five Hundred Passages

Comments: On the question of the meaning of the title *Analects* (論語 *Lunyu*), there are various opinions. Modern scholar Zhao Jibin 趙紀彬 (1905–1982) explained:

> The character *lun* 論 means "to organize," "to select and put in order," and so on. *Yu* 語 means "two persons speaking to each other on equal footing," "discussing difficulties," or "answering and exposition."[1] If we translate literally, then, *Lunyu* means conversations that have been organized, selected, and put in order, or "collected conversations." Ban Gu 班固 [32–92] remarked, "The *Analects* contains Confucius's conversations with his disciples, his disciples' conversations with their contemporaries, and the words they heard from the Master. At the time, each disciple had his own notes on these conversations, so that when the Master died, the followers together edited and compiled them; thus it is called *Lunyu* (the *Analects*)." (Quoting from the "Yiwen zhi" of the *History of the Han*).[2]

In the present work, I adopt this view of the meaning of the title. Actually, if we take the words literally, *Lunyu* means "words of discussion." This would not be an impermissible translation. To quote Zhao Jibin again, "The book, the *Analects*, was referred to during the pre-Qin period simply as *Confucius* (*Kongzi*)," and "The *Analects* is simply a book that collects the remnants of the *Confucius*," and so on.[3] This is also defensible. Later annotators and disciples of Confucius also added to it, as I have discussed in the introduction.

Book 1

1.1. 子曰：「學而時習之，不亦說乎？有朋自遠方來，不亦樂乎？人不知而不慍，不亦君子乎？」

Confucius said, "To study and frequently put into practice, is this not happiness? To have a friend come from afar to see you, is this not pleasure? To find that no one understands you, and yet feel no frustration or resentment, is this not what it means to be a noble person (*junzi*)?"

Notes: *Zhu Xi, in his commentary on the Four Books, notes that the character* xi 習 *refers to a bird's frequent flying. To study unceasingly is like a bird that constantly flies.*

Comments: Just because this is the first passage of the *Analects*, it does not necessarily follow that it must contain some profound truth. But because of the two references to happiness, joy, or pleasure (in the characters 悅 *yue*[4] and 樂 *le*), it seems appropriate here to speak of one of the most fundamental themes we will raise in this contemporary reading of the text. That is, just as Western culture is guilt-based, while Japanese culture is "shame-based" (as Ruth Benedict and certain Japanese scholars have pointed out), we can say that the spirit of the Confucian-based Chinese culture is that of a "culture of delight" (*legan wenhua* 樂感文化). This type of culture is based on the fundamental supposition that there exists only "this world," only the present moment in time. There is little attention to or construction of a metaphysical world that transcends the present (to put it philosophically) or of heaven and hell (to put it in religious terms). This cultural disposition is concretely manifest in pragmatic idealism (in terms of methods of thought or theoretical habits) and emotion-as-substance (*qinggan benti* 情感本體) (in terms of the essence of human life or its destination, or perhaps one could call it the realm of Heaven and Earth, or the realm of supermoral quasi-religious experience). A "culture of delight" and "pragmatic reason" are both hallmarks of the Chinese cultural tradition.

At the root of Confucian thought, then, is the "happiness," "pleasure," or "joy" of this first passage. It is a present happiness that does not depart from the world of human affairs or the senses, while at the same time it transcends them. To study the way of "being human" (*weiren* 為人), to obtain knowledge and skills and put them into practice, must be of benefit to people, the world, and the self, and thus the heart rejoices in it. This is a mature, deeply rewarding happiness. For a friend to come from afar to see you was always understood to refer to a fellow student (*tong men yue peng* 同門曰朋 ["'friend' means being of the same school of thought"]) who has come to discuss what one is learning, to compare notes, and aid in mutual self-cultivation. This is similar to the notion of friendship in ancient Greece, where "friend" connoted one with whom a person discussed philosophy and wisdom. But actually, why should we confine the meaning to this rigid definition? For a friend to come to see you, drink wine with you, speak with you, is this not also a joy? This is especially so if the person comes from afar, which implies that you have not seen him or her for a long time. In ancient times, this would have been particularly difficult to arrange, and thus all the more precious, and would produce even more happiness. This joy or pleasure is entirely this-worldly, and yet at the same time it is spiritual. It is an "I and Thou" kind of pleasure, in which the "pleasure" (*le* 樂) goes beyond mere "happiness" (*yue* 悅) (see 6.11). "Happiness" (*yue*) is confined to one's own individual experience, while "pleasure" (*le*) is communal, encompassing the relational feelings of subjective intercourse (*zhuti jian xing* 主體間性). It is the pleasure of genuine friendship.

In this regard I would like to quote a set of Tao Qian's poems[5] on missing a friend.

Hanging Clouds 停雲

Thick and dusky the hanging clouds,
Misty, misty, the season's rain.
In all directions the same dusk—
The level road is blocked.
Quietly settled at the eastern window

Alone I grasp my cup of spring wine.
My good friend is far away,
I scratch my head and linger long.

The hanging clouds are thick and dusky,
The seasonal rain is misty, misty.
In all directions the same dusk—
The level ground becomes a river.
I have wine, I do have wine,
Lazily I drink at the eastern window.
I want to speak with the one I miss—
Boats and carriages can't help.

The trees in the eastern garden,
Their branches are arrayed once more,
As if by their fresh newness
To call out my feelings.
People have always said,
"The sun and moon are on the march."
How can we sit down together
And speak of each other's lives?

靄靄停雲, 濛濛時雨. 八表同昏, 平路伊阻.
靜寄東軒, 春醪獨撫. 良朋悠邈, 搔首延佇.

停雲靄靄, 時雨濛濛. 八表同昏, 平陸成江.
有酒有酒, 閑飲東窗. 願言懷人, 舟車靡從.

東園之樹, 枝條載榮. 競用新好, 以怡余情.
人亦有言, 日月于征. 安得促席, 說彼平生?

These poems are sincere and profound, and require no complicated explication. The poet in composing these poems, and the reader in reading them, find their feelings going deeper. That is to say, some fundamental human emotions are actually animalistic—animals also feel friendship and affection. Dogs and horses feel a closeness and attachment to their owners. But to preserve, extend, and elevate that feeling to this high level, causing the scene to strike a chord in the heart, and infusing the landscape with emotion in this way, is the handiwork of culture. Like

Confucius's remark, this poem can shape people's emotional psyche. Culture causes the emotions to become humanized. Friendship and the joy of feeling friendship are cultivated in the psyche through the accumulation of culture and especially through direct formation by literature and artistic works. Tao Qian's poem is an example. For young people it may be difficult to appreciate the poem (or indeed any of Tao Qian's poems), but when one has accumulated a certain degree of life experience, it is a different story. This is an example of what I call "sedimentation." Sedimentation refers to a type of cultural-psychological formation, or what may be called the "humanization of nature," the locus of the distinction between people and animals, or the locus of "human nature."

Of course, there are many different levels of "emotion." In *Four Essays on Aesthetics*, I distinguished three levels of aesthetic experience, "pleasures of the ear and eye, of mind and heart, and of aspirations and moral integrity."[6] Of these, the latter is the level that approaches or enters the religious realm or religious experience. At this level, it takes the "relationship between Heaven and humans" or the "unity between Heaven and humans" as its solace or purpose. The pleasure of aspirations is suffused with tragic spirit, especially because there is no established faith in an anthropomorphic deity, so that each person must construct grace or faith for him or herself on his or her own path, must establish for him or herself that the "movement of Heaven is full of power" (天行健 *tianxingjian*);[7] he or she "knows something is not possible, yet goes and does it" anyway (*Analects* 14.38). There is no external source of salvation, hope, or support, and therefore the inner suffering and difficulty, the management of one's gloom, and the spiritual burden are heavier than in cultures with an anthropomorphic god.

The reason that Chinese pragmatic reason emphasizes the spirit of tenacity, difficulty, and struggle is found here. What prevents China's culture of delight from becoming superficial or vulgar is also here. The reason that so much of Chinese philosophy and ethics approaches common sense but remains profound, lies here as well. Loftiness in the common, greatness in the ordinary—this is the spirit of Chinese culture of which Confucius is representative. This cultural spirit takes feelings that are both worldly and other-worldly as its source and foundation, its truth and its substance or final reality (*benti* 本體). Because the meaning of human existence is found in this-worldly relationships, this locus of moral responsibility is also where the solace of human life is to be found. This is what distinguishes Confucianism from other religions and philosophies.

As for "To find that no one understands you, and yet feel no frustration or resentment," this is something that will be discussed in later passages, and so I will not discuss it extensively here.

This passage makes clear from the very beginning that, in sum, "study" means the study of what it means to be human. To learn to be human and to take pleasure in it because this is the substance or final reality of humankind—the commonly held reality—this is pleasure. To take pleasure in the arrival of a friend from afar demonstrates that this pleasure is communal and not individual. "To find that no one understands you, and yet feel no frustration or resentment" demonstrates that although this truth is communal, it does not lose the respect for, or the recognition or value of, the individual. These three levels cycle ever deeper; they are the root of the understanding of "humaneness," and the crux of the culture of delight and of pragmatic reason. For the opening passage of the *Analects*, this is "only natural, isn't it?" (*Analects* 19.23).

1.2. 有子曰:「其為人也孝弟, 而好犯上者, 鮮矣; 不好犯上, 而好作亂者, 未之有也。君子務本, 本立而道生。孝弟也者, 其為仁之本與! 」

Youzi said, "It is rare for someone to show filial respect to parents, reverence and love for older brothers and elders, and yet like to offend superiors or officials. Even more unheard of are those who do not like to offend their superiors, yet rebel and sew chaos. The noble person (*junzi*) works on the root. When the root has been well established, the way of humanity grows out of it. It seems that filiality to parents and respect for one's elders must be the root of humanness."

Notes: *Cheng Shude quotes Chen Shan's* 陳善 *[Southern Song dynasty] "Menshi xinyu"* 捫蝨新語*: The ancients often used false cognates. An example is Analects 1.2, "It seems that filiality to parents and respect for one's elders must be the root of humanness* [ren 仁]*." Or, "If you observe someone's mistakes, you will understand what type of person* [ren 仁] *he is" (4.7). Or, "someone* [ren 仁] *has fallen into a well" (6.26). I would venture that in all these cases, the character* ren 仁 *[meaning humaneness] should be* ren 人 *[meaning person]. [Cheng also quotes] Wang Shu's* 王恕 *(1416–1508)*

"Shiqu yijian" 石渠意見: *The* ren 仁 *in [the last line] should be* ren 人, *since it follows the above line,* 其為人也孝弟 *("for someone to show filial respect to parents, reverence and love for older brothers and elders"); filiality and respect for elders is the root of humanness* (ren 人).

Comments: "Humaneness" (*ren* 仁) is a fundamental Confucian category. It is the ideal for the formation of human nature. The move from ritual (*li* 禮) to humaneness (*ren*) is Confucius's creative theoretical contribution, as I discussed in my *History of Classical Chinese Thought*. It is by way of *ren* that Confucius begins to mold a cultural-psychological formation, or in slightly exaggerated terms, how he creates the Chinese spirit. This is how it is possible for me to say that Confucianism is half religion, half philosophy. For although it does not possess an anthropomorphic deity, in terms of its shaping of and influence on the spirit of the Chinese people it plays a role not dissimilar to that of Christianity in the West. Furthermore, one of the main reasons that Confucianism is not some sort of abstract philosophical theory, school, or thought system is that it makes thought speak directly to emotion; it builds its fundamental reasons and theories onto the foundation of the emotional psyche, always requiring the blending of reason and emotion, so that to this day Chinese people like to speak of something "making sense" using the phrases *he hu qingli* 合乎情理 ("it accords with feeling and reason"), and *he qing he li* 合情合理 ("it accords with feelings and accords with reason"). This passage is similar. When we read it today, we should cast aside the outdated specific recommendations or demands about "offending superiors" or "fomenting chaos," and so on. We should set aside the naive fantasy that in this way we will achieve clean government or world peace (more on this in the next passage), and pay attention instead to the crucial element here, viz., that the "root" of humanity (*ren* 人) or humaneness (*ren* 仁) is in the emotional relationships among family members in everyday life. Many animals also nurse and take care of their young, but when the young are grown, they leave "home," become independent, and never return, so that it would be difficult to argue that they retain any of the feeling a child has for its parents. One of the main characteristics of Confucian doctrine, from the so-called "three years of mourning" to what Mencius and Wang Fuzhi 王夫之 (1619–1692) called "what differentiates men from beasts," is to place primary emphasis exactly here, on the conscious cultivation of this "family" based feeling of children for their parents. Confucianism regards this as the root of "human nature," the source of order, and the foundation for society. It places "family values" on a par with humanistic feelings, and makes them the basic content of education.

How to maintain society's stability and continuation has been a difficult question from the time of Confucius to today. Jurgen Habermas thinks that today's conflict between liberalism (individual rights, equality, anti-corruption: the strong rule the weak) and democracy (the will of the masses, the people's democracy, the good of society: the many bully the few) can be resolved through "intersubjective" "discourse ethics." **Now that the Chinese Confucian emphasis on people instead of the law has been overturned to give primacy to the rule of law, is it still possible to absorb the traditional Chinese use of the formation of human nature to stabilize society, and its emphasis on the emotions, self-cultivation, family values, and intersubjectivity, in order to make a sort of transformative creation? There are many concrete issues here that are worth considering.**

1.3. 子曰:「巧言令色, 鮮矣仁!」

Confucius said, "Where there is clever, flowery speech, false appearance, or sham expression, there is rarely kindheartedness."

Comments: The previous passage addresses humaneness (*ren*) from a positive standpoint; this passage addresses it from a negative standpoint. This passage emphasizes that humaneness does not refer to any sort of external beauty or magnificence, and points out that external appearance and speech should follow upon the molding of the inner spirit. Too much polish or ornamentation not only has no benefit, but actually may be harmful to this sort of inner molding. In early shamanistic ritual, clever speech and false appearance without true sincerity was a great sin and utterly impermissible.

The hallmark of humaneness is love. Zhu Xi defined humaneness as "the principle of love, the virtue of the heart-mind."[8] He constructed a universal ethical order based on Heavenly Principle and human desire in order to govern the people (see 2.8). Modern thinkers Tan Sitong 譚嗣同 (1865–1898) and Kang Youwei treated humaneness as an ultimate universal reality that unites all things, like ether or electricity, and used it as the philosophical basis for modern concepts like freedom, equality, and universal brotherhood (see my *Zhongguo jindai sixiang shi lun* [*History of Modern Chinese Thought*]).[9] Today if we attempt to reconstruct a philosophical foundation for regarding humaneness as the substance or final reality, that would be what I have called the psyche- or emotion-as-substance. It is certainly not a universal "ether," nor is it (internal or external) transcendent "nature" (*xing* 性) or "heart-mind" (*xin* 心), much less any sort of outward magnificence or beauty.

1.4. 曾子曰:「吾日三省吾身: 為人謀而不忠乎? 與朋友交而不信乎? 傳不習乎?」

Zengzi said, "Every day I examine myself many times: In trying to find solutions for others, have I done my utmost? In friendship, is there anywhere I have been unfaithful? Those things that I pass on to others, have I put into practice myself?"

Comments: People exist in an "intersubjective" "common space." To make this common intersubjective space truly meaningful, valuable, and vital, from a Confucian point of view one must always begin with the self. This is not only the way of the noble person (*junzi*) in making friends and dealing with the world—it also applies to the mass of human relationships, and elevates these relationships to a very high level of self-cultivation and self-consciousness. The hallmark of this passage is self-examination of one's level of faithfulness within this "intersubjective" space. It has a heavily religious feeling to it and carries the flavor of the pursuit of religious morality, with "intersubjectivity" standing in for God and self-examination (of one's faults or inadequacies) taking the place of repentance before God. Zengzi is the transmitter of religious morality among Confucians. But in Confucianism (including in Zengzi) this is quite different from the concept of repentance from sin in Christianity. Although it may accommodate pangs of conscience as if one is teetering on the edge of the abyss, China still does not have the concept of original sin or the deep sense of sinfulness that accompanies it, and thus there is relatively less terrifying self-torment or devastation. On the contrary, Confucianism sees the existence of the universe and nature and human life itself as good and approaches the task of explaining and governing them with a positive, active emotional tone. This supreme principle of "intersubjectivity" refers to this-worldly human relationships, human community, and human life. Rather than being a response to a command by God to love people, this love for people itself is God. The "many self-examinations" (*san xing* 三省) here refers to examining oneself in this light. "Three" in the original does not indicate the number, but simply "many," and as such this contrasts with the Catholic practice of giving thanks at each meal or Islam's five mandatory prayers a day, or we could as well say, with any practice of undertaking repeated external forms in order to consolidate one's faith.

The last sentence of the passage could just as well be translated as follows: Those things which I have lectured or written about, have I thoroughly thought through, researched, and put them into practice? This is a good warning to myself, as I am quite sure there are many ways in which I today "disseminate errors that do people harm," especially where words do not match actions, and character diverges from learning.

1.5. 子曰: 「道千乘之國: 敬事而信, 節用而愛人, 使民以時。」

Confucius said, "In governing a country of a thousand chariots, be careful and respectful in handling of administrative affairs, scrupulous in upholding the people's trust, frugal in expenditures, loving and protective of the people, and leave to the common folk the choice of when the slack season begins."

Comments: The *Analects* has much to say about government. For the most part the passages agree, though there are differences in small particulars. I will return to this discussion in later passages. Here we should first point out that the *Analects* and Confucius himself frequently addressed the topic, and gave it quite a prominent place. This can still be seen even in the later writings of Zengzi's school. Confucians by no means limit their teachings to morality, human nature, and the heart-mind. This is the reason I emphasize the great importance of the question of "how to live," and the reason the question of "how to live" had primacy over the question of "why we live" (morality, etc.).[10] Song-Ming Neo-Confucians and modern New Confucians both gave grossly inadequate attention to this distinction. The word "respectful" (*jing* 敬) is an important term found commonly throughout the *Analects*. Although it refers to an external attitude, it even more indicates an internal emotion. Respect arose from the fear and reverence toward the gods and spirits in shamanistic ritual practice, which underwent rationalization to become an attitude of life and an emotional requirement, finally becoming a part of how human nature is shaped.

It is worth noting that despite the transformation from the reverence and fear of gods and spirits to reverence and respect in the realm of human affairs, relationships, and governmental duties, this sentiment still expresses itself as reverence and respect for objective principles. The Chinese term *jing* is similar to the "moral feeling of respect" Kant emphasized, in the sense that it is not related to joy or happiness, and thus is far removed from any sort of utilitarianism. However, Kant's categorical imperative is supremely sublime, sitting high above the sensible world, while in Confucianism, with its basis in humaneness and its inseparability from the sensible realm, it can be equally sublime. Here we see again the distinction between a two-world (kingdom of heaven/human world) system and one based upon a single human life. The reason China is "this-worldly" has to do with the direct rationalization of the shamanistic worldview (by way of the *Book of Rites* and the *Book of Changes*). This is the lynchpin of the history of ancient China and Chinese thought, and the reason for what Liang Shuming 梁漱溟 (1893–1988) called the "early maturity" of Chinese culture.[11] More on this below.

1.6. 子曰:「弟子入則孝, 出則弟, 謹而信, 汎愛眾, 而親仁。行有餘力, 則以學文。」

Confucius said, "Young people should be filial and obedient to their parents at home, and respectful and loving towards older brothers and elders abroad. They should be circumspect, faithful, loving towards the people, and associate closely with people who are humane and virtuous. If having done all these, they still have strength, let them pursue book learning."

Comments: This passage contains no particular "philosophy," "wisdom," or "knowledge," but concerns itself squarely, again, with the very concrete norms for "being human" (*zuo ren* 做人). Yet it is more than an aphorism about how to conduct oneself in society. The respect and esteem for older brothers and elders is known as *ti* 悌. It refers not just to the elder brother of one's modern nuclear family but to anyone older than oneself but in the same generation, whether in one's extended family, clan, or nation. "Loving towards the people" also refers to general amicable relations with the adults of one's own clan.

1.7. 子夏曰: 「賢賢易色, 事父母能竭其力, 事君能致其身, 與朋友交言而有信。雖曰未學, 吾必謂之學矣。」

Zixia said, "To regard virtuous behavior as important rather than appearances; to be able to exert one's utmost in service of one's parents and give one's life in the service of one's ruler; in dealing with friends to be true to one's word and keep one's promises—even if such a person should be said to have never studied at all, I would certainly say he was educated."

Notes: *Liu Baonan quotes the Guang ya shi yan* 廣雅釋言*:* Yi 易 *means "like or similar." In Wang Nianshu's* 王念孫 *(1744–1832) "Annotations and Proofs" ([Guangya] Shuzheng* 疏証*) Wang Yinzhi* 王引之 *(1766–1834) remarks: In [the first line of Analects 1.7,]* yi *means "like." It means loving virtuous behavior as much as one loves beauty.*

Comments: These two passages clearly illuminate how the Confucian concept of "study" is primarily concerned with real, practical behavior, and not book learning. Thus "learning" or "study" in the *Analects* and other Confucian texts has a broader and a narrower meaning. The narrow meaning is that of the word "study" in the previous passage, "If having done all these, they still have strength, let them study documents and knowledge"—that is, book learning and all the things we today associate with "studying," like reading books, researching, and so on. These were of course also valued by Confucians. But on the whole, what Confucians emphasized more was the broader meaning of "study" or "learning": viz., that moral action is superior to knowledge, and behavior has primacy over words. As for the relationship between virtue (behavior) and knowledge (language), one could compare the differences with Greek philosophy and Socrates, and in various passages of this book I will bring up this topic. This is the question I have raised before about the difference between "In the beginning there was action (the Way)" and "In the beginning there was language (the Word)," to which many differences between East and West can be traced.

My translation departs from the explanation of the word *yi* 易 given in the Notes. According to that definition, the first line should read, "Those who love virtuous action as much as they love appearances." *Yi* can also be understood to mean "easy to get along with," so that here it would mean "take pleasure in beauty." *Se* 色 is usually taken to refer to feminine beauty, so that it is also possible to read this as referring to the "way of husband and wife," in keeping with the classical Confucian Three Obediences, starting with husband and wife, then father and son, and finally ruler and minister.

1.8. 子曰:「君子不重則不威，學則不固。主忠信，無友不如己者，過則勿憚改。」

Confucius said, "If a noble person is not serious and dignified, he will lack authority, and the things he studies will not be firmly learned. He should make faithfulness and trustworthiness his rule. He does not have friends that are not his equal. If he makes a mistake, he is not afraid to correct it."

Comments: Why should it be that if someone "is not serious and dignified, he will lack authority"? Because "study" here implies practice, and if you are not serious and diligent, your behavior and practice will not be truly secure. You will not progress sturdily, each step leaving its imprint, and others will not trust or respect you. Thus, the word *wei* 威 ("authority") here does not mean a solemn, dignified appearance. In later years many put on a dignified, sanctimonious expression, making a great show of seriousness while being inwardly wretched and acting basely. This is what is called the "false study of the Way." Is it not true that these official stooges and "Mister Leftists" 左派先生 are all of this ilk? It is also possible to read *gu* 固 ("secure") as *bi* 蔽 (meaning covered or sheltered) (as for example Chen Daqi 陳大齊 does in *Lunyu yijie* 論語臆解).

To say that "he does not have friends that are not his equal" means that you should look at the strong points of your friends. Others will always be superior to you in certain respects. This is not really saying you should not make friends who are not as good as you, or that all your friends should be superior to yourself. This last would be impossible to put into practice, since if it were a general principle, logically no one would be able to have any friends. Thus, it is simply meant as an encouragement.

"Faithfulness" (*zhong* 忠) and "trustworthiness" (*xin* 信) are two important terms that touch on both the emotions and on the shaping of character. But they are subordinate to terms like humaneness (*ren*) and filiality (*xiao* 孝). It is here that the different path of Chinese culture becomes apparent, as I shall discuss later.

1.9. 曾子曰:「慎終追遠, 民德歸厚矣。」

Zengzi said, "Be devout in taking care of the funerals of your parents and in remembering and sacrificing to your ancestors, and the character of the common people will be deeply faithful and honest."

Comments: The great importance accorded to funerary rites is a common characteristic of primitive ancient clans. This is well-documented in the annals of world anthropology. According to modern anthropologists, the burial of the dead or the carrying out of some sort of funerary rites for them (e.g., the spreading of red powder around or on the body of the deceased in the rites of Shandingdong man) **marks the beginning of the self-consciousness of the human race** as well as the beginning of the human cultural psyche. Animals, in general, have no such practices. In other words, funerary rites add to the vague and indistinct animalistic rational and emotional psychic elements a particular social, clan, or racial direction and meaning that affirms the self's belonging to this race or clan; this is the earliest "self-consciousness" of "race." Funerary rites in honor of the dead all share this emotional-rational function (on which, see Xunzi), which constitutes the earliest social consciousness, human psyche, and emotional behavior. Confucius and his disciples were inheritors of this great historical tradition and added theorization and rationalization to it, turning it inward to create the "humaneness—ritual" construct. **External ritual (human culture) and internal humaneness (human emotion) in this way became the root of what it meant to be human.**

Devoutness in funerals and remembrance of ancestors are primarily required of the upper classes and rulers, and [as a result] the "character of the common people will be deeply faithful and honest." This demonstrates another major characteristic of Chinese tradition: how, as the superior acts and the inferior follows, the greater and lesser traditions, elite and popular culture, mutually infiltrate and intermingle, so that there is not a large gap between them. The reason for this influence of the superior on the inferior can be found in the emphasis in Confucianism from the beginning on "transformation by education," which unifies superior and inferior: the devoutness of the upper classes in funerals of parents and sacrificing to ancestors can cause the lower classes to follow suit or fall in line, because both originally come from the same clan. As Xunzi said,

> Hence the sacrificial rites originate in the emotions of remembrance and longing. . . . The sage understands them, the noble person (*junzi*) finds comfort in carrying them out, the officials are careful to maintain them, and the common people accept them as custom. To the noble person (*junzi*) they are a part of the way of man; to the common people they are something pertaining to the spirits.[12]
>
> 祭者、志意思慕之情也 …… 聖人明知之, 士君子安行之, 官人以為守, 百姓以成俗; 其在君子以為人道也, 其在百姓以為鬼事也。 (*Xunzi*, "Li lun," 32).

Clearly, Confucian concepts and categories are not just theories for individuals to argue about; rather, they are largely principles for communal application and practice.

1.10. 子禽問於子貢曰: 「夫子至於是邦也, 必聞其政, 求之與? 抑與之與?」子貢曰: 「夫子溫、良、恭、儉、讓以得之。夫子之求之也, 其諸異乎人之求之與?」

Ziqin asked Zigong, "Whenever the Master arrives in a country, he is certain to hear about its administration and government. Does he himself ask for this information? Or do the rulers of those countries invite him to do so?" Zigong answered, "The Master obtains it by way of his gentleness, goodness, respect, simplicity, and modesty. His way of asking is probably quite different from that of others."

Comments: The student has respect for his teacher and emphasizes how the teacher's good character inspires strong admiration on the part of the rulers of the various states. Note, however, that he does not deny that Confucius does "ask"; he takes a great deal of initiative in actively seeking a way to have input into government. This takes almost the same shape as the characteristic we see in later Confucianism and in Confucian scholars' shared quest to actively enter into government and social activity. This is in marked contrast to the Buddhist monk's effort to put off or distance himself from human relations, forsaking family, as well as to the practicing Daoist. It is also in contrast to later Neo-Confucian and Daoist concern with the cultivation of human nature and unconcern with "thorough knowledge of the classics put to practical use." Of course, this is not to say that today's intellectuals should learn from Confucius and all become like ancient Confucians. On the contrary, today you can be concerned about and participate in politics and social action, or you can specialize in a particular profession and pay no attention to these things. Today there is a need not only for specialized people who pursue "science for science's sake, art for art's sake," but also for a class of people who keep a distance from politics and are dedicated to the "bureaucracy." For we are no longer in a time of imminent danger to the country, where the whole people are mobilized to ward off enemies, a time of "workers, peasants, merchants, students, and soldiers, coming together to save the country from destruction." We have moved toward a modern pluralistic and developed society in which each has his or her own role to play.

1.11. 子曰:「父在, 觀其志; 父沒, 觀其行; 三年無改於父之道, 可謂孝矣。」

Confucius said, "While your father is alive, observe his aspirations and intentions; when your father is dead, look at his actions and behavior. To follow the father's path or direction for three years without changing it—this can be called filiality."

Notes: *In Zhu Xi's commentary, he quotes Yin Tun (尹焞, 1070–1142): "If the ways of his father are in accordance with the Way, it would be perfectly acceptable to go his entire life without changing them. If they are not in accordance with the Way, though, why does he wait three years to change them? Even in the latter case, the filial son goes three years without making any changes because his heart is blocked by a certain reluctance."*[13]

Comments: There are different opinions about whether the word *qi* 其 (here translated "his"), which occurs twice in the first sentence, refers to the father or the son. I take it to refer to the father. "Without changing" refers to a hesitancy to lightly make changes to the father's way of doing things when it has passed into your hands; this is in accordance with the demands of clan tradition. If you do make changes, they should be made slowly, thus the "three years" (i.e., many years) you should wait before beginning. Some commentaries (like that quoted in the Notes above) summarize this as an inner "discomfort" (or "reluctance"). Although this reading is suffused with the Confucian spirit of connecting ritual (external, traditional custom or principle) with humaneness (inner emotion), it does not hold water from a historical standpoint. The real reason for this prohibition against changing the father's practice for three years after his death is the importance of maintaining the experiential existence of one's clan; this is the real crux of the matter. Later commentators for the most part ignored the fact that one cannot explain the passage from either a purely moral or a purely emotional standpoint. Even though these practices were just the vestiges of primeval clan society, it is also quite clear that they were neither required of nor indeed possible for later generations to carry out. The formal requirement mandating three years leave from office on the death of one's parents to carry out the funeral and the required three years of mourning was the last trace of this, with the original meaning of the norm being now long lost.

From this it is possible to see how, from ancient times, ethics (between father and son) and politics (between ruler and minister) were the same; when these were united with sacrifices and worship of ancestors, this created the trinity of "ethics, politics, and religion," or the Chinese version of the unity of church and state: a unity of conceptual thought, ideologies, and social systems. Although in later years the concrete form of this principle would undergo changes, this tradition would remain unshaken. And despite the later appearance of Buddhist and Daoist organizations, rituals, and doctrine, none of these could displace the strong tradition of this Confucian "trinity" well enough to unify systems, laws, and public and private life. Mou Zongsan's and Du Weiming's 杜維明 (b. 1940) assertion that Confucianism had a distinction between the "tradition of the Way" (*dao tong* 道統) and "tradition of politics" (*zheng tong* 政統) is completely without merit.[14]

1.12. 有子曰: 「禮之用, 和為貴。先王之道, 斯為美; 小大由之。有所不行, 知和而和, 不以禮節之, 亦不可行也。」

Youzi said, "Of all the functions of ritual, the most precious is to be 'fitting.' In earlier dynasties, the sage kings' regulations were beautiful in this sense; this was the case whether in small matters or larger affairs. Yet there are times that this does not work, for even if something is 'fitting,' if it is not regulated by or judged in accordance with ritual, then it will not work."

Comments: The readings of this passage are many and various, with vastly differing interpretations. It is also possible to parse the line "知和而和不以禮節之" differently, with a break after the second character (as Cui Shi does in his *Lunyu yu shuo*). Many commentators explain *he* 和 as "harmony," taking its musical sense, and take it to mean that even if (musical) harmony is not the goal, it still serves "ritual." This reading is also tenable. In the first chapter of my book *The Chinese Aesthetic Tradition* (華夏美學), entitled "The Rites and Music Tradition," I extensively discussed the opposition and mutual complementarity between the rites (or ritual, *li*) and music (*yue*). Actually, in clan society and ancient tradition, ritual was human culture and encompassed everything, including music. Although "rites" and "music" often appear in parallel with each other, "music" is actually one aspect of the ritual system, and thus musical "harmony" manifests, supplements, and is subordinate to "ritual."

"Rule by ritual" is unlike "rule by penalty," and "rule by a person" is not the same as "rule by law." The difference lies in that one must emphasize not only the objectivity of external rules and regulations but also the affectionate emotional identification with and harmonizing unity of human relations built upon the foundation of the blood clan. It is still worth considering how, in the context of the modern political and social system with its rule of law, we can maintain as much as possible of this tradition, for example how to increase harmoniousness and reduce litigation, explain more and judge less, and so on. Of course, this would be extremely difficult and would affect efficiency, but it is certainly worth making some effort to initiate movement in this direction. But perhaps it is premature to suggest moving in this direction at this time.

A more important issue in this passage is this notion of "fitting" or "suitable." What is "fitting" is "harmonious" and "beautiful," and is also a question of being in proper "measure" (*du* 度). The idea of "measure" is one of the characteristics and important categories of Chinese philosophy, and especially Chinese dialectics. For example, there is the expression "too much is just like not enough" (*guo you bu ji* 過猶不及), A ≠ A ±, or the quotes from the *Zuozhuan* "straight but not rigid, bent but not crooked . . . sad but not gloomy, happy but not intemperate,"[15] or the *Analects* passage "impressive and yet not violent, respectful and composed" (7.38). All of these address this concept. Today when people speak of having a "sense of propriety," this is what they mean. In art or any creative endeavor, we rely on grasping this sense of "measure" or "propriety," which is another aspect of beauty: "If you add a bit it would be too long, take away a bit and it would be too short." It is the capability to grasp the proper degree in action and is very different from any abstract notion (like "quality" or "amount") that serves only analysis. This is the crux of Chinese dialectical thought, also known as the "Mean": "The Mean is the highest when it comes to humaneness and virtue" (see 6.29).

1.13. 有子曰:「信近於義, 言可復也; 恭近於禮, 遠恥辱也; 因不失其親, 亦可宗也。」

Youzi said, "If you invoke trust in keeping with [your] principles, that is the only way you will be able to make good on your promises; if you speak of respect in ways that are in keeping with the ritual systems, that is the only way to avoid shame. If someone relies only on his or her own relations, this is an example that can be followed."

Comments: Here again the tradition offers an abundance of possible readings. The explanation here of the need for and possibility of qualities like trustworthiness and respect for the individual is very concrete and realistic. As for the last line, there are many different readings, and I will not list them here. My reading is chosen based upon the historical roots of Confucianism in clan blood relations.

What exactly is *yi* 義 in the first line (here translated "principles"), and how is it achieved? This is a big question. *Yi* can be translated "righteous," "suitable," "reasonable," "fitting," "self-evident truth," "rule," or "obligation," and so on. *Yi* is related to ceremony (*yi* 儀), and dance (*wu* 舞), owing to the character's suggestion of a feathered headdress (*yang* 羊) worn by a person (*wo* 我) dancing. It thus suggests careful conformity to the principles and regulations of shamanistic ceremonies. Both *yi* (ceremony) and *yi* (righteousness) were later rationalized to refer to the concrete language and formal bearing to adopt when carrying out the rites (thus phrases like "the three thousand rules of demeanor" *wei yi san qian* 威儀三千).[16] Later they underwent a process of abstraction, taking on the meanings of "appropriateness," "in proper measure," "reasonable," "obligatory," or "just," all of which have a sense of external coercion, authoritativeness, or objectivity. Finally, these terms were extended to mean simply "reason" (as in "reasonable," "truth," "principle"), or "just right" (as in "just at the right time," "suitable," or what "ought" to be). From an individual point of view, *yi* came to refer to standards, regulations, and obligations of behavior. It is basically a rational principle or category for practical use.

Because *yi* was not directly connected to inner emotion, as was *ren* (humaneness), from the time of Mencius onward statements about *yi* tended to arouse various opinions or arguments about externals, namely, how it can be both a question of a sort of general necessity for individuals to carry out absolute standards of objective (external) behavior and at the same time be a question of self-conscious individual requirements for (inner) moral self-discipline. Gaozi believed "humaneness is internal, righteousness (*yi*) is external,"[17] while Mencius believed both were internal, and Dong Zhongshu believed "humaneness is external, righteousness is internal"; Song-Ming Neo-Confucians advocated a return to the Mencian view; and so on. In sum, when placed in contrast with humaneness, *yi* becomes a category or standard for the regulation of behavior. It is the highest category of the Confucian moral ethic (while *ren* transcends morality). It is both categorical imperative and moral autonomy. Here there are some similarities with Kant. But Kant makes this into something transcendent and external, while according to Mencius it is a priori and internal (and emphatically not "internal and transcendent"). In Confucianism as a whole, however, *ren* (humaneness) is always superior to *yi*. The reason why China has lacked or found it difficult to accept a Kantian brand of transcendental formal principle has to do with the this-worldly focus of its tradition. I remarked on this above (1.5), and bring it up here again, and not for the last time, for this is a crucial point indeed.

1.14. 子曰:「君子食無求飽, 居無求安, 敏於事而慎於言, 就有道而正焉, 可謂好學也已。」

Confucius said, "The noble person does not seek satiety in eating and drinking, nor comfort in his dwelling place. He is diligent in action and cautious in speech. He draws near to people of virtuous action in order to improve himself. This can be called a love of learning."

Comments: We eat to live, we do not live to eat. Eating good food and living comfortably are not life goals for the noble person (*junzi*). In the Confucian view, life is difficult, and does not afford opportunity for rest. This is what is meant by the sayings "doing one's utmost" (*jin lun* 盡倫) or "doing all that is humanly possible" (*jin ren shi* 盡人事). The *Xunzi* records the following story:

> Zigong made a request of Confucius, saying, "I am worn out from learning. I wish to rest and serve a lord."
>
> Confucius said, "The *Odes* says:
>
> Day and night, with warmth and reverently,
> They performed their tasks assiduously. [Mao 301]
>
> Serving a lord is difficult. In serving a lord, where can one find rest!"
>
> "In that case, I wish to rest and serve my parents."
>
> Confucius said, "The *Odes* says:
>
> Those filial sons will be untiring.
> They will grant to you blessings unending. [Mao 247]
>
> Serving one's parents is difficult. In serving one's parents, where can one find rest!"
>
> "In that case, I wish to rest and have a wife and child."
>
> Confucius said, "The *Odes* says:
>
> He served as a model to his wife-mate,
> Then to his elder and younger brothers;
> He thereby brought order to clan and state. [Mao 240]
>
> Having a wife and child is difficult. In having a wife and child, where can one find rest!"
>
> "In that case, I wish to rest and carry on friendships."
>
> Confucius said, "The *Odes* says:
>
> A thing in which friends do help each other:
> They help with awe-inspiring deportment. [Mao 247]
>
> Carrying on friendships is difficult. In carrying on friendships, where can one find rest!"
>
> "In that case, I wish to rest and do farming."
>
> Confucius said, "The *Odes* says:

In the day thatch-reeds you go gathering.
At night you bind them together with string.
Up top to patch the roof, hasten to go.
Soon the hundred grains you'll begin to sow. [Mao 154]

Doing farming is difficult. In doing farming, where can one find rest!"

"In that case, is there nothing in which I can find rest?"

Confucius said, "Behold the grave: so final, blocked up, and cut off! With this, one knows where to find rest."

Zigong said, "How great is death! The gentleman finds rest in it. The petty man comes to an end in it."[18]

Only in death is rest possible. This lofty sense of human responsibility is also the locus of the "meaning of life," and for Confucius's disciples, it is also the meaning of "study," that is, religious moral cultivation. In later generations this becomes foundational for such ideas as Buddhism's emphasis on "universal liberation of all sentient beings," and "if I don't enter hell who will."[19] It can also be compared with the "salvation" emphasis of Christianity. The Confucian version of "salvation" might be more "secular" (as I discussed above, rooted in everyday life) and realistic (this-worldly), but the spirit of its "salvation" is not inferior to that of religious people. The Confucian notions of "If one has realized the truth in the morning, one can die the same evening" (4.8) and "perfect humaneness, choose righteousness" (*cheng ren qu yi* 成仁取義) or "view death as a returning" (*shi si ru gui* 視死如歸)[20] are not purely moral in their meaning. They are an excellent footnote to the metaphysical quest found in the statement "If you don't understand life, how can you understand death?" (11.11). More on this below.

1.15. 子貢曰:「貧而無諂, 富而無驕, 何如?」子曰:「可也。未若貧而樂[1], 富而好禮者也。」子貢曰:「《詩》云:『如切如磋, 如琢如磨。』其斯之謂與?」子曰:「賜也, 始可與言詩已矣! 告諸往而知來者。」

Zigong said, "To be poor but not fawning or servile, prosperous but not proud or haughty—what do you think of that?" Confucius answered, "That is good. But to be poor but happy, and prosperous but love ritual—that is better."

Zigong said, "In the *Book of Songs* it says, 'As from the knife and the file, / As from the chisel and the polisher!'[21] Is this what you mean?" Confucius said, "Ah, Zigong, this is exactly how we can begin to discuss the *Songs*! If I tell you the past, you can use it for the future."

Notes: *Zhu Xi comments: Zigong for his own part felt that to be without haughtiness or arrogance was of prime importance. When he heard the Master's answer, he realized the unfathomableness of* yili 義理 *[the principle of righteousness], and although he could grasp it, he was unable to live up to his own principles.*

Comments: In ancient editions the character *le* 樂 ("happy") is followed by *dao* 道 ("the Way"), which would make the meaning more clear.[22] This passage does not speak of rejoicing *in* poverty, but of rejoicing *despite* poverty. Perhaps when Zigong raises this question, it is after he has already grown very rich. This is the reason for the second part of the discussion about the *Songs* quotation. Of course, this type of reading of the poem does not accord with its original meaning. One characteristic of Chinese pragmatic reason is its lack of emphasis on logical argument in favor of analogical association. If one draws inspiration from analogy, the scope is broad and the instinctual sense strong, all of which is conducive to creativity being aroused through experience. This can be seen as a way of thinking different from logical inference, and can be called "analogical thinking." The creative potential of this manner of thinking and the pros and cons of its function and expression in Chinese culture is worth investigating. The *Book of Songs* in ancient times was not just a collection of expressive poetry, but was more of a source of analogical reasoning and associative thought that functioned in both public life (e.g., in diplomatic language) and private life (as in the above conversation). Confucius's use of the *Songs* to instruct Zigong is just one example. Ordinarily, associative thought does come into play in logic, but in China, this vassal became itself a great state—it became the mainstream.

1.16. 子曰：「不患人之不己知，患不知人也。」

Confucius said, "Do not be afraid that others will not know you; what is to be feared is that you not know others."

Notes: *Cheng Shude quotes Wang Fuzhi in his "Sishu xunyi"* 四書訓義 *[Lessons on the Four Books]: They fear that they will not receive early recognition, and so bend over backward to pander to the ways of the world.*

Comments: This type of language is common in the *Analects*. In *Analects* 1.1, we had, "To find that no one understands you, and yet feel no frustration or resentment." Chinese intellectuals have always struggled with the quest for a "name" or reputation (*ming* 名). As the line from the *Lisao* says, "Old age comes on steadily, soon will be here, / I fear my fair name will not be fixed firmly" 老冉冉其將至兮, 恐脩名之不立.[23] Because of the relationship between "name" and immortality, many have placed their hope in it. Actually, tens of millions of ordinary people will labor their whole lives without having any name to pass on, and although their labor may be anonymous, it has certainly not decayed like the grass and trees. Thus, it is really true that "the masses create history" is an earth-shattering truth, and one I believe to this day; though I may be blamed for holding to Marxism unto death, I still cheerfully accept it. There are many in this day and age who in the pursuit of fame stoop to "pander to the world's opinions."

What is really worth considering is the question of the present and future social function and fate of intellectuals. Will they continue to play the role of the enlightened "prophet" who "takes responsibility for the good of the world," or will they play the role of the social critic? Will they become technical and academic supports for the market economy? Or will they be able to escape this real ethical dilemma? My personal hope is that the progress of history will allow this objective possibility of escape. Only in this way will intellectuals lose their "special" status and cease to require the instruction, practice, or cultivation that leads them to "find that no one understands [them], and yet [they] feel no frustration or resentment." This is why I have emphasized that "the Way is in everyday human relationships," and why I made "emotion-as-substance" the conclusion of my "Zhexue tanxun lu" ["Notes on Philosophical Pursuits"].

But the crux of the injunction not to "be afraid that others will not know you" lies in grasping the value and dignity of the individual—the importance of going your own way, doing what you must do, "not moved by praise or blame, not counting glory or shame," for the sense of self really resides in self-knowledge and not in the recognition of others.

Book 2

2.1. 子曰：「為政以德，譬如北辰，居其所而眾星共之。」

Confucius said, "Use virtuous action to govern the country, like the North Star in the heavens: it sits in its place and all the other stars revolve around and encircle it."

Comments: This passage has been explained in many different ways. Daoists use it to explain the "ruler's way of non-action [*junzi wuwei* 君子無為]." Legalists explain it as "the ruler enjoys leisure while the ministers work." It is apparent that the idea of non-action is an ancient Chinese concept of government that is common among Confucians, Daoists, and Legalists. Elsewhere in the *Analects* there are passages like, "What did [Shun] do? He himself respectfully sat in his place [facing South], that is all" (*Analects* 15.5). Should a "ruler" rule by "action" or "non-action"? We will discuss this later in various chapters and so will not get into this question here. In this passage Confucius is simply emphasizing that one should use the *de* (德 "virtue," "power," or "moral force") of customary laws and regulations to manage governmental affairs. Thus it is not here a question of the *de* that Daoists speak of in the pairing *daode* 道德 ("the Way and its Virtue or Power"), and that is synonymous with "nature." What then is *de* exactly? Speaking from a societal point of view, I believe it refers to a principle of the clan system involving the wide bestowal of benefits and the unification of the collective. Speaking from the point of view of the individual, I believe it probably has roots in the ancient shamanistic leader's supernatural and mysterious magical power. Both of these later transformed into the personal moral character that Confucians advocated for leaders and rulers, by which the behavior and life of clan members could be guided, controlled, restrained, standardized, and [otherwise generally] led. Ritual (*li* 禮), as I have said many times in the past, is simply the customary laws and regulations of the clan. The *Zuozhuan* says, "In all cases when the leaders of the princes rescue others from trouble, share the burden of their disasters, and chastise crime, it is in accordance with ritual" 凡候伯, 救患, 分災, 討罪, 禮也 (First year of Duke Xi).[1] Here the original relationship between *de* and ritual (*li*) is still apparent. This can also explain the relationship in 2.3 below, "If you use virtuous action to manage and lead, and ritual to govern and regulate" 導之以德, 齊之以禮, which is also a principle of the clan system. These customary laws and regulations were carried on for a long period of time. They originally had a markedly religious function and content, but Confucius and the Confucians completely rationalized them and turned them into morality. For example, the "inner sage" originally referred to a mystical, magical sorcerer with a [special] connection to Heaven, but was transformed into a leader (a monarch) of high noble character and great prestige. The trinity of religion, ethics, and government of the remote past developed into a kind of pan-moralism and became the mainstream of thought that continued for over two thousand years. This pan-moralism mixed and melded together into a unified and organized system the personal *religious* pursuit of integrity and spiritual perfection with regulation of the *political* order and principles of behavior. In it, formal principles equal essential principles. Beginning from Confucius and Mencius, through Han Confucianism and Song-Ming Neo-Confucianism, this [system] has continued to be influential to this day. Because it has already developed into a very complex and complete regulatory and theoretical system and psychological habit, on the one hand it has caused China to lack independent social and political systems of regulation; and on the other hand, it has also caused China to lack an independent consciousness of religio-psychological pursuit. Both of these melded into "relational morality," so that it became impossible to differentiate or separate out any one society or period's respective laws and regulations from "universal, inevitable" absolute law. This is why the "false Daoists," "fake *junzi*," or "Marxist-Leninist old ladies" could run amuck with their absolute law of moralism throughout the country (in the form of such slogans as "struggle against selfishness and repudiate revisionism," or "revolution bursts forth from the depths of the spirit").

2.2. 子曰：「詩三百，一言以蔽之，曰『思無邪』。」

Confucius said, "The three hundred poems of the *Book of Songs*, if summarized in one sentence, would be: No falsehood."

Notes: *Zhu Xi quotes Cheng Yi: "No falsehood" means* cheng 誠 *("sincerity"). Cheng Shude quotes Zheng Hao's* 鄭浩 *(1863–1947) "Lunyu jizhu shuyao"* 論語集註述要*: The ancient meaning of* xie 邪 *is* xu 徐 *(meaning "to slow") . . . so "no falsehood" means that one's mind has no other aim. . . . It is saying that the three hundred poems, whether they have to do with filial sons, loyal ministers, resentful men or sorrowful women, all arise from the overflow of extreme emotion, the direct expression of grief over wrongs done, and have no trace of falsity or pretense.*

Comments: There has been much discussion of this passage. The line "No falsehood" comes from the *Book of Songs* poem 297 on horses. The character *si* 思 should not be taken as [having its typical meaning of] "thought," nor should *xie* 邪 be taken as [having its typical meaning of] "evil."[2]

2.3. 子曰：「道之以政，齊之以刑，民免而無恥；道之以德，齊之以禮，有恥且格。」

Confucius said, "Using policy to manage and lead, and using punishments to govern and regulate, the people will seek only to avoid being punished, and will have no sense of shame in their hearts. Using virtuous action to manage and lead, and ritual to govern and regulate, the people will have a sense of shame, an inner recognition and conversion."

Notes: *Cheng Shude quotes Zheng Hao: [The character]* ge 格 *[in the last line] means "come." Yang Bojun's Lunyu yizhu quotes the Ziyi* 緇衣 *chapter of the "Liji"* 禮記*: "As for the people, one must teach them with virtue, order them with ritual, then the people will have a mind to follow. If you teach them with policies and order them with punishments, the people will have a mind to avoid or escape [the rule or punishment]"* 夫民，教之以德，齊之以禮，則民有格心；教之以政，齊之以刑，則民有遁心. *This passage could be regarded as the first commentary on Confucius's statement; this is quite credible. Here the "mind to follow" and the "mind to avoid" create a* *pattern of opposition. The character* dun 遁 *means "to avoid" or "escape." The opposite of avoiding or escaping is drawing near to, submitting to, or moving toward.*

Comments: The character *ge* 格 [in the last line] has many readings. As I already explained under 2.1, this passage again compares ancient clan customary regulations (virtue and ritual) with contemporary administrative regulation (punishment and policy), and in doing so emphasizes, again, the importance of taking inner pleasure in complying. Why would it be bad for people to "seek only to avoid being punished, and . . . have no sense of shame in their hearts"? Because if one only cares about external behavior and results and does not address the inner world of the heart, this will be far from the unity of body and spirit, the inward and outward "sincerity" (*cheng* 誠) originally demanded in shamanistic rites and ceremonies. After Confucius, Mencius moved from "inner nature is good" to speak of the "four beginnings" (*si duan* 四端),[3] developing the psychology of Confucianism. Xunzi emphasized that "actually the rites and music, policies and punishments, are one and the same," setting aside the psychological aspect and emphasizing instead the establishment of systems of regulation. The former developed religious morality and returned to mystical experience, while the latter developed social morality and moved toward government and law. Subsequently, when Daoists and Legalists took the upper hand, they discarded the whole ancient clan structure. But because in the long term small-scale agricultural production and blood relations continued to form the important pillars of the social structure, when the Han dynasty emphasized *xiao* 孝 ("filial piety"), ethics, and government in their grasp of the empire's government systems, these [clan structures] became inseparably melded with the new forms. In Song-Ming Neo-Confucianism, this was pushed to even greater theoretical preeminence, and this was also the case in practice. This kind of religious morality encompassed everything, including government, as is reflected in expressions like the "the great duke is impartial" 大公無私, "dying for a righteous cause" 成仁取義, and "worry about the world's worries first, rejoice when the world rejoices after" 先天下之憂而憂, 後天下之樂而樂.[4] Precisely because China's unity of church and state is characterized by this type of broad moralism, it has been more difficult to separate from secular governmental affairs than irrational religious faith or doctrine.

2.4. 子曰:「吾十有五而志于學, 三十而立, 四十而不惑, 五十而知天命, 六十而耳順, 七十而從心所欲, 不踰矩。」

Confucius said, "At fifteen I made up my mind to study, at thirty I established myself, at forty I was no longer confused, at fifty I recognized my own fate, at sixty I naturally accepted all kinds of criticism, at seventy I did whatever my heart desired to do, but without going against the prescriptions of ritual."

Comments: This passage is one of the most famous of ancient texts, and has been in continual use to the present day. It is very interesting to use age to describe the various stages and states of individual maturity. Accordingly, the passage has a variety of explanations. These have focused on, for example, "making up one's mind" (*zhi* 志) to study what? What does it really mean to "establish" (*li* 立, "to stand") oneself? Does it refer to success in one's work or to moral accomplishment? "Confused" about what? And how should we understand *ershun* (耳順, literally, "ear complies," here translated as "accepted criticism")? Could it be that having "recognized my fate," everything goes smoothly without a hitch (*shunshun dangdang* 順順當當)? And so on. Actually, each can understand this passage in his or her own way, there is no need to be strict about it. For example, some emphasize that "at thirty I had established myself" must be read in connection with "establish yourself with ritual 立於禮" (*Analects* 8.8). That is to say, if a man starts to study ritual at six, by thirty he can be said to have mastered it. Later commentators, however, for the most part do not read this as narrowly addressed to ritual, but rather as pertaining more broadly to the maturity of the human personality, and I find these readings preferable. The most difficult to understand is what is meant by *zhi tianming* (知天命, here translated "recognized my own fate"). One might read it to mean that by fifty, one has developed an understanding and recognition of life as a whole—in all its randomness—understanding on the one hand one's own limitations and on the other hand one's potential. No longer is it the boundless prospects of youth, "Mounting the tall tower alone, / To gaze all the way to the horizon."[5] Nor is it the reckless empty ambition of "If I don't do Heaven's work, who will? 天下事舍我其誰."[6]

Why would one want to turn religious morality into a "categorical imperative," [consisting of] the individual pursuit of spiritual perfection? Theism regards this as the will of Heaven, or divine command. But an anthropological historical ontology (*renleixue lishi bentilun* 人類學歷史本體論) regards this as the responsibility and duty of the individual toward humanity as a whole, for which reason it is both inescapable and unrefusable. This is so not because of the heteronomous or experiential demands of any particular society, time period, or collective, but because of the directive of a universally "inevitable" so-called "a priori" autonomy, that is, free will, or the locus of final reality or substance. It is higher than any experience, yet still rooted in the emotions of human relations—rooted in them yet able to transcend them, because of the solidification of reason within it, to become a psychological formation or structure. Therefore, although it pertains purely to individual self-cultivation, it is not something that everyone can attain, and this is where the distinction between the sage and the common person lies. It is also only in this way that we can distinguish between ethical absolutism and relativism in philosophy, or between religion and politics in praxis, or between personal religious morality and public social morality, so that each is in its proper place.

As for the "will of Heaven" (*tianming* 天命), "fate" (*ming* 命), "establishing one's fate" (*liming* 立命), or "rectifying one's fate" (*zhengming* 正命), this is something Confucius and Mencius frequently speak of, but that is not at all easy to explain. It has various implications. "When a thing comes about though no one brings it about, then it is decreed 莫之致而至者, 命也" (*Mencius* V.A.6), meaning something that is not within the power of humans to control. But Wang Fuzhi says in his commentary on the Four Books (*Du Sishu da quan shuo* 讀四書大全說 [*Great Compendium on Reading the Four Books*]):

> It is commonly said that every drink and every bite are determined ahead of time, and any inevitable thing you can speak of, however trivial, we call "fate." Even life before death, and poverty before the accumulation of wealth are all considered to belong to fate—things requiring every human effort to attain, but one simply hasn't attained them—is this not error? Therefore, if a scholar-official is in poverty, it is not that Heaven has deprived him; and if a person does not die or a country is not destroyed, this is not something given by Heaven. In other words, those areas where people should expend their effort cannot be blamed upon Heaven. (*Du Sishu da quan shuo* 讀死書大全說)

This comes a bit close to Xunzi. But it is still emphatically within the spirit of the shared Confucian tradition that includes Confucius and Mencius. In other words, people live amid unpredictable randomness, but this does not at all mean that they lose control. This is what is meant by "knowing the will of Heaven" (*zhi tianming* 知天命), or here, "recognizing my own fate." As we read in *Mencius*:

> Whether he is going to die young or to live to a ripe old age makes no difference to his steadfastness of purpose. It is through awaiting whatever is to befall him with a perfected character that he stands firm on his proper destiny. 殀壽不貳, 修身以俟之, 所以立命。(*Mencius* VII.A.1)

> That is why he who understands destiny does not stand under a wall on the verge of collapse. He who dies after having done his best in following the way dies according to his proper destiny. 知命者不立乎巖牆之下; 盡其道而死者, 正命也。(*Mencius* VII.A.2)[7]

"Standing on destiny," "understanding destiny," and one's "proper destiny" all address the ability of individuals to influence and direct their own fates. There is no trace here of obeying fate, submitting to fate, or fatalism. This is also what is meant by "knowing Heaven." Thus when we speak of "knowing the will of Heaven," or "fearing the will of Heaven," this should not be understood as an external law or control, but rather as the diligent, reverent shouldering of external chance, neither "resenting Heaven" nor "blaming other people" 不怨天不尤人 (*Analects* 14.35), but establishing oneself in the process of living through and experiencing this life with all its difficulties and obstacles, without losing the necessity of exercising control. Recognizing one's own limitations, and using these very limitations to overcome obstacles, bear responsibility and establish [oneself]—these are also what is meant by "establishing one's fate," one's "proper destiny," and "knowing the will of Heaven." "At fifty I recognized my own fate" has its significance in the perfection of bearing of responsibility and establishing [oneself], that is, the self's thorough grasp of fate. This in general is probably quite difficult for anyone under about fifty to achieve. In sum, the recognition of and contentment with the limited nature of one's own existence, and yet persistence in the establishment of oneself—this is not pessimism, anxiety, or endless futile pursuits. The

Chinese-style emotional transcendence involved in the "knowledge of fate" or "following fate" is quite different from that in the West. In our discussion we will frequently return to this idea.

2.5. 孟懿子問孝。子曰:「無違。」樊遲御, 子告之曰:「孟孫問孝於我, 我對曰『無違』。」樊遲曰:「何謂也?」子曰:「生事之以禮; 死葬之以禮, 祭之以禮。」

Meng Yizi asked about how to be filial. Confucius answered, saying, "Do not disobey."

Fan Chi was driving Confucius's chariot, and Confucius said to him, "Meng Yizi asked me about how to be filial, and I answered that you should not disobey." Fan Chi asked, "What does this mean?" Confucius said, "While your parents are living, serve them in accordance with the ritual system; when they have died, bury them in accordance with the ritual system, and make sacrifices in accordance with the ritual system."

Notes: *Yang Bojun notes: Meng Yizi was an official of the state of Lu, and a member of the Three Families. In ancient times, ritual applied differently to different levels: the Emperor, the feudal lords, officials, knights, and common people. The Three Families of Lu were of the official class, but sometimes adopted the ritual practice of the Lu lords, and even sometimes that of the emperor. This type of behavior was known as* jian 僭 *("overstepping") and was most distressing to Confucius. His answers in these lines may have been directed at this phenomenon.*

Comments: To use the observance of the ritual system to explain "filial piety" (*xiao* 孝) would seem to have little relationship with psychology. This reply is directed at a specific person (a well-known and powerful official of the state of Lu) and addressed a concrete situation (the over-stepping of ritual bounds, *jian li* 僭禮).

The phrases "asked about filial piety" (*wen xiao* 問孝) or "asked about benevolence" (*wen ren* 問仁)" are sometimes translated, "asked what filial piety is" or "asked what benevolence is," and so on. Confucius always answers such questions with how to act (or behave) in order to be filial or humane. Thus, it is more correct to translate these questions as "asked about how to be filial" or "asked about how to be humane." China has never been very interested in questions of "what is," or in questions of Being or Idea, but instead has been interested in questions of "How" (*ruhe* 如何). This is a major characteristic of Chinese pragmatic reason, which is totally different from Greece in its point of view, approach, questions, language, and patterns of thought. **In this respect, Chinese philosophical tradition is non-essentialist and anti-metaphysical. What it emphasizes are the various states and functions of existence, rather than fixed realities or essences. This is equally true of Confucians, Daoists, Legalists, and yinyang theorists. After the arrival of Buddhism, this changed, as its strong influence on Song-Ming Neo-Confucianism resulted in movement toward the notion of two worlds.** But Buddhism also gave rise to the Chan school within it, which constituted a return to native tradition. The relationship among these schools is complicated, however, and not like that described by many of today's historians of philosophy.

2.6. 孟武伯問孝。子曰: 「父母唯其疾之憂。」

Meng Wubo asked about how to be filial. Confucius said, "Make your parents worry only about their sons and daughters falling ill."

Notes: *Cheng Shude quotes the "Shuo Lin" chapter of the Huainanzi: "The one who worries about his parents' illness is the son; the one who treats it is the doctor." The "Qu li" chapter of the Liji says: "When his father or mother is ill, (a young man) who has been capped should not use his comb, nor walk with his elbows stuck out, nor speak on idle topics, nor take his lute or cithern in hand. He should not eat of (different) meats till his taste is changed, nor drink till his looks are changed. He should not laugh so as to show his teeth, nor be angry till he breaks forth in reviling. When the illness is gone, he may resume his former habits."[8] Both of these take a son's worry for his parents' illness to be [a sign of] filiality.*

Comments: This passage has many interpretations. Does it refer to sons and daughters being very solicitous of their parents' health (as in the Note)? Or does it mean that sons and daughters only cause their parents worry over sickness, and not over anything else, so that they are able to be completely at ease about other things? From Meng Wubo's posthumous title, Wu 武 [meaning "martial"], it appears that he may have been full of valor, and his parents may have feared that he would be indifferent to death, and meet with difficulties or disasters. Perhaps this is the reason Confucius responded to the question in this way?!

The several passages that fall before and after this one all contain Confucius's answer to the question of how to be filial, but all answer this question differently. Just as it will later, when disciples and others come to ask him about benevolence or government, Confucius's response varies according to the person. This is a very important point. It not only shows that Confucius responded differently depending upon the situation (different people, issues, contexts, and different needs, weaknesses, and problems). More importantly, in comparison with Plato's dialogues, the latter worked from concrete things and concepts (e.g., a beautiful vase, a beautiful woman, etc.) to abstract a universal, inevitable, and even transcendent ideal form (e.g., the idea of beauty), thinking that that ideal form is the locus of truth, and then used this abstractly argued ideal form as the standard or principle by which to regulate the concrete world. Here we see just the opposite. **Confucians always see "Truth" as something concrete and multifarious that is found in the actions and practices of these various concrete persons, affairs, and objects. In other words, "The Way is found in everyday human relationships" 道在倫常日用之中.** To depart from this multiplicity and concreteness to seek for something universal—as to leave this human life in pursuit of transcendence—is not something that Confucianism elects to do. This is the reason for the fact that in faith, Confucians do not speak of spirits, in thought they do not emphasize abstraction, and in method they do not use logic. This is where "pragmatic reason," emotion-as-substance in place of reason-as-substance, and the this-worldly (human) vs. other-worldly character [of Chinese thought] come from. This is a theme I have already discussed in the comments to the previous passage (2.5).

In the introduction to this book I discussed how "Heaven and Earth, country, parents, and teacher" have traditionally been objects of worship for Chinese people. Of these, filial piety to one's parents is the core. The *Classic of Filial Piety* (*Xiaojing* 孝經) came out in the Han dynasty, and Tang legal codes mandated the duty of sons to care for their aging parents. "Filial piety," and therefore family, has from start to finish been a key concept in Chinese culture. At times it has been preached ad nauseum, as in the "Twenty-Four Exemplars of Filial Piety" (*Ershisi xiao* 二十四孝).[9] But as to how "family values" should be estimated today or in the future, this is something that still seems to require deep consideration. Is it possible for the natural blood-based sense of kinship, with the addition of intentional and modern cultivation, to become a kind of healthy, stabilizing element of society? And filial piety can be extended to include siblings, friends, the extended family and the village. . . . If people regard emotion as reality, existence, and substance—could this be the way for society to find a new path? Based on the experience of China, the Mohists opposed emotion, with meager funerals and opposition to music, and the Daoists negated emotion with concepts like "free and easy" (*xiaoyao* 逍遙) and "making all things equal" (*qiwu* 齊物). Neither of these emphasized the centrality of the interpersonal emotional relations based on parent-child kinship feelings, and thus both lost out to the Confucians. Confucianism moves from concern to happiness, and the interplay of concern and happiness causes people to realize that the ultimate reality of human life is to be found precisely in these emotions. It does not need to be sought on the "other side," and thus Confucians actively enter the world, exerting themselves tirelessly, to make the ways of humans accord with Heaven and Earth. This has given Chinese culture the ability to undergo suffering and devastation without breaking down or being obliterated. Could this be a starting point for considering its future?

2.7. 子游問孝。子曰:「今之孝者, 是謂能養。至於犬馬, 皆能有養; 不敬, 何以別乎? 」

Ziyou asked about how to be filial. Confucius said, "These days, what is meant by filial piety is simply being able to support one's parents. People support and feed their dogs and horses. If there is no respect, then what difference is there?"

Comments: The word for "respect" (*jing* 敬) can be explained in two different ways. One is love and respect for parents, the other is respect for moral laws. The latter can be explained as what Kant referred to as "moral feeling," and indicates a reverence and fear of the absolute law. Of course this greatly elevates the metaphysical stature of ethical behavior, but I am afraid it does not capture the original Confucian meaning of the word. In Confucianism, respect (*jing* 敬) refers rather to the former, to the loving respect of a child for his parents. It can echo (and be echoed by) the "attitude" in the following passage. Here, Confucians take public social morality ("being able to support") and elevate it to the level of private religious morality ("If there is no respect, then what difference is there?"). This demonstrates that private religious morality is founded upon a kind of holy emotion ("respect" originates in the feeling of fear when sacrificing to the gods). The difficulty with the "moral theology" that Kant envisioned is that it lacks this emotional foundation, so that it is difficult to reach the "theological" (because Kant's moral feeling is the reverence for objective law, and not the emotional love of the object). This is a crucial point, and should be underlined as Xiong Shili (熊十力 1885–1968) did: "Critical, critical."

2.8. 子夏問孝。子曰: 「色難。有事弟子服其勞, 有酒食先生饌, 曾是以為孝乎?」

Zixia asked how to be filial. Confucius said, "By not giving your parents attitude. If there is something to be done, the young offer their services; if there is wine and food, they allow the elders to eat first—is that all filial piety is?"

Comments: These two passages emphasize again that "filial piety" must first and foremost be the cultivation and extension of a kind of inner emotion. In the comments on the previous passage and on 1.5, I have already discussed how "respect" (*jing* 敬) originated in the emotions of fear, reverence, and worship found in ancient sacrifices to ancestors and the gods. It is not simply some external ceremonial regulation of attitude or behavior. What is important, therefore, is to attain this kind of personal emotional experience; it is neither an external heteronomous behavior, nor is it an abstract, transcendent ideal.

One of the biggest problems of both Song-Ming Neo-Confucianism and modern New Confucianism is that they have not given adequate attention to this point. This is particularly the case with the Cheng-Zhu school, which takes "Principle" (*li* 理) as "substance." In Zhu Xi's commentary on *Analects* 1.2, "It seems that filiality to parents and respect for one's elders must be the root of benevolence" (小弟也者, 其為仁之本與), he says. "Benevolence (*ren* 仁) is the principle of love, and the virtue of the heart-mind." Benevolence here becomes "love," the transcendent and speculative principle or virtue of the sensuous feelings of the heart-mind (*xin* 心). Zhu Xi also says, "To be humane is to act humanely"

(為仁猶言行仁). "Benevolence" here has become just a kind of external principle, norm, or heteronomy.

Cheng Yi's commentary on *Analects* 1.2 says, "Someone asked, 'If filiality and respect for elders is the root of benevolence, does that mean that from filiality and respect for elders one can arrive at benevolence?' He said, 'No. It means that practicing benevolence begins with filiality and respect for elders; filiality and respect are one aspect of benevolence. To say it is the root of the practice of benevolence is also possible, but to say it is the root of benevolence is not possible. For benevolence is nature (*xing* 性), and filiality and respect are function (*yong* 用). Nature has only these four: benevolence (*ren* 仁), righteousness (*yi* 義), ritual (*li* 禮), and wisdom (*zhi* 智). When were filiality and respect ever part of it?'" And again, "In speaking of nature (*xing* 性), then we can take benevolence as the root of filiality and respect." This is precisely the above-mentioned Platonic method, or Platonic orientation, for it abstracts the notion of benevolence out from the concrete (filiality and respect) and calls it metaphysical reality ("nature," or "root"). In the process, filiality, respect, and other concrete emotional psychology becomes the realization or manifestation of reality ("nature" or "root"). This "Principle-as-substance" of the Cheng-Zhu school came under intense criticism by Lu Jiuyuan and Wang Yangming, and particularly by modern-day New Confucian Mou Zongsan. But although the Lu-Wang school and Mou Zongsan both take the heart-mind (*xin* 心) as substance, because they emphasize the distinction between the "Dao mind" (*daoxin* 道心) and the "human mind" (*renxin* 人心), and the opposition and distinction between "nature" and "feeling" in the formulation, "the mind unifies nature and emotions" (*xin tong xingqing* 心統性情), the result is the domination and control of the moral-metaphysical "Dao mind" and "nature-as-substance" (*xing ti* 性體).

If we say that the Cheng-Zhu school takes Principle as the reality or substance that structures knowledge and systems of authority, then the Lu-Wang school and Mou Zongsan take the heart-mind as that reality or substance. Both have strayed far from the concrete emotions of the human heart-mind that is closely linked with "human desire," and thus are not far from the Cheng-Zhu school. But because the Cheng-Zhu school makes transcendent Principle and nature into the master that governs and controls concrete interpersonal emotions and desires, Dai Zhen, Tan Sitong, and others cry out that they are "killing people with Principle." And because the Lu-Wang school holds that the heart-mind is not separable from the body (*shen* 身), it is able to move toward a theory of natural human desire in which "desire" is "nature," thoroughly eschewing a moral metaphysics.

Apparently, it is only by deconstructing these views of "Principle-as-substance," "nature-as-substance," and "heart-mind-as-substance," and returning to the "emotion-as-substance" in which principle and desire are melded together, that we can perhaps approach Confucius and Mencius more closely and reconstruct the original, classical Confucianism. How this looks in Confucius will be discussed in detail in the following passages. Mencius's notion of the "Four Beginnings" is even harder to [connect with] New Confucianism's emphasis on "a priori" or "transcendent and inner," because what it addresses does not depart from the emotional. Mou Zongsan emphasizes that the "heart of compassion" (*ceyin zhi xin* 惻隱之心) is the "point of sensitivity" (*lingming yi dian* 靈明一點) that is "unable to be at peace about or bear" (*bu an bu ren* 不安不忍) things; if that is not emotion, what is it? Of course this emotion is not natural physiological sentiment, but rather has social rationality sedimented within it; it is emotion that melds together desire and principle.

It is possible to have strong feelings for dogs and horses, and for dogs and horses to feel strongly for people, but this type of feeling is not "respect." Clearly, although respect is an emotion, it has absorbed a distinctly social rationality. This is precisely what is meant by "human nature." The reason that the "heart of compassion" is a "human" feeling ("No man is devoid of a heart sensitive to the sufferings of others")[10] is precisely because of the rationality sedimented within it.

2.9. 子曰: 「吾與回言終日, 不違如愚。退而省其私, 亦足以發。回也, 不愚。」

Confucius said, "If I talk to Yan Hui a whole day, he will not express any different opinion [from mine], as if he were stupid. But if I later observe his behavior and so on, it inspires even me. Yan Hui is not the slightest bit stupid!"

Notes: *Zhu Xi notes: The word* si 私 *refers to the times that Yan Hui is alone, when he is not engaged in discussions. The word* fa 發 *means to expound upon what has been said.*

Comments: There is another way to understand the word *fa* 發, which I have translated as "inspired." It is often taken to mean that Yan Hui "develops," "elaborates," or "expounds" on Confucius. This is the meaning taken in the above note, but I do not follow it here; 11.3 is similar. In the *Analects*, Yan Hui always appears "stupid," quiet, and mysterious.

2.10. 子曰:「視其所以, 觀其所由, 察其所安。人焉廋哉? 人焉廋哉?」

Confucius said, "Look at what he does and how he acts, observe where he begins and ends, understand what he finds sustenance in—where will he be able to hide then! Where will he be able to hide?"

Comments: People always, whether purposefully or not, wear all kinds of masks. They are born on the earth and live among people, and thus there is this "looking" and "observation." The world of "I and Thou" is always obstructed by the world of "I and It."

2.11. 子曰:「溫故而知新, 可以為師矣。」

Confucius said, "Review the past in order to know the future; in this way you will be able to be a teacher."

Comments: In China there has always been an extreme emphasis on historical experience, and the recording of various experiences and lessons to serve as warnings to others in the future is one of the great marks of its civilization. The number of historical works China has produced is without equal in the world. The attitude of starting from experience, facts, and history, of learning from the old in order to inform the new, not [trusting in] miracles or superstition, nor indulging in pure speculation—this is the concrete manifestation of "pragmatic reason." "Pragmatic reason" is in some senses the same as historical reason. Both speculative reason (knowledge) and practical reason (morality) originate in and are subordinate to this "historical reason." No wonder it is said that Kant in his later years was planning a work entitled *A Critique of Historical Reason*.

2.12. 子曰：「君子不器。」

Confucius said, "The noble person (*junzi* 君子) is not a tool."

Comments: Today this passage could be rendered, "The noble person is not a robot." In other words a person should not be controlled, should not become some sort of specialized tool or machine. A person is alive and is not a tool or part of a (technical, social, or political) tool. He is not a slave to his own creation, which then oppresses, occupies, or controls his power of "dissent" (whether against a technological achievement, authoritarian will, or consumerist advertising). People should allow their latent talents and individuality to obtain full development and expression. This is what it means to "live," from a philosophical standpoint. Sociologically speaking, in traditional Chinese society this statement, "the noble person is not a tool," meant that the literati (who derived their economic wealth from the land) were to be the "backbone of society." They were not, could not, should not belong to any specialization. They were to study, hold office, and act as humans (morally) in order to "govern the state and pacify all under heaven" (治國平天下). Their duty was to hold together and guide the existence of the entire society. In the twentieth century, in the particular context of domestic trouble and foreign invasion, modern Chinese intellectuals still played this "backbone" role (see my *History of Contemporary Chinese Thought*) for about six generations.[11] For the sake of awakening and national salvation they shouted slogans, carried out movements, and fomented revolution, from carrying out literary creation to scientific, educational, and cultural work, to leading the peasant revolution. Although they may all have had "occupations," they were also all "worried about the world," and were "not tools."

But when it comes to present-day society, the situation is very different. It is no longer the intellectuals but the broad bourgeoisie that holds together the framework of society's existence. Intellectuals have become specialists whose work is very narrowly defined, like doctors, lawyers, engineers, managers, teachers, professors, journalists, and so on. They have become no more than a kind of apparatus for this society. In today's society, people have all become "professionalized." Thus, the "noble person *must* be a tool" (taking "noble person" as a loan word here of course—there is no so-called petty person).

I am speaking in general terms, as the actual situation is more complicated. First of all, among these specialists there are those whose scope of work, research, and publication expresses views or opinions about the "whole" (the world, nation, humankind, society); that is, there are still "noble people" who are "not tools"—viz., today's "public intellectuals." Secondly, even if they do not publish along these lines, there are those who are not hindered from having an interest and concern beyond their specialization. In both of these senses, it is still possible to say "the noble person is not a tool." It may be said that China is now in the process of shifting from a traditional society in which the literati and intellectuals ("noble persons") are the leaders and framework to a modern society in which the bourgeoisie are the leaders and framework. The various attendant phenomena and problems, including the loss of a sense of mission, the increasing emphasis on specialization, the fading away of "thinkers" and the emergence of "scholars," and so on—all are indicators of this shift from "the noble person is not a tool" to "the noble person must be a tool." This process will only speed up and become more widespread. But it is still even more worth emphasizing how public intellectuals can carry on the tradition of "the noble person is not a tool" in today's highly specialized context.

2.13. 子貢問君子。子曰:「先行其言而後從之。」

Zigong asked what is a noble person (*junzi*). Confucius said, "He first carries out what he expresses, then speaks about it."

Comments: Zigong was very intelligent and good at speaking, so Confucius answered him in this way. This touches on the question of whether language is the foundation and home, which I will discuss in the comments on a later passage.

2.14. 子曰:「君子周而不比，小人比而不周。」

Confucius said, "The noble person is broadly magnanimous toward people, and is not partial or pandering; the petty person is partial and pandering, and not broadly magnanimous."

Comments: This type of brief parallel antithesis is common in the *Analects*. Terse but comprehensive, this construction was able to express the opposition between right and wrong, black and white, good and evil, beauty and ugliness, in a way that was easy to recite and remember. Chinese parallel antitheses are beautiful, and hopefully can be preserved and continued in the present day.

2.15. 子曰: 「學而不思則罔, 思而不學則殆。」

Confucius said, "To study but not think is to be perplexed; to think without studying is dangerous."

Comments: In epistemology, we have Kant's formulation, "Perception without conception is blind, conception without perception is empty";[12] this is almost the same line of thinking. This truth is still not outdated today. Whether in East or West, this is the same idea, the same truth. Ye Shi, in his *Xi xue ji yan* (習學記言) says, "One who imitates, practices, and models himself on the old ways, superficially carrying them on, this is like 'not thinking'; one who creates far-fetched interpretations of *xing* and *ming* (穿穴性命), empty and self-satisfied, this is like 'not studying.' A scholar does not overstep in either of these two ways." Scholars from the Han to the Song, from Chinese purists to those who go after Western fashions, from ancient times to today—this applies to all.

2.16. 子曰: 「攻乎異端, 斯害也已! 」

Confucius said, "To attack heterodox teachings that are different from yours, it is there that the danger lies."

Comments: There are three different ways to read this passage, most of which take the word *gong* 攻 (attack) to mean to specialize, study, or devote oneself to, yielding the reading, "To study heterodox teachings is dangerous." In a manuscript of the *Analects* unearthed ten or so years ago, in place of this character *gong* 攻 was *gong* 功 (meaning work or skill), which would seem to support that reading.

A second possible reading would be, "Attack and suppress heretical teachings, and thus they will lose their danger." This is Yang Bojun's reading. This would seem to be an interesting reflection of the philosophy of struggle of the Mao period. In the traditional commentaries there are also some advocates of this reading.

I have chosen a third possibility, which I believe expresses the broad spirit of Confucianism: it advocates looking for commonalities and allowing differences to remain, not driving out those who differ with oneself. When the emperor Liang Wudi (464–549, r. 502) became a devout Buddhist in the Sui and Tang dynasties, he placed the Buddha above Confucius. In the modern period, with the veneration of Marx and Lenin, when these foreign men's portraits were hung in Tiananmen Square the Chinese people did not object. Mencius scolded the Yangists and Mohists, yet recognized Gaozi, who believed that "the inborn is what is meant by 'nature,'" as his disciple.[13] Han Yu 韓愈 (768–824) refuted Buddhism and Daoism, yet believed that "Confucius had to use Mozi, and Mozi had to use Confucius."[14] Su Shi 蘇軾 (1036–1101) took Confucianism in and out of Buddhism and Daoism, and [his brother] Su Zhe 蘇轍 (1039–1112) used the "Doctrine of the Mean" to explicate Laozi; subsequently, scholar-officials and the lower classes alike all adopted the "unity of the three faiths" [Confucianism, Buddhism, and Daoism]. Chinese religion has not had any passionate religious fervor or doctrinal disputes but has persisted in following the maxim, "Whoever has the truth, that's who we listen to." This breadth explains why in the modern period China readily received Western technology, culture, administration, and even philosophy, and was so quick to change thousands of years of thought, clothing, customs, and lifestyles. This breadth, in turn, is precisely the manifestation of that pragmatic reason that emphasizes praxis, experience, and "accomplishing things through facts." **And it is just this breadth of pragmatic reason that gives Confucianism itself and Chinese culture the ability to continuously take in and assimilate objects and thought from abroad, while continuing its own existence and development.** If it were not for this reception and assimilation of Daoism, Legalism, and yinyang theory, Han Confucianism, as represented by Dong Zhongshu, could never have existed. If it had not absorbed Buddhism, Song-Ming Neo-Confucianism would not have been possible. If it had not absorbed the concepts of Western natural sciences, we would never have had modern Confucians like Kang Youwei or Tan Sitong. "If one can absorb, then one will be great"—where is this not true, whether for people, schools of thought, cultures, or traditions.

This broad spirit of Confucianism is an important resource for the construction of today's public social morality. Today's public social morality has two major characteristics. The first is its broad spirit—it recognizes and allows for the variety of values that exist in the world, and does not meddle with the rights and freedoms of individual choice.

The individual's ultimate concerns, religious faith (or lack of it), concepts of values, and attitude toward life, and so on, should occupy the central position. The second is shared norms and standards: in order to maintain the minimum requirements for that society's life, individual members should have the moral conscience to follow common norms of behavior. Because this aspect is closely related with economics, law, and government, the content will differ according to time period, nationality, and so on, and people should tolerate and harmonize with one another.

In addition to common norms, there are two additional aspects: first, a strict respect for the individual struggle for freedom, autonomy, and equality—human beings are the goal, not a tool. Secondly, there should be special care taken of those members of society who are disadvantaged, such as the old and weak, women and children, as well as the disabled, and even of the animal world. This is what is meant by, "All people are my brothers and sisters, and all things are my companions" 民吾同胞, 物吾與也.[15] Clearly, not only in terms of personal religious morality but also in terms of public social morality, traditional Confucianism does have objectionable teachings that must be abolished (like the "Three Cardinal Guides" *sangang* 三綱, "Three Obediences and Four Virtues" *sancong side* 三從四德, etc.),[16] as well as resources that can prove productive (like this passage and "the ritually correct way to assist a blind person" in 15.42, etc.).

2.17. 子曰: 「由! 誨女知之乎? 知之為知之, 不知為不知, 是知也。」

Confucius said, "Zilu, let me tell you what it means to seek knowledge: you know what you know, you don't know what you don't know. This is true 'knowledge.'"

Comments: The emphasis here on an attitude of pursuing knowledge is yet another manifestation of pragmatic reason. To construct a large system that encompasses everything in reality is to take not knowing for knowing; to force a lack of knowledge to be knowledge is both a bad habit of the common people and a common failing of "religious founders." One of the characteristics of Confucius and Confucians is that they deny being either great talents or the founders of a religion, and acknowledge that there are things they do not know or understand.

Here, the "lack of knowledge" is seen as a type of "knowledge," which shows that "knowledge" will always be limited, just as human existence is limited. Only by continual accumulation can we continue to make progress toward the limitless or eternal. This is also the reason why Confucius rarely spoke of life, death, or spirits, or of human nature or the Way of Heaven. This truth seems very plain and simple, yet it is actually very deep. The passage brings to light the way that people must acknowledge their own limitations in order to be able to transcend or escape them; it is only by recognizing what one "does not know" that one can truly "know." This is wisdom. This idea is borne out in the common sayings, "It is important to know one's own limitations" 人貴有自知之明, and "It will only display how much he overestimates himself" 多見其不知量也 (*Analects* 19.24), and so on. "Raise it to its greatest brilliancy, that is the way of the Mean"[17] of Confucianism; here we see a bit of it: it is not only lofty and deep truth, but more than that, it is training in life. This is the religious morality aspect of Confucianism, addressing the individual's quest for the perfection of the personality, which is still beneficial to us today. However, it is not required that every person be able to study or carry this out, because this never became part of public social morality, but remained the province of the individual's ultimate concerns. As for statements like the Bible's "Let your 'yes' be 'yes,' and your 'no' be 'no,' so that you may not fall under condemnation" (James 5:12 ESV), Confucianism does not employ this type of external threat or coercion, which seems [to me] to be better. Actually there are many areas in which the *Analects* could usefully be compared with the New Testament, to see if they are similar or different, or half similar and half different, and where the significance of these similarities and differences lies, but unfortunately that task is outside the scope of the present work.

2.18. 子張學干祿。子曰:「多聞闕疑, 慎言其餘, 則寡尤; 多見闕殆, 慎行其餘, 則寡悔。言寡尤, 行寡悔, 祿在其中矣。」

Zizhang asked about how to obtain office and an official salary. Confucius said, "Listen much, and set aside the things you are unsure about, but carefully speak of those aspects of which you can be certain; in this way you will make few mistakes. Watch much, do not undertake risky affairs, but carefully carry out those things you can be sure of; in this way you will make few missteps and have few regrets. If you make few mistakes in your speech and have few regrets over your actions, you will naturally attain the office and the salary."

Comments: The saying "Speak late, speak little, dare to speak" (晚說, 少說, 敢說), was how a particular high-ranking cadre during the Cultural Revolution passed on their life experience with a great deal of self-satisfaction. Let me attempt to explain: "Speak late" meant to wait for the opportune moment to speak, not to speak rashly. If the crucial moment has not yet arrived, although you speak it may not be effective. If you first watch the mistakes of others in their speech, you can reap benefits for your own speech afterward. "Speak little," for if you talk a lot you are sure to misspeak, and you do not want to speak to the point of being irritating. Complex vocabulary and superfluous words only make people tire of listening. "Dare to speak" means that you cannot let the opportunity pass, but when you spot the right moment you speak. In this way you will naturally win the heart of the ruler, gain favor, and rise in the ranks. This follows upon Han Feizi's "Shui nan" 說難 ("Difficulties of Persuasion") chapter. It is the application of pragmatic reason to politics.

Perhaps I should be a bit more clear: Why did students come to study with Confucius? For the great majority of them, they came to "study to attain office," that is, they studied the Six Arts in order to become officials. "If you study well then you will be given office" (學而優則仕) is the conventional course and is very different from knowledge for the sake of knowledge, virtue for the sake of virtue. It is only after Confucius and his disciples that the great importance of religious morality itself was understood, and that "study" became no longer for the sake of attaining office. This aspect was further developed by Yan Hui, Zengzi, and other disciples and their schools. The reason that Confucianism had a more transcendent and religious flavor than the Yinyang school, the Daoists, or the Legalists—the reason Confucius and Mencius were and still are more attractive to people than other thinkers—is because on this point they touch on ultimate concerns, the meaning of life, and the quest for the spiritual realm; that is, because of their religious morality.

2.19. 哀公問曰:「何為則民服?」孔子對曰:「舉直錯諸枉, 則民服; 舉枉錯諸直, 則民不服。」

Duke Ai asked, "How can I make the common people follow me?" Confucius answered, saying, "Employ upright people, and cast off the crooked, and the common people will follow you. Employ crooked people, and cast off the upright, and the common people will not follow you."

Comments: Before modern democratic systems, there was always this question of "whether or not to employ people." This is why the common people today are still very concerned with the affairs of the upper echelons, unfortunately and sadly. Without systemic safeguards, what advantage is there in "employing the upright and casting off the crooked"; but if the system safeguards good order, then it makes more sense to have "men who create order."[18] It is really as Huang Zongxi put it, "One must first govern the law, then one can govern people" (有治法而後有治人).[19] This statement of Huang's constitutes a major development in the study of Confucian social morality. It reasserted the "outward kingship" strain, which we must surely not regard as a solely Song-Ming Neo-Confucian concept.

2.20. 季康子問:「使民敬、忠以勸, 如之何?」子曰:「臨之以莊則敬, 孝慈則忠, 舉善而教不能, 則勸。」

Ji Kangzi asked, "How can one make the common people respectful, faithful, and diligent?" Confucius answered, saying, "If you approach them with dignity, the common people will be respectful; if you are filial and obedient to your parents, and loving towards children and youth, the common people will be faithful; if you elevate good people and educate those who lack ability, the common people will be diligent."

Comments: The notion that if you are filial and loving the people will be faithful is a life principle based upon the consanguineous small-scale farming family as the basic structural unit of society, which developed into Confucian ethical government. The "tenderness" it entails is today significant only as it concerns the private religious morality of individual perfection, and not as required by any contractual or rational public social morality. But the former can still exert a sort of regulative function upon the latter. In my *History of Classical Chinese Thought* (中國古代思想史論) I showed how in the Qin dynasty Yunmeng 雲夢 bamboo slips[20] *The Way of the Mandarin* (*Wei li zhi dao* 為吏之道), there were such statements as

> Treat those below you with kindness and do not insult them. 慈下勿淩。
>
> Respect others and defer often, govern with leniency. 恭敬多讓, 寬以治之。
>
> Be abundantly generous, devoted and faithful; be peaceful, and do not lay blame. 寬裕忠信, 和平毋怨。

These statements "seem to demonstrate that the real government of the Qin was not entirely as extreme as Hanfeizi's theories or Qin Shihuang's practices."[21] This could be taken to support Chen Yinke's notion that Qin administrative practices were still a manifestation of Confucian ideals, and that Qin-Han government and concepts still for the most part constituted a development and extension of Confucianism and Xunzi. Today's histories of philosophy and thought seem to give little attention to this, as Legalism and Confucianism on a surface level seem to be in opposition, while in reality they were mutually alternating, and actually Confucianism remained dominant.

2.21. 或謂孔子曰:「子奚不為政?」子曰:「《書》云:『孝乎惟孝、友于兄弟, 施於有政。』是亦為政, 奚其為為政?」

Someone said to Confucius, "Why don't you go into government?" Confucius said, "In the *Book of Documents* [*Shang shu* 尚書] it says, 'Filial piety! There is only filial piety! If you also know how to love your older and younger brothers, then you can be of use in government.' This is government; what other government would I go into?"

Comments: The Confucian notion of "cultivate yourself, order your family, govern the nation, bring peace to the world," as I have often emphasized, has its origins in practical historical realities: this type of "ethical" pursuit that extends from family to country is the political order of "family-tribe-clan-clan alliance." Here, ethics is government, and from the Yin and Zhou through the Spring and Autumn periods, what was called *bang* (邦 "state"), *guo* (國 "country"), the "eight hundred fiefdoms," and so on, were just such family-tribe-clan states. Therefore, the relationships of father and son, older brother and younger brother, and husband and wife were not simply the "private" individual relationships between family members but rather a kind of shared governing system and norm. In a patriarchal clan unit built on the relationship of fathers and sons as its core and skeleton, the leaders of clan society had of course first to be able to claim legitimacy and establish their authority and position within their own family, tribe, clan, or alliance, and only after that would they be able to take the further step of gathering together and uniting other tribes, clans, and alliances in order to "unify all under heaven" 一統天下. We must understand this historical reality if we are to understand why Confucians emphasized "filiality" as the foundation of government. In clan society, tradition, mores, and authority had undergone a long process of formation and been carried on from generation to generation; they could not be lightly or easily changed. I have already discussed all this under earlier passages. **It was precisely because human relationships (filiality and fraternal duty) equaled government, and because these relationships were imbued with a lofty, substantial quality, that the intermingling of emotion and rationality, religion, ethics, and government became so deeply ingrained.**

2.22. 子曰: 「人而無信, 不知其可也。大車無輗, 小車無軏, 其何以行之哉? 」

Confucius said, "A man who does not keep his word? How can that be? If an oxcart or a carriage does not have the pin for the drawbar used to drive it, how can it go?"

Comments: Keeping one's word comes up many times in the *Analects*, similarly to Kant's use of "not lying" as a universal moral law. Keeping one's word is probably the universal etiquette and "moral" regulation required of the individual by the collective of any society; without it a society cannot hold together. It is not a priori, but for the sake of the existence of the whole of humankind. This is from the society's religious morality aspect; but telling lies to one's enemies and being unwilling to betray one's comrades (for the benefit of a collective, nation, party, or group) is also a part of social morality. The relationship between these two types of morality is very complex. One seeks absolute universality, as if it came down from heaven, and transcends experience. The other seeks only relative objectivity, and is produced by and decided upon within a particular time period and environment. Although the two often coincide, they are also opposed to each other and sharply conflict in many respects, in a manner that calls for more specific analysis.

2.23. 子張問:「十世可知也?」子曰:「殷因於夏禮, 所損益, 可知也; 周因於殷禮, 所損益, 可知也; 其或繼周者, 雖百世可知也。」

Zizhang asked, "Is it possible to know what ten generations hence will be like?" Confucius said, "How the Yin [Shang] carried on and adapted the ritual system of the Xia, adding to it and paring it down, can be known. How the Zhou carried on and adapted the ritual system of the Yin, adding to it and paring it down, can be known. Thus, it may be that those who carry on and adapt the Zhou will be able to be known, though it may be a hundred generations from now."

Comments: Less than three hundred years were to pass before the Qin and Han systems, which arose to replace the Zhou, would already differ greatly from the Xia, Yin, and Zhou. Although later Confucians repeatedly sought "the prime of the Xia and Three Dynasties," it was completely impossible to attain. Instead, it was the government system put into place by Qin Shihuang after he unified China that would basically persist and be carried on for over two thousand years. Mao Zedong spoke of the "Qin system that was carried on by a hundred generations," and liked to compare himself to Qin Shihuang. But the Qin and Han systems of government were also heirs of the Warring States period. The Three Ritual Texts[22] had their origins in deep antiquity, but were written down and formalized during the Han, which would seem to demonstrate that the Han government was still related to the rituals of the Zhou; that is, although they practiced the teachings of the Legalists, they still emphasized "government through ritual propriety" (*li zhi* 禮治). In other words, in any change or reform there will always be elements of continuity; one never starts with a blank slate. This is why we have phrases like "the revolutions of Tang and Wu,"[23] as well as the phrases in this passage, "How the Yin [Shang] carried on and adapted the ritual system of the Xia," and "How the Zhou carried on and adapted the ritual system of the Yin." Those who parade the banner of "totally new" usually end up with "totally old" instead. The Cultural Revolution is an example. Clearly, gradual improvement is preferable to revolution, and carrying on someone's legacy is superior to criticism.

Interestingly, Kang Youwei in his comments on the *Analects* was severely critical of Zengzi, and elevated Zizhang. This was because Zizhang emphasized government characterized by shared objective norms—that is, public social morality. The reference here to "ten generations" has a similar meaning; Zizhang paid attention to questions of the systems of society and government, rather than individual moral self-cultivation, in contrast to Yan Hui and Zengzi. Kang Youwei had great praise for Zizhang, and in so doing was in fact praising himself. It is said (in *Hanfeizi*) that after Confucius, Confucianism formed eight schools, of which the details are unknown. But there were at least two trends that can be descried, one of which, the school of the "inner sage" marked by the cultivation of the heart-mind, is represented by Yan Hui and Zengzi and culminates in Song-Ming Neo-Confucianism. The other is the school of "outer kingship" that addresses ritual systems, worldly accomplishment (*shigong* 事功) and the "spirit of the Spring and Autumn period" (*Chunqiu dayi* 春秋大義) (e.g., "Being familiar with the Three Unities, extending the Three Ages" 通三統, 張三世). This school is represented by Zigong, Zizhang, and Zixia and followed by numerous politicians and thinkers by way of Xunzi and Dong Zhongshu. The former is ahistorical—or perhaps even anti-historical—moral metaphysics, while the latter is socio-political thought that emphasizes history and experience. The former absorbed Buddhism and Chan, the latter absorbed Daoism, Legalism, and the Yinyang school. Both, however, are fundamentally Confucian. This is the only truly complete view of Confucianism; the tendency of modern New Confucians to call the theories of mind and nature the "spirit and marrow" of Confucianism, and to regard the strain represented by Confucius, Mencius, the Cheng brothers, Zhu Xi, Lu Jiuyuan, and Wang Yangming as its "lifeblood" (*mingmai* 命脈), is actually one-sided.

Over the past decades, terms like "primitive society," "slave society," "feudal society," and "capitalist society" have been used indiscriminately to describe Chinese history; this has been like "cutting the feet to fit the shoes," or trying make a square peg fit in a round hole, and has aroused great dissension over the periodization of ancient history and the long-stagnant question of feudalism, which now seem to beg a fresh rethinking. China's neolithic age was long and well-developed, with frequent large wars and a complete tribal system structure that had a great deal of tenacity and was difficult to dismantle. This is an important characteristic, and because of it, in the development of society and culture, the blood family/clan has remained unchanged as the basic element or pillar of society, despite the many stages society has gone through (viz., patriarchal systems, early patriarchal clan systems, systematized clan systems, regional states, large unified autocratic states, familial aristocratic systems, secular landowning imperial power systems, the emergence of contemporary trends, etc.), comprehending all the important historical transitions of the Qin-Han, Wei-Jin, Sui-Tang, and modern periods. This characteristic has governed and influenced every aspect of society, even if "ten generations hence." This is where the true character of or key to Chinese history lies. How to use an understanding of this characteristic in order to look ahead toward the future would really merit deep inquiry. For the greatest development of today's Chinese society has been the dismantling and collapse of this pillar in order to enter the modern period.

2.24. 子曰:「非其鬼而祭之, 諂也。見義不為, 無勇也。」

Confucius said, "To sacrifice to a spirit that does not belong to one's own clan is flattery. To come across something just and not do it is to lack courage."

Comments: The first half of the passage explains that according to the primitive ritual system, one only sacrificed to the ancestors or members of one's own clan. The origin of this [system] did not lie in merit or benefit but in unconditional reverential worship and emotional support. Sacrifice to other spirits was for the most part for the sake of asking for grace or blessings or the avoidance of disaster and so on. The second half of the passage explains that "courage" is a psychological quality. As to how these two halves are related, there seems to be [a relationship], and yet seems not to be. In the end they can only be united on the basis of the shaping of emotion.

Here I would like to reiterate what I said in the discussion of previous passages, namely, that in modern life we should distinguish clearly between two types of morality that were traditionally intermixed—private religious morality (concerned with obedience to the ritual system) and public social morality. Both are often present in the same behavior, activity, or mentality, although they have different content, as in the "flattery" or "courage" of the present passage. The latter (public social morality) has to do with social justice, fairness, and reason; the former (private religious morality), in contrast, has to do with the formation of emotions, faith, and qualities related to the individual. The former is marked by a certain degree of coercion, temporality, and relativity, while the latter for the most part is consciousness-driven, historically accumulated, and absolute. Thus, what we should seek today is neither the unity of benevolence (*ren* 仁) and ritual (*li* 禮) (as in ancient times), nor the opposition of benevolence and ritual (as in modern times), but rather a division of labor between benevolence and ritual. This division of labor is, of course, not complete. Religious morality, [which has to do with] ultimate concerns and the emotional support of the individual, will still have a regulative function and position vis-à-vis social morality. In the past I have compared them to Kant's regulative principle and constitutive principle.[24] But the whole aim of the present work is to return to origins, to conduct a new exploration of Confucianism. It should not be the same as the Han Confucianism characterized by the mutual reflection of Heaven and humans and represented by Dong Zhongshu; nor should it be the same as the Song-Ming Neo-Confucianism characterized by the theory of mind and nature and represented by Zhu Xi and Wang Yangming, or its modern version, moral metaphysics ("modern New Confucianism"). In contrast to these efforts to construct a system of knowledge or authority that will account for everything, a new interpretation of original Confucianism will take emotion as the substance and will emphasize multiplicity, individual personality, and psychological sedimentation; it will stress tolerance, not the construction of systems, and thus will differ from the intolerant and combative nature of the fundamentalism of other religions. This is also the reason I have adopted such a spontaneous and fragmentary approach in this book.

Book 3

3.1. 孔子謂季氏:「八佾舞於庭, 是可忍也, 孰不可忍也?」

Confucius criticized the head of the Ji clan, saying, "In his own courts he goes so far as to perform the dances the Son of Heaven enjoys. If this is tolerable, then what is intolerable?"

Notes: *Yang Bojun notes:* 佾 *is pronounced "yi (*逸*)." In the music and dance of ancient times, eight people in a row were called a* yi 佾. *Eight* yi, *then, were eight rows, so eight times eight is sixty-four people; only the Son of Heaven could have employed [such a display].*

Comments: In the creation of human civilization, the ritual system had certain customs or practices; to use them indiscriminately is to harm the maintenance and stability of human civilization.

3.2. 三家者以雍徹。子曰:「『相維辟公, 天子穆穆』, 奚取於三家之堂?」

The Three Great Families used the "Yong" ode at the end of their sacrifices, as the places were being cleared away. Confucius said,

"The lords are all around, assisting at the sacrifices;
The Son of Heaven's appearance is glorious and solemn.
How can this be used in the temples of the Three Families?"

Notes: *Zhu Xi notes: The Three Families are the families of the great officials of Lu, the Meng, Ji, and Shu families. Yong is the title of one of the Odes of Zhou. The character* 彻 che *means to clear the sacrificial stand. In the sacrifices in the imperial temple there would be song and dance during the clearing away.*

Comments: Above I have commented on the tolerance of Confucius and the Confucians. Here we see Confucius's intolerance: He cannot tolerate behavior that goes against ritual. This could perhaps be read as "tolerant in thought, strict in behavior." In thought, doctrine, or political opinion, he advocated the pursuit of common ground and the tolerance of differences, but standards of behavior and social systems must be respected by all, otherwise each would act according to what he or she thinks right, and society would disintegrate. Any society must have commonly respected order, norms, and standards—this is a universal principle that has stood through the ages. Of course, in music and dance this has not necessarily been the case. At the time, however, much of music and dance was sacred ritual, rather than mere entertainment or enjoyment, and this is an important distinction to keep in mind. However, much music and dance actually was being gradually liberated from solemn, sacred rites and ritual systems [during this period] and taking on independent significance and appreciation, and Confucius, in the purely governmental point of view he takes in this passage, is a bit behind the times.

3.3. 子曰:「人而不仁, 如禮何? 人而不仁, 如樂何?」

Confucius said, "If a person has no humaneness, what can he have to say about ritual? If a person has no humaneness, what can he have to do with music?"

Comments: This is a major passage. It is saying that the external forms of the rites and music must take psychological emotion as their true basis. Otherwise they will be nothing but an empty shell or surface appearance. Although certain types of music may have a melody and may appeal to the ear, one can perceive that they are empty inside. **A fundamental characteristic of Confucianism is its [emphasis on] shaping the psychology of human nature,** as I have discussed above. If we want to be a bit more concrete, **this "psychology of human nature" for the most part should be [understood to be] a type of emotio-rational structure (*qingli jiegou* 情理結構), that is, an amalgamation of rationality (reason, understanding) and emotion (sentiment, passion), in varying degrees, relationships, and proportions—in other words, the establishment of a "humanized emotion" on the sensuous foundation of natural animal existence.** This is the "humanization of inner nature" I have emphasized in my work on aesthetics. From the enjoyment of ear and eye to the happiness of sexual love, from social behavior to ritual morality, all have to do with this. I believe this particular type of "emotio-rational structure," the deep psychology created by cultural sedimentation, is one of the keys to understanding Confucianism and Chinese culture.

3.4. 林放問禮之本。子曰:「大哉問! 禮, 與其奢也, 寧儉; 喪, 與其易也, 寧戚。」

Lin Fang asked what was the foundation of ritual. Confucius said, "This is a big question. In ritual, simplicity and economy are better than elaborate extravagance. In matters of mourning, true sorrow is better than grand ceremonies."

Comments: "A big question" could also be translated as "a good question" or "an important question." This passage again concretely emphasizes how emotion (*qi* 戚, sorrow or woe) is the foundation, and is more important than external ceremonies. Its ancient shamanistic-historical culture (*wushi wenhua* 巫史文化) caused China to be unable to develop independent religion or independent government.[1] Instead, it built an external edifice and ideology that unified ethics, religion, and government, founded upon a ritual system with sacred magical-religious properties (i.e., ethical familial relationships and order under a clan patriarchal system). For this reason, both human relations and government were encompassed within and permeated by this sacred religious emotion. **From fear (in the Shang) to reverence (in the Zhou) to love (in Confucius), this type of emotion in which rationalization is being cultivated is the main characteristic of Confucianism.** It underwent continuous development and was generalized into a universal principle (in Han Confucianism: "Humaneness is the heart-mind of Heaven" 仁, 天心也) and moral law (in Song Neo-Confucianism: "Humaneness is the principle of love, the virtue of the heart-mind" 仁, 愛之理, 心之德也), such that emotion (humaneness, love) became the locus of the substance of the "heart-mind of Heaven" (*tianxin* 天心) and the "Heavenly Principle" (*tianli* 天理). Whether "the mutual complementarity of Confucianism and Daoism" or "the mutual alternation of Confucianism and Legalism," whether for "inner sageliness" or the "outer kingship," this substance or characteristic constitutes its inner spirit from start to finish. Therefore,

it is not Heaven, *qi*, Principle, the heart-mind, or human nature as substance, but "emotion-as-substance" (*qing benti* 情本體) that is the crux of Confucianism, as I will repeatedly state in this book.

3.5. 子曰:「夷狄之有君, 不如諸夏之亡也。」

Confucius said, "Although the barbarian tribes have rulers, they are not [as good as] China without rulers."

Notes: *Liu Baonan notes: This passage specifically addresses matters related to the rites and music. Although the rulers of the states of Chu and Wu repeatedly allied with China, their violence exceeded the bounds of the [ritual] system, and they were unable to equal the rites of the Zhou. Therefore they were inferior to the Chinese without rulers.*

Qian Mu in his "Lunyu xinjie" (hereafter referred to simply as "Qian Mu") notes: This passage has two explanations. First, that the Yi and Di [barbarian tribes] also had rulers, but were not equal to the Chinese even under usurpers, whether with a ruler or without. Another explanation is that even when the Yi and Di have rulers, they are not equal to the Chinese without a ruler. . . . When the state of Jin [moved their capital] across the river into the South, in the North the Five Barbarian Tribes created chaos. For scholars of that time, when the status of aristocratic clans was at its height and the king's palace was despised, in effect this amounted to not having a ruler, while they [themselves] needed to strictly observe the barrier between Chinese and barbarian for the sake of self-preservation. Thus [scholars of that period] mostly favored the latter reading. The Song inherited the late Tang and Five Dynasties' longstanding problem of breakaway barrier towns, and failed to advocate for the significance of reverence for the ruler; it was thus difficult to maintain the various reaches of the area under unification, so that the infiltration and rise of barbarians was to be expected. Most of [the scholars of this period] preferred the former reading. . . . When the "Analects" speaks of government, it must be on the basis of the greatness of the Way of humanity, and respect for the ruler is also the way to respect the Way; it does not mean that the position of the ruler should be regarded as above the Way itself. Thus we can see that the latter reading is superior.

Comments: Here I follow Qian Mu's reading. The Way (*dao* 道) is greater than the ruler (*jun* 君), and the whole of civilization is greater than systems of government. Chinese tradition emphasizes the concept of "culture," above "race" and even governmental systems. Among ancient clans and tribes, the concept of "race" was originally extremely important, as in the saying "If he is not of my clan, his heart must not be like ours 非我族類, 其心必異."[2] Even though in the Spring and Autumn period there was still a concept of "Just Retribution" (*da fuchou* 大復仇) (which was actually inter-clan feuding), it seems that beginning with the Confucians, later generations ended up much more seldom either acting or speaking in this manner. It is only when resisting invasion by more lowly and backward people groups (still determining "advanced" or "backward" in terms of culture) that [they] would strongly advocate the "barbarian-Chinese distinction." Otherwise there were only isolated cases of sons avenging their fathers, and quite rarely would there be large-scale racial massacres. This should be seen as an important phenomenon of Chinese history and culture. Of course, there have still been instances in Chinese history of violent massacres and extermination of minority peoples, including Wang Yangming's "exploits," and the Qianlong emperor's "Ten Great Campaigns." But on the whole, over the two-thousand-plus years from the Qin and Han to the Qing dynasty, the Chinese people and its culture for the most part assimilated minorities naturally and without violence. Including events like the "Uprising of the Five Barbarians" in the Jin dynasty, and the Manchu conquest, the result of these events was that the dominated and oppressed Han people in the end assimilated those who had dominated or oppressed them, so that the latter lost their original language, writing system, culture, and so on. This phenomenon is remarkable in world history. Thus the term "Chinese" is really a cultural concept, not a racial one. The blood in the veins of today's Chinese people is not purely Han. This is the exact opposite of Hitler's Nazi conceptual theory. The facts of Han cultural history can thus refute any racist ideology.

3.6. 季氏旅於泰山。子謂冉有曰:「女弗能救與?」對曰:「不能。」子曰:「嗚呼! 曾謂泰山, 不如林放乎?」

The head of the Ji clan was going to make sacrifices to Mt. Tai. Confucius asked his student Ran You, "Can you prevent him?" He answered, "I cannot." Confucius said, "Alas! I wouldn't have thought that Mt. Tai is unequal to Lin Fang!"

Comments: As only the Son of Heaven could sacrifice to Mt. Tai, the head of the Ji clan is violating ritual propriety. Confucius asks Ran You, who serves as an official with the Ji clan, whether he could not prevent this from happening, and he answers that he cannot. Therefore Confucius utters a great sigh, bemoaning the fact that Mt. Tai, the recipient of the sacrifice, is not as careful about ritual as Lin Fang [see 3.4 above]. What does Mt. Tai know or perceive? Confucius is using it as a stand-in for the Ji clan. Liu Fenglu 劉逢祿 (1776–1829), in his *Lunyu shuhe* 論語述何 says, "He uses this to be severe with Ran You for his obsequiousness 舉以厲冉有之詭隨也"; that is, he uses Lin Fang to severely criticize Ran You for following the lead of the head of the Ji clan and being unable to correct him.

3.7. 子曰: 「君子無所爭, 必也射乎! 揖讓而升, 下而飲, 其爭也君子。」

Confucius said, "The noble person has nothing to contend for, apart from archery competitions. Bowing to and saluting one another, entering the field for the competition and, when it is over, leaving the field and drinking wine—this is the competition of the noble person."

Notes: *Cheng Shude quotes the "Song Yang jiang yi"* 松陽講意[3] *as follows: In the world there is a rank of person who only knows how to hide and protect himself, and contends with no one, refusing to discuss what is right and wrong, permitted or not permitted. This is what Zhu Xi called a "circumspect and honest scholar"* jin hou zhi shi 謹厚之士, *and not a noble person* (junzi). *There is another type of person who knows only to fawn and toady to the world, and who purposefully obscures right and wrong, permitted and not permitted, saying of himself that he has no quarrel with anyone. This person is what the Master [Confucius] called a "village worthy'"* (xiang yuan 鄉原),[4] *and is not a noble person* (junzi). *There is yet another type of person, who is eager to make lofty speeches, arguing for the oneness of all things, that he is the same as others, that there is no difference, and nothing to quarrel about. . . . This, too, is not the noble person.*

Comments: Archery competitions are a custom handed down from antiquity. Before agricultural society, people relied on hunting for their livelihood, and archery was the main (and perhaps earliest) important technology. For this reason, it became one of the "Six Arts" (rites, music, archery, charioteering, calligraphy, mathematics) of later generations, up to Confucius's time.

The comments that Cheng Shude quotes from the "Song Yang jiang yi" are very interesting in that they emphasize that if one does not contend, one is not a noble person (*junzi*). For a noble person there will always be times that he or she must "contend." The commentary is very insightful when it concretely finds fault with three types of people, seemingly just and fair, capable, and high-minded, who "do not contend." Clearly, although Confucius is here speaking of "not contending," later generations of Confucians could have very different opinions. This is an illustration of the internal tolerance of Confucianism: it is not the case that every single thing Confucius said was true, for Confucius himself allowed his disciples to disagree and argue with him. Wang Chong 王充 (27–ca. 100 AD) had his chapter, "Questioning Confucius" (*Wen Kong* 問孔),[5] and Liu Zhiji 劉知幾 (661–721) in his "Understanding History" (*Shitong* 史通) chapters questioning antiquity and doubting the classics also expresses dissatisfaction with Confucius. Wang Yangming said, "If you inquire of your heart and find that it is wrong, even if Confucius said it you should not take it for right" 求於心而非也，雖其言於孔子不敢以為是也, and Li Zhi 李贄 (1527–1602) further has the famous formulation "Don't take Confucius's right and wrong for right and wrong" 不以孔子之是非為是非. These demonstrate the true spirit of pragmatic reason that characterizes Confucianism and Confucians. Neither Confucius nor the *Analects* should be regarded as ossified sacred idol or religious dogma. Both Song-Ming Neo-Confucians and modern New Confucians get this wrong.

3.8. 子夏問曰：「『巧笑倩兮，美目盼兮，素以為絢兮。』何謂也？」子曰：「繪事後素。」曰：「禮後乎？」子曰：「起予者商也！始可與言詩已矣。」

Zixia asked, "'A beautiful smile, dimpling slightly; / Beautiful eyes, vivid in black and white; / On pure white paper, resplendent color.' What does this mean?"[6] Confucius said, "First you have the white background, and only then the painting."

Zixia said, "Then ritual should follow after?" Confucius said, "The one who is inspiring me is you! Now, finally, I can talk to you about the *Songs*."

Comments: This is like 3.3. If "ritual" is like a flower, one needs a background of white silk (psychological emotion) against which to paint it. In other words, the inner emotions (*ren* or humaneness) are the foundation for outward systems (*li* or ritual). Xunzi says, "Overall, ritual works to ornament happiness when serving the living, to ornament sorrow when sending off the dead, to ornament respect when conducting sacrifices, and to ornament awe-inspiring power when engaged in military affairs. 凡禮, 事生, 飾歡也; 送死, 飾哀也; 祭祀, 飾敬也; 師旅, 飾威也."[7] The character *shi* 飾 [to ornament or decorate] is very deep, and worth probing more closely. On the one hand, the "rites" are the expression or transmission of emotion, while at the same time giving emotion a definitive shape as it becomes a ritualized ceremonial form. That "humaneness is inward, ritual is outward," and therefore "humaneness comes first, ritual after," seems to have become a settled conclusion. Yet where does this inner "humaneness" come from? This became the biggest question. Mencius traced it to an a priori ethical disposition or "sprout" of goodness (*shan duan* 善端), which is very difficult to separate from sensibility. Zhu Xi traced it to "Heavenly Principle" (*tian li* 天理), which seems to make it heteronomous. Neither of these is as good as Xunzi's [decision to] dispense with humaneness and speak of ritual, moving from the outward regulation to the inward disposition, which is much more clear and consistent. I believe **ritual is human culture, while humaneness is human nature. The two actually are co-occurring historical facts, for the content of human nature (humaneness) cannot be separated from the form of human culture (ritual) at their source: the emotion of human nature must be given a particular form in order to be cast or formed. Without the form there would not be the emotion; without the "ornament," there would be no "happiness," "sorrow," "respect," or "awe."** This is also the reason that "ritual" can be considered an art. This explanation of Confucius, humaneness, and ritual, although it might not hit the mark exactly, is not far off. And Xunzi, of course, must not be ignored.

3.9. 子曰:「夏禮, 吾能言之, 杞不足徵也; 殷禮, 吾能言之, 宋不足徵也。文獻不足故也, 足則吾能徵之矣。」

Confucius said, "The rituals of Xia I can speak about, but the state of Qi already has inadequate documentation. The rituals of Yin (Shang) I can speak about, but the state of Song already does not have adequate documentation. [This is] because both their written materials and their living [human] materials are too scarce; if these were plentiful, I would be able to use them as documentation."

Notes: *Zhu Xi notes: Qi is the successor state of Xia; Song is the successor state of Yin [Shang].* Wen 文 *refers to books and records;* xian 獻 *refers to sages* (xian 賢). *The passage is saying that while I may speak of the rituals of the two dynasties, these two states have too little [remaining] to document [those rituals], for both their written documents and their worthies are not adequate. If these were adequate, then I would be able to cite them to corroborate what I say.*

Comments: The ancient rites that Confucius spoke of were all impossible to document. Perhaps this is precisely what inspired Kang Youwei to so emphasize Confucius's "reform in the name of the ancients," taking this as the slogan for his own legal reforms. To truly originate something or find the original meaning is hard, [so] China early developed this tradition of explication. Do you not see how Chinese tradition has undergone numerous renewals by way of this type of continuous annotation, commentary, explication, and interpretation? Have not Dong Zhongshu, Zhu Xi, Wang Yangming, and many other major and minor Confucians all done this? They have no need to advocate other slogans or create other theories, as if "without destruction there can be no construction 不破不立." Rather, they can "wipe away the old as if it were new 拭舊如新," "weed through the old to bring forth the new 推陳出新"—these are the very "transformative creation[s]" that seemingly can still today be considered a kind of avenue of progress for China.

3.10. 子曰: 「禘自既灌而往者, 吾不欲觀之矣。」

Yang Bojun's translation: Confucius said, "In the ceremony of the *di* sacrifice, after the first time the wine is poured, I do not want to watch anymore."

Notes: *Yang Bojun comments: The* di *ritual refers to an extremely solemn great ancient sacrificial rite, which could only be carried out by the king. However, King Cheng of the Zhou, because Duke Dan of the Zhou had accomplished great things for the Zhou dynasty, allowed him to carry out the* di *sacrifice. Afterward, the rulers of the State of Lu all followed suit in "misusing"* (jian 僭) *this* di *ritual, and thus Confucius did not want to watch it.*

Qian Mu's interpretation: With the passage of time and change of generations, the later generations often have things they do not understand the meaning of. As with this passage, later Confucians one after the other have researched it but have been unable to come to an agreement.

Comments: This passage has always been difficult to understand. I have followed Yang Bojun's translation and annotations as my interpretation.

3.11或問禘之說。子曰:「不知也。知其說者之於天下也, 其如示諸斯乎!」指其掌。

Yang Bojun's translation: Someone asked Confucius to explain to them about the theory of the *di* sacrifice. Confucius said, "I don't know; the one who does know, when it comes to ruling the world, would find it as easy as putting something here!" As he said this, he indicated his palm.

Notes: *Yang Bojun notes: The* di *was a rite of kings, and for the State of Lu to carry it out, in Confucius's opinion, was entirely inappropriate. But Confucius did not want to come out and say this openly, so he had to say "I don't want to watch," or "I don't know," or even "If someone understood this, he would be able to rule the world as easily as putting something in the palm of his hand."*

Comments: The reason I elected not to translate these two passages and to adopt Yang Bojun's translation instead is because both passages have been explained in various ways, all demonstrating the concrete content and significance of this "rite," but all offering very unclear and often forced explanations. Researching these two passages is the duty of a small minority of historians—they are not for the average reader to understand. What is worthy of inquiry for us is this: ceremonial rites are human culture; they are the sacred system of any ancient people, through which groups are unified, social order is solidified, and human nature is established. They started as magic or witchcraft, a type of symbolic spiritual production, and the earliest human higher-level structure or form of consciousness. As Max Weber says, "Thus, all areas of human activity were drawn into this circle of magical symbolism," "since the slightest deviation . . . might render the procedure inefficacious." "Among the magicians of the American Indians, faulty singing during ritual dances was immediately punished by the death of the guilty singer, to remove the evil magic or to avert the anger of the god."[8]

In China, the question of how these ancient magical ceremonies gradually developed and progressed into the ritual system of the Xia and Shang, how they were gradually rationalized and politicized (in China, this happened in a single process), and how their religious and political aspects were organized and constructed is still an important one that students of the history of ancient thought have yet to answer. As I said above, I believe China's shamanistic-historical culture has caused the melding of primitive shamanism and ethical government, to form a "trinitarian" ritual system, which is at once ethical, political, and religious. It is precisely this "trinity" that formed the "emotion-as-substance" that characterizes Confucianism, "Confucian-Daoist mutual complementarity," and the "Confucian-Legalist mutual alternation" that followed later. When Daoism or Legalism was the form, Confucianism remained the heart, precisely because it originated in the shamanistic cultural tradition and became ancient China's shamanistic-historical culture.

The characteristic of shamanism is the ability of people to take initiative in making use of the gods; it emphasizes action and manipulation. By way of various complex actions or manipulations, one can communicate with the gods or spirits, and urge them to do things in service to oneself. This is very different from making a god the object of prayers for grace, where people are in a completely passive position of contemplative prayer. All primitive peoples have magic, and in our modern life today we have the traces of witchcraft. But because the tradition of shamanism in China was intermixed and melded with the political system and with ancestor worship, and because of the extent and speed at which it was rationalized in the direction of these, it formed a unique tradition: the shaman (religious leader) is also the king (political leader)—Kings Yu 禹, Tang 湯, and Wen 文 were all great shamans, and after their death became even greater objects of worship. **The ancestors became the center of sacrificial worship, by way of the intermediary step of shamanism, and people and gods were connected (for the ancestors were originally human) to form a union; this is why China is "this-worldly."** The worship of ancestors was originally connected with blood-based clan hierarchical relationships, and in fact was built upon this order of relationships. All of this, up to the Duke of Zhou's "establishing ritual and creating music," formed an extremely ethical, systematized trinitarian system of religion, politics, and ethics.

The reason Confucius used humaneness to explain ritual was in order to avoid the collapse of this precociously rationalized ritual system, by enlisting the help of the emotion of the primitive shamanistic tradition. But because of the high degree of rationalization that had already occurred, this "emotion" was no longer mystical or ineffable, but rather became the simultaneously this-worldly and other-worldly respect, reverence, sincerity, humaneness, and so on. All of this happened in an extremely complex historical and philosophical process.

3.12. 祭如在，祭神如神在。子曰：「吾不與祭，如不祭。」

When sacrificing to the ancestors, it seems as if the ancestors are present. When sacrificing to the gods, it seems as if the gods are present. Confucius said, "If I do not personally attend a sacrifice, it is as if I did not sacrifice."

Comments: From social history we know that in ancient times "as if present" (*ru zai* 如在) originally referred to someone receiving sacrifices on behalf of the dead (*shi* 尸); that is, if a living person (the "king") represents the ancestors (the king's forbears) in receiving sacrifices, then those ancestors can communicate with those offering the sacrifice (his children and grandchildren). Clearly, the unity of people and gods has existed in China for a very long time—it is one of the traces of shamanism. Even today, a family's ancestral tablets are still placed in rooms in which people live. China's "this-world" orientation is still the basic tradition, is fully expressed in every aspect of its culture, and has determined the shape of its philosophy. It would be a mistake to give too little attention to history while speaking inordinately of philosophy.

From the point of view of cultural-psychological formation, the two uses of "as if" here clearly neither prove the existence of gods and spirits nor prove their non-existence. What is emphasized is that when offering sacrifices, one must assume that the gods and spirits (ancestors) exist. What is required **is a sort of psychological-emotional offering, and not rational knowledge or proof.** This is why Confucius says that if one does not personally participate, one will not make this sort of psychological-emotional offering, and this will be equal to "not sacrificing." Clearly, for Confucius, the important thing about sacrificial rites is not the ritual or form, but the personal participation in order to attain this psychology, emotion, or quality. The *Book of Rites* says in the "Ji tong 祭統" ("About Sacrifices") chapter, "Sacrifice is not a thing coming to a man from without; it issues from within him, and has its birth in his heart 夫祭者, 非物自外至者也, 自中出生於心."[9] Xunzi says, "What is the purpose of the three-year mourning period? I reply: it is a form which has been set up after consideration of the emotions involved 三年之喪何也, 曰稱情而立文."[10] And so on. All these are saying almost the same thing. In the whole of the *Analects*, whenever sacrifices are discussed, the emphasis is always on this type of inner emotion, which is used as evidence for the origins of and need for the external ceremonies and ritual systems. Although this is the opposite of the historical reality, it serves to show that attention to psychological formation and the formation of human emotions are characteristic of the foundation Confucius laid for Confucianism. God or spirits are objects of emotional offering, support, and belonging, not rational proof or logical deduction (as in the various proofs of God's existence in medieval Western theology and philosophy); this is the "doctrine" of Confucianism. **But within this emotion there is still a rational element; there is no sense of the anti-rational spirit or attitude of "credo quia absurdum."**[11] Originally, it was very easy for shamanistic ceremonies to lead to irrational moods or attitudes, and to the fostering and development of this type of fanatical sentiment. Still today, this is true of some folk "witches" or "sorcerers." The meaning and weight of these two "as if" statements of Confucius from two thousand years ago had already reached this point: they demonstrate the molding in the Chinese people of a particular kind of psychology that drew rationality into emotion (*yin li ru qing* 引理入情). Every culture cultivates emotions; the key is how it cultivates them, and what kinds of emotions and emotio-rational structures it cultivates.

3.13. 王孫賈問曰:「與其媚於奧, 寧媚於竈, 何謂也?」子曰:「不然, 獲罪於天, 無所禱也。」

Wangsun Jia said, "What does it mean when it is said, 'It is better to curry favor with the kitchen god than with the god of Heaven'?" Confucius said, "This is not correct. If one offends against the god of Heaven, then however much one curries favor or prays, it will be useless."

Notes: *Zhu Xi comments: Heaven means Principle (*li 理*); in respecting it there is no opposition—it is unlike the comparison between the stove and the corner shrine.*[12] *To go against Principle is to offend against Heaven; what prayer to the kitchen god or the god of the corner shrine would do anything to make up for it? This passage is saying one should follow Principle, not particularly that one should not appease the kitchen god nor that one should appease the god of the corner shrine.*

Comments: This passage has elicited a great many different readings. Wangsun Jia was probably comparing himself to the kitchen god and wants Confucius to attach himself to him. Zhu Xi's note elevates this passage far above the human realm of the "kitchen god" and "corner shrine" to encompass "Heavenly Principle." From it we can infer once again the implication or question of "following the Way, not the ruler" (*cong dao bu cong jun* 從道不從君).[13] In Confucianism, there is quite a tight relationship between the tradition of the Way (*daotong* 道統) (represented by the teacher, respected for his virtue) and the tradition of government (*zhitong* 治統) (represented by the ruler, respected for his position), or between the emperor and Confucius. Which of these ultimately has precedence? Apart from this, there is also the very close connection between the minister-ruler relationship (of loyalty) and the son-father relationship (of filiality). Mencius's imagined story of Shun carrying his father and fleeing,[14] the Song dynasty "Pu Controversy,"[15] and the Succession Controversy of the Ming,[16] as well as the sacrifices at the temple of Confucius, the norms for the conferral of titles, and so on—all these were famous instances in which Confucian officials fiercely opposed the emperor, even to the point that many were beaten to death. The question of how later generations, under authoritarian rule, adapted to the democratic flavor that classical Confucianism carried from its origins in clan society, is worth attention and research. It is equally one-sided and simplistic to overgeneralize Confucianism into either an accomplice of authoritarianism (from Tan Sitong's notion of "just village worthies working to emulate a great robber" 惟鄉原工媚大盜 to today's progressive anti-traditional views), or a solider of democracy (categorically dividing the tradition of government [authoritarianism] from the tradition of the Way [democracy] and emphasizing their opposition, as in today's "modern New Confucianism").

Zhu Xi's reading of "Principle" for "Heaven" has elicited quite a bit of opposition. Some have pointed out that **"praying to Heaven" is certainly not "praying to Principle."** From this one can actually see that the reason "Heaven" cannot be made equal to Principle is precisely because it still retains an emotional element. **Although it has been naturalized, rationalized, and de-humanized, just below the surface it still retains traces of the gods worshipped by people in primitive shamanism and as such is directly related to human emotion.**

3.14. 子曰: 「周監於二代, 郁郁乎文哉! 吾從周。」

Confucius said, "The Zhou dynasty drew lessons from the Xia and Shang dynasties' experiences and achievements; how perfectly beautiful and cultivated is its rites and music tradition! I will follow the Zhou dynasty."

Comments: Clearly, Confucius advocated neither a return to the ancients nor revolution, but rather accumulation and progress.

3.15. 子入太廟, 每事問。或曰: 「孰謂鄹人之子知禮乎? 入太廟, 每事問。」子聞之, 曰: 「是禮也。」

Confucius walked into the Great Temple, and asked about everything. Someone said, "Who says this son of a man from Zou village understands ritual? He walks into the Great Temple, and asks about everything." When Confucius heard it, he said, "This is ritual."

Notes: *Zhu Xi notes: Zou is a district of Lu, where Confucius's father Shuliang He* 叔梁紇 *had served as an official. Confucius had been known to be well-versed in ritual from a young age, which is perhaps why someone criticized him for this.*

Comments: This passage demonstrates that Confucius is humble and diligent; he neither pretends not to understand and feigns inquiry, nor is he completely without understanding; rather he asks for confirmation, genuinely seeking to verify what he knows and does not know. Is this not a very good method of study?

3.16. 子曰: 「射不主皮, 為力不同科, 古之道也。」

Confucius said, "In an archery competition, one is not judged on how far one's arrow penetrates, since everyone's strength is different. This was the regulation in ancient times."

Notes: *Zhu Xi cites Yang Bojun: Hitting the mark is an ability that can be learned, while strength cannot be arrived at through effort.*

Comments: Archery competitions are based upon hitting the target, not upon penetrating deeply into it. Perhaps at the time there were those who were boasting about their strength, which is why Confucius commented on it.

3.17. 子貢欲去告朔之餼羊。子曰: 「賜也, 爾愛其羊, 我愛其禮。」

Zigong wanted to dispense with the butchering of a sheep at the sacrifices on the first of each month. Confucius said, "You cherish the sheep, I cherish the ritual."

Notes: *Yang Bojun notes: The* gao shuo xi yang 告朔餼羊 *was an ancient system. . . . On the first of every month, a live sheep would be sacrificed at the temple, then they would return to court to hear about issues of government. This sacrifice was called* gao shuo 告朔 *["announcing the new moon"], while the hearing on issues of government was called* shi shuo 視朔 *["new moon inspection"],* or ting shuo 聽朔 *["new moon hearing"]. By the time of Zigong, on the first of every month not only would the ruler not personally attend at the ancestral temple, he would not hear about governmental issues, but would only kill the live sheep.*

Comments: Even if a particular ceremony or ritual has lost its meaning and its concrete content, the form in itself still holds some value. This is a concrete trace of primeval culture, which in later generations exerts an aesthetic attraction on people, so that it cultivates and shapes a sort of aesthetic emotion. This is the case for many ancient relics and some practical articles that are no longer valued for their utility, so that today they are called "art" or "art objects." The sacred character and importance of ceremonial form has been discussed in great detail by Herbert Fingarette (see his *Confucius: The Secular as Sacred*). Benjamin Schwartz makes a similar argument that the forms of revering the gods are more important than reverence for the gods itself (in *The World of Thought in Ancient China*). Ancient ritual ceremony employs tangible, materialized forms (dance, incantations, music, sculpture, painting, architecture, writing, etc.) to condense and manifest in time sacred and incontrovertible norms of behavior, mental concepts, emotional experiences, and communal order. By way of the continual practice and repeated solidification of these ceremonial forms, people attain the internalization of reason (as knowledge) and the condensation of reason (as virtue). Subsequently, these forms themselves become aesthetic objects (the sedimentation of rational emotion, on which see my essays on aesthetics).

3.18. 子曰: 「事君盡禮, 人以為諂也。」

Confucius said, "When serving a ruler, if you do everything in accordance with ritual propriety, people think you are being obsequious."

Comments: Times have changed, and by the Spring and Autumn period, people no longer had the same reverence for the ruler as in traditional times. For this reason, when one acted in accordance with the ritual system, as in the descriptions in Book 10 of how Confucius acted and conducted himself (including how, when the ruler summoned him, he would immediately set out, or how when the ruler was present, he would adopt various types of respectful, reverent postures), of course people were not used to this and saw it as "being obsequious." Confucius here seems to be defending himself; actually it makes sense that people were unused to such actions. The way that Confucius insists on keeping the ancient rituals, not recognizing that times have changed, is not something worth emulating.

The reason for such fearful, careful ritual observance in ancient times was that at the time the ruler was a "sage king," at once an administrative leader and a great shaman, able to communicate with the gods. By the Spring and Autumn period, the "king" had long ceased to be a "sage," and had lost his halo, so that, like an ordinary person, he ceased to require the same degree of reverence. But as for the autocratic emperors after the Qin and Han with their absolute authority, they once again commanded immense reverence and awe among the ordinary people who were their subjects. The appellation of an authoritarian emperor as the "Son of Heaven" (*tianzi* 天子) still contained an element of religious submission, yet was quite different from the type of mystical reverence accorded them in ancient times.

3.19. 定公問:「君使臣, 臣事君, 如之何? 」孔子對曰:「君使臣以禮, 臣事君以忠。」

Duke Ding asked, "How should a ruler make use of his ministers, and how should ministers serve their ruler?" Confucius answered, "The ruler should make use of his ministers according to ritual propriety; ministers should serve their rulers with faithfulness."

Comments: This is quite different from the view of Legalist-influenced Han Confucianism that emphasized "The ruler guides the subject" 君為臣綱 (from Dong Zhongshu through the *Baihutong*), or the later authoritarian system of ruler-minister relations characterized as "The ruler is sagely and bright; when the minister commits wrong he should be executed" 天王聖明, 臣罪當誅 (Han Yu).[17] In later generations, the humiliation and bullying by rulers of their ministers and people knew no bounds. That both ministers and subjects would owe their ruler unconditional, absolute obedience and acceptance, and so on, did not at all belong to the ritual system advocated by Confucius and classical Confucianism. Confucius, after all, was someone who received and passed on the clan system, and thus still retained traces of the primitive democracy and humanism of the clans. Mencius also had the saying, "I have indeed heard of the 'outcast Zhou'" 聞誅一夫紂矣.[18] Even Xunzi, who emphasized the authority of the ruler, still stressed that one should "follow the Dao, not the ruler; obey righteousness, not the father" 從道不從君, 從義不從父 (*Xunzi* 29.1). "Confucius said . . . if a son simply obeys his father, how would that son be filial? If a minister simply obeys his lord, how would that minister be exercising fidelity? To be careful about the cases in which one obeys another—this is called filiality, this is called fidelity" 孔子曰 . . . 故子從父, 奚子孝? 臣從君, 奚臣貞? 審其所以從之之謂孝、之謂貞也 (*Xunzi* 29.2).[19] Neither "fidelity" nor "filiality" is blind obedience or unthinking emotion; instead, both are actions characterized by the melding of understanding into emotion. In Confucianism, the Dao and righteousness are higher than the ruler or the father, which is markedly different from the later emphasis on submission to being a "cog in the [revolutionary] machine"[20] or "carrying out [orders] even if you don't understand" (this originally referred to military operations). The tragedy of the suicide of the assassin Chu Ni 鉏麑, praised by Confucians (centering on the conflict between being "loyal to the Dao" and "loyal to the ruler") is a concrete demonstration of this characteristic, and is quite different from the notion of loyalty in the Japanese Bushido or "Code of the Samurai" (loyalty to the feudal lord).[21] **Confucians advocate loyalty and filiality but at the same time oppose ignorant or blind loyalty or filiality, requiring that one should ask the reason for or explain the rationale for all things, opposing both systemic (communal) and emotional (individual) blind faith or blind obedience; this is where Chinese pragmatic reason resides.** As for why it was not possible from this to develop a social morality according to the modern conception, that is, some sort of contractual relationship between ruler and minister, on the one hand this was probably due to the inherent limitations in the level of development of society itself (from the mid-Ming forward, with the flourishing of the commercial economy, Confucianism did not prohibit commerce or speaking of profit and personal gain, from which foundation there arose the new political thought of people like Huang Zongxi and Tang Zhen 唐甄 [1630–1704]). On the other hand, this was also due to the fact that, again, the foundational trinitarian structure of religion, politics, and ethics in Chinese Confucianism could never be self-consciously dismantled.

3.20. 子曰: 「關雎, 樂而不淫, 哀而不傷。」

Confucius said, "The poem, 'The Ospreys,' is happy without being excessive, and sad but not to the point of being harmful."

Comments: The characters *fu* 淫 and *shang* 傷 both refer to excessiveness, so the passage says that this poem expresses the emotions of joy and sorrow appropriately, and in no way to excess. Excess is damaging to the spirit of the individual and harmful to society as a whole. In my book *The Chinese Aesthetic Tradition* (華夏美學), I argued that China has no "Dionysian spirit," it has no self-indulgent revelry. On the contrary, what it emphasizes is that **even happiness must be restrained. That restraint must, of course, be accomplished with the help of reason.** Greek philosophy also discussed the role of reason in leading and controlling the emotions. What is characteristic of Confucianism is that **reason does**

not simply guide, lead, or control the emotions; more importantly, reason must be drawn into, permeate, and meld with the emotions, so that the emotions themselves—for example happiness—receive a truly human, and not instinctual, animalistic release. This is the concrete shape of the humanistic emotions as psychological formation. In this formulation, reason is not simply a sort of conceptual ability, attitude or process; rather, it is something that is directly related to people's behavior and actions, and thus to their emotions and desires. This tradition emphasizes the natural melding and mutual permeation of rationality and the emotions, so that reason and desire are harmonized and unified. This is also why the "rites and music" were spoken of together, with formulations like "Music comes from within, the rites are accomplished from without" 樂從中出, 禮自外作,[22] "Devote yourself to music in order to govern the heart" 致樂以治心,[23] and others, that emphasize the principle of "governing the heart." In the workings of human psychology and therefore also in behavior, this relationship between reason and the emotions plays a very important part. Fundamentally, so-called human psychology means an "emotio-rational structure" (*qingli jiegou* 情理結構). Feeling (*qing* 情) originates in animal instinct, and is often linked with various desires, instincts, and physiological elements, so that it includes the non-rational. Reason (*li* 理) arises from communal consciousness, and is often linked with various normative or societal elements, and as such requires rationality. The combination of the two is what makes people both distinct from animals and different from machines. It is, in fact, what we call human nature; the various proportions of the composition or construction of this combination can create a different national or individual character. In China (including Confucianism), this combination takes the form of a mutual interpenetration and melding, rather than one in which the two are opposed, one controls or overpowers the other, or in which one or the other is given lopsided development.

We should also emphasize here the problem of "moderation" (*zhong* 中) and "proper measure" (*du* 度), or A ≠ A ± ("happy without being excessive, and sad but not to the point of being harmful"). This is one of the characteristics of China's dialectics, quite distinct from simple obedience to the law of identity in formal logic, and from Hegelian dialectic. This dialectical concept of "proper measure" (moderation [*zhong* 中], the Mean [*yong* 庸], or "going too far is as bad as not far enough" [*guo you bu ji* 過猶不及]) arises from pragmatic reason, rather than from linguistic argument or rules of thought (as in Greece).

Both "happiness" and "sadness" are psychological states, not linguistic ones, but where do they reside? How could they reside in language?! One of Heidegger's greatest contributions was to take the psychological experience of the troubles of life and fear of death and elevate it to the ontological realm of Dasein ("existence"). But because it lacks true concrete real-life experience, this [ontological view] flows into nothingness, and ultimately can easily morph into a life force of indignant emotions and rash actions. In later years Heidegger took refuge in Being, acknowledged Nature, sank into happiness, and returned to language. I believe this constituted a departure from the psychological character of indignation and exertion of his earlier period, not without loss.

3.21. 哀公問社於宰我。宰我對曰：「夏后氏以松，殷人以柏，周人以栗，曰使民戰栗。」子聞之曰：「成事不說，遂事不諫，既往不咎。」

Duke Ai asked Zai Wo about the type of wood to use to make the ancestral [tablet]. Zai Wo answered, saying, "In the Xia dynasty they used pine, during the Yin they used cypress, and in the Zhou, chestnut. The meaning of the chestnut tree [*lishu* 栗樹] was to cause the people to be fearful (*zhanli* 戰栗)." When Confucius heard this, he said, "Years-old debts should not be brought up; things that have already been done cannot be taken back; since it is already in the past, don't go investigating it."

Comments: This passage shows that Confucius did not advocate the ancient system of control that used religious terror to cause people to fear. He emphasized a government based upon clan relations, that starts from "humaneness (*ren* 仁)/filiality (*xiao* 孝)" and eschews terror and slaughter, instead giving great attention to maintaining the warmth and affection of interpersonal relationships. Primitive tribes all had rituals involving blood sacrifice; archaeology has demonstrated this throughout the world. From this, one can see the progressiveness of the rationalized, humanized strand of the Duke of Zhou and Confucius, with its emphasis on emotion.

"Since it is past don't go investigating it" 既往不咎 (or "let bygones be bygones") became an aphorism still widely used today, which has applications in people's behavior and actions, and even in government. On the one hand, it takes historical experience seriously, while on the other hand having an eye to the present and future, rather than thoroughly inquiring about an individual living person's past mistakes. This may seem "irrational," or lacking in "fairness," but actually it is just like China's folk disputes, which traditionally always advocated "prizing harmony" (和為貴), "smoothing things over" (和稀泥), and being a "peacemaker" (和事佬), seeking mediation in order not to "damage harmony" (不傷和氣), and did not value taking things before a court of law, asking the court to decide right or wrong or the merits of a case, in pursuit of some sort of "justice."

3.22. 子曰: 「管仲之器小哉! 」或曰: 「管仲儉乎? 」曰: 「管氏有三歸, 官事不攝, 焉得儉? 」「然則管仲知禮乎? 」曰: 「邦君樹塞門, 管氏亦樹塞門; 邦君為兩君之好, 有反坫, 管氏亦有反坫。管氏而知禮, 孰不知禮? 」

Confucius said, "Guan Zhong's capacity is really small!"

Someone asked, "Is Guan Zhong frugal?" Confucius said, "Guan Zhong collects large amounts in taxes and levies, and employs many specialized people; how could this be considered frugal?"

"Then does Guan Zhong pay close attention to ritual?" Confucius said, "The ruler erects a palace with resplendent walls, and Guan Zhong also builds resplendent walls; the ruler in his diplomatic banquets has special implements for putting down the wine cups, and so does Guan Zhong. If we say Guan Zhong is careful about ritual, then who is not careful?"

Notes: *Zhu Xi notes: "Small in capacity" means he does not know the Way of the sages and the Great Learning. Therefore his capacity is cramped and shallow, his scope is low and narrow, and he cannot regulate his body and cultivate virtue in order to attain mastery of the kingly Way.*

Comments: Confucius criticizes Guan Zhong for not being careful of "ritual," yet he praises his "humaneness" (see 14.16, 17). The positive outweighs the negative, for not only is "humaneness" clearly superior to "ritual," but the achievement and greater virtue (*da de* 大德) of creating benefit for the people is superior to certain details of behavior, or minor individual virtue. This is quite different from the Song-Ming Neo-Confucian standards for evaluating personality, which favored individual, personal virtue. Some able ministers (in times of peace) and swashbuckling heroes (in times of chaos), from Sang Hongyang 桑弘羊 (152–80 BC) and Cao Cao 曹操 (ca. 155–220), to Li Mi 李泌 (722–789), Yang Yan 楊炎 (727–781), and Zhang Juzheng 張居正 (1525–1582), and so on, all received the disapprobation of Song-Ming Neo-Confucians for their lack of concordance with the standards of the Neo-Confucian "inner sage." Right and wrong have been confused for a long time. This tradition continues unabated through today. This is the Chinese version of the "unity of church and state" phenomenon. Zhu Xi's comment above linking "self-regulation and cultivation of virtue" with the "kingly Way," is an example. Classical Confucianism arose out of clan society, in which the traditional concept of "inner sageliness and outer kingship" still remained, but conflict and contradictions had already begun to appear. From this point on, politics and virtue should gradually have separated, but this was never possible, for they were deeply rooted in primitive clans, and thus familial blood relations became carriers for the characteristics of both religious ethics (in ancestor worship) and political ethics ("Nearby, it can be used to serve one's father, and afar to serve one's ruler" [*Analects* 17.9], and "seek the loyal servant at the door of the filial son" [*Zizhi tongjian*]). This prevented the development of independent religion or independent government.

3.23. 子語魯大師樂。曰:「樂其可知也: 始作, 翕如也; 從之, 純如也, 皦如也, 繹如也, 以成。」

Confucius said to the Grand Music Master of the state of Lu, "Music is something that can be understood. At the beginning, it is excited and intense; as it goes on, it is harmonious, pure, and quiet, it grows clear, it continues, and then it finishes."

Notes: *Cheng Shude quotes [Wang Fuzhi's] "Du Sishu da quan shuo": Mencius did not discuss music in any of his seven chapters; due to the things he did not attain, he was great but did not transform (大而未化).*

Comments: I know absolutely nothing about music, and thus am unable to comment. Wang Fuzhi pointed out that Mencius spoke little on music, which should have been a significant discovery; yet until today, no one has developed this further. Perhaps this has to do with Mencius's sole focus on the cultivation of *qi* among officials, and his emphasis on the heart-mind (*xin* 心) and nature (*xing* 性) to the exclusion of emotion (*qing* 情), since in these respects he greatly influenced later Song-Ming Neo-Confucianism (which also spent a lot of time discussing Principle [*li* 理], *qi*, the heart-mind, and nature, and gave little attention to emotion). Wang's statement that [Mencius] was "great but did not transform," may be understood to mean that although he attained great brilliance, he could not address the Mean, and remained [on the level of] purely external regulation, the reason for this being that he lacked [discourse on] the emotions or music.

3.24. 儀封人請見。曰：「君子之至於斯也，吾未嘗不得見也。」從者見之。出曰：「二三子，何患於喪乎？天下之無道也久矣，天將以夫子為木鐸。」

A certain minor official of the city of Kaifeng asked to see Confucius, saying, "Of the rulers who come here, there is none that has not received me." Confucius's disciples allowed him to see [the Master]. When he came out, he said, "Why do you people fear being underutilized? It has been a very long time since China has lost its standards, [but now] Heaven wants to make your teacher a spiritual guide!"

Comments: "Heaven wants to make your teacher a spiritual guide," has been taken by modern scholars to prove that Confucius can be interpreted theologically. Actually, there is inadequate evidence for this. First of all, this phrase comes out of the mouth of an official of Kaifeng, not Confucius himself. Secondly, the phrase is simply an ordinary exclamation of praise, and should not be read too literally. Of course, like his contemporaries, Confucius probably still believed in gods and spirits. However, he simply took the attitude of "keeping the question open," that is, he refrained from using reason (rationality, understanding) to explain the existence of the spirits, but rather took a certain understanding, for example about the existence of the universe and its regularity ("the four seasons are set in motion" 四時行焉 [17.19] etc.), and allowed its realization to sink into the emotions, thus creating a certain psychological spirit of faith. In passage 3.12 above, the three instances of "as if" (*ru* 如) are another example of this.

3.25. 子謂韶，「盡美矣，又盡善也。」謂武，「盡美矣，未盡善也」。

Confucius evaluated the music of Shao, saying, "It is extremely beautiful, and extremely good." When it came to the music of Wu, he said, "It is extremely beautiful, but not good enough."

Comments: This is a difficult passage to explain. Exactly what relationship there is between "goodness" and "beauty" is not clear. When the passage says it is "beautiful," yet not "good" enough, is this to say that the music is mostly the "sound of killing and fighting," and not graceful enough or pleasing to the ear? Or is it to say that its art fails to more clearly and directly promote the cultivation of virtue? But if this were really expected [of music], then it would usually be "good" but not "beautiful," and thus it would be impossible to use aesthetics to "store up goodness" (*chu shan* 儲善).[24] Many later literary works that sought to "aid human relations, and beautify education" ("*zhu ren lun, mei jiao hua*" 助人倫，美教化), including the poetry of the Neo-Confucians, constituted moralistic propaganda or hidden teachings about Heaven and humans, and for the most part were failures as works of literature. These are indeed good, but not necessarily beautiful.

3.26. 子曰：「居上不寬，為禮不敬，臨喪不哀，吾何以觀之哉？

Confucius said, "To sit in a high position, but treat people without generosity; to carry out ritual without solemnity or earnestness; to attend funerals without sorrow—what is there here to regard?"

Comments: The meaning is that such people are not worth bothering with.

Book 4

4.1. 子曰:「里仁為美。擇不處仁，焉得知？」

Confucius said, "To live in a kindhearted neighborhood—this is beautiful. In where one lives, if one does not choose humaneness, how can one be said to be smart or wise?"

Comments: This is extremely concrete. If today's neighborhood committees could consciously move in this direction, and greatly broaden their function to regulate, consult, harmonize, care for, and help their neighborhoods, would they not be a great form of organization? They could break out of the maladies of both atomistic individualism and mechanistic collectivism, with the effect of intensifying human relations and humanistic feeling.

Because it takes emotion as substance, Confucianism has always affirmed that life in this world is beautiful and good, and has not needed to seek the beauty or goodness of another world or a heavenly kingdom. The poem "Summoning the Soul" ("Zhao hun" 招魂) from the *Songs of Chu* describes the frightening beasts of prey and evil spirits of heaven, under the earth, and the four directions; if one cannot live in these places, then it is better to return to one's old home among humans. This sentiment seems to bear a deep Confucian influence, and **this is the deeper meaning of "to live in a kindhearted neighborhood."** I have always emphasized the fact that Chinese culture is characterized by "this worldliness," that is, the real world, full of human emotion and love—"a kindhearted neighborhood"—**which is quite different from the two-world (heavenly/human) view of other cultures.**

4.2. 子曰:「不仁者不可以久處約, 不可以長處樂。仁者安仁, 知者利仁。」

Confucius said, "People who are not humane (*ren* 仁) cannot long stand difficult circumstances, nor can they long remain in peaceful, happy circumstances. Kind-hearted people naturally return to humaneness, smart people keenly seek humaneness."

Comments: This is what Mencius spoke of when he said "He cannot be led into excesses when wealthy and honored or deflected from his purpose when poor and obscure, nor can he be made to bow before superior force" (III.B.2).[1] Confucius expresses this in a tactful but sincere way, Mencius in a vigorous and resounding fashion, reflecting a different time period and a different style. For the phrase "keenly seek humaneness" (*li ren* 利仁), see the *Mean*: "Some carry it out peacefully, some keenly (*li*)," where *li* can be understood as *ruili* (銳利, "sharp" or "keen") (see 15.10). Most commentators read *li* here as "benefit" or "profit from," readings that I do not follow here.

4.3. 子曰:「唯仁者能好人, 能惡人。」

Confucius said, "Only the kindhearted person is able to like others or hate them."

Comments: Who is unable to like or hate? Here again, even though it is a question of liking and hating, these are not purely emotional or natural, but should have some element of rational judgment in them. The idea in the "Bowing" section of the *Book of Rites* of "loving and yet knowing the evil [of what you love], hating yet knowing the good [of what you hate]" (愛而知其惡, 憎而知其善) is an even better expression of this. Only in this way can likes and hates be more than just reflections of sentimentality or even biology, and it is only the "humane person" (*ren ren* 仁人) (the person who truly has a human nature) who can attain this. Clearly, "humaneness" cannot equal principle or reason (including "Heavenly Principle" *tianli* 天理), rather is something that contains within it both reason and emotion, that is, again, it is the manifestation of a type of emotio-rational structure. The fact that the "emotion" in question includes hate (dislike, loathing) shows that the humane person is not someone who does not distinguish between good and evil or ask what is right or wrong in order not to offend anyone. But this mindset of distinguishing good from evil involves not just rational judgment, or an attitude of following an a priori law; it is a human attitude that melds reason into emotion. This differs greatly from the Western notion of Good and Evil or Kant's practical reason. "Right and wrong" in the Chinese tradition are not neutral factual statements, but always to greater or lesser extent contain value judgments and emotional attitudes within them. Qian Mu in his *Lunyu yao lue* 論語要略 notes, "In humane people, it is in genuine emotion that their quality as people is shown, which is why they are able to have their own likes and hates. . . . Those who have explicated this passage have always . . . failed to recognize the word *neng* 能 ['can,' 'be able to']." "Knowledge stands for learning, humaneness for emotion, courage for will. And among these three—knowledge, emotion, and will—emotion is really the main thing. The emotions are the hub of psychological activity. If genuine emotion can flow freely, that will be [like] the axis of Heaven [or the whole truth]."[2] Liang Shuming says, "In emotion, a person always sees the other party and not him or herself; on the other hand, in desire, he or she only knows to serve self and has no regard for the other."[3] All of these emphasize emotion as the main characteristic of Chinese culture.

4.4. 子曰:「苟志於仁矣, 無惡也。」

Confucius said, "If one truly and diligently sets one's heart on humaneness, one cannot do bad things."

Comments: "Humaneness" here is almost like "magic." If one only sets one's heart toward it, one can readily follow goodness, or change from bad to good. Zhu Xi explains *ren* as "the principle of love, the virtue of the heart-mind" 愛之理, 心之德, and thus calls *ren* "Heavenly Principle" (*tian li* 天理). He little imagined that in taking it to this level of abstraction, he would lose the lively vitality of its concrete, sensuous emotional content, making it into an external law that governs things, and thus would distort the basic characteristic of *ren*, viz., that it does not depart from the emotions (the substance does not depart from the phenomenon). In this way, not doing bad things becomes simply a matter of following external rules, and not a matter of the shaping and reform of the psychological emotions. This is a crucial point for grasping classical Confucianism, as I have pointed out many times already, but which I repeat here yet again. This passage also touches on the question of "intentionality" (the will), which I will leave aside for the moment.

4.5. 子曰: 「富與貴, 是人之所欲也, 不以其道得之, 不處也; 貧與賤, 是人之所惡也; 不以其道得之, 不去也。君子去仁, 惡乎成名? 君子無終食之間違仁, 造次必於是, 顛沛必於是。」

Confucius said, "Growing wealthy and gaining an official position are things that people wish for, but if one does not attain them by way of right methods, one should not accept them. Poverty and lowliness are what people abhor, but if one does not break away from them by way of just methods, one should not cast them aside. If a noble person (*junzi* 君子) loses humaneness, how can he or she be considered a noble person? The noble person does not depart from humaneness even for a moment—when busy and pressed the noble person is [still] like this, as well as when in difficulty."

Comments: The reason that "humaneness" can encompass all sorts of behaviors, actions, attitudes, and lifestyles is not because it is a moral regulation, "Heavenly Principle," or "Substance of Human Nature" (*xingti* 性體),[4] but rather because it is a psychological quality and emotio-rational structure that has undergone self-conscious construction. If we want to develop Confucianism today, this is an important point that needs to be made in distinguishing it from Song-Ming Neo-Confucianism as well as from modern New Confucians (as represented by Feng Youlan 馮友蘭 (1895–1990) and Mou Zongsan). Note that these lines may also be punctuated as follows: 不以其道, 得之不處也, and 不以其道, 得之不去也.

4.6. 子曰: 「我未見好仁者, 惡不仁者。好仁者, 無以尚之; 惡不仁者, 其為仁矣, 不使不仁者加乎其身。有能一日用其力於仁矣乎? 我未見力不足者。蓋有之矣, 我未之見也。」

Confucius said, "I have never seen a person who loves humaneness nor one who abhors the lack of it. As for one who loves humaneness, we need say no more; as for one who abhors the lack of humaneness, his humaneness lies in preventing non-humaneness from touching him. Is there anyone who can devote a day of time towards attaining humaneness?

I have not seen anyone lacking the strength for this. Perhaps there really is such a person, but I have not seen him."

Comments: The *Analects* contains many sayings that directly contradict each other. For example, on the one hand this passage emphasizes that "humaneness" is rare, hard to find, difficult to obtain, and not easy to carry out, to the point that the most highly praised disciple, Yan Hui, could only go "three months without violating humaneness" (6.7). On the other hand, it emphasizes that everyone is to strive for it, and should not depart from it even for a moment; that as long as one sets one's heart on it, humaneness is easy to achieve, and so on. Clearly, these statements should not be seen as philosophical arguments or logical debates, but rather as a semi-religious, practical teaching. On the one hand it is difficult to obtain, on the other hand, easy to do; and as long as one can do it, one can obtain salvation. This kind of vagueness, indeterminacy, and breadth in the Chinese manner of thinking is by no means contradictory with receiving contemporary training in strict Western thought. Chinese can still very quickly receive Western science, logic, and ethical philosophy; this phenomenon is worth investigating. Mencius was not interested in logic, and his arguments do not hold water logically (Mou Zongsan also demonstrates this; see his *Yuanshan lun* 圓善論 [On the *summum bonum*]). Xunzi's logic is very strong, and that of his student Han Feizi even stronger, and the School of Names and the Mohists even more so. Clearly, the Chinese people did not lack logical thought or the capacity for close reasoning, yet without relying upon or developing this aspect, they were somehow able to maintain the existence of their people for so long—Why? How is this possible? All of these questions are worth deeper investigation. Here we see secular ethical behavior, including political behavior, all with a layer of the religious-sacred on top—yet another manifestation of what I have dubbed the "trinity" phenomenon. Thus, the distinction Max Weber described between the "religious state" and the "ordinary state" does not exist in Confucianism. Confucianism causes everyday secular behaviors and attitudes to have a sacred meaning and quality; this where we see the characteristic of "ritual" and the "Way in everyday life." Religiosity melds with secular behavior and political ethics to endow these with emotional content, which rationality alone cannot control. This is also why it was difficult [for China] to develop concepts or theories like the charters of the rights of independent individuals, or "God-given human rights."

4.7. 子曰:「人之過也, 各於其黨。觀過, 斯知仁矣。」

Confucius said, "In making mistakes, people have their types. If you observe someone's mistakes, you will understand what type of person he is."

Comments: Interesting. It is not through observing someone's good points, but rather through observing someone's mistakes, that one can understand the person's characteristics, interests, tendencies, and personality, and thus distinguish between types. Probably strengths are often similar, while weaknesses and mistakes can reflect individual character traits?

4.8. 子曰:「朝聞道, 夕死可矣。」

Confucius said, "If you realize the truth in the morning, you can die the same evening."

Notes: *Zhu Xi comments: The Way is the principle of the way things must be. If one is able to hear it, then life will go smoothly and one can die in peace, without any need for regret.*

Comments: This is a very famous passage, which speaks of how it is not easy to "realize" the "Way," and how one can easily exhaust a lifetime in seeking it. The religious quality of this passage is very strong, as it touches on questions of life and death. I use "truth" to translate "Way" because "truth" is part of our everyday parlance today, and not necessarily in order to suggest a Western philosophical notion of "truth." I'm afraid China does not have the same notion of purely objective truth as in the West. Thus, "truth" here refers not to knowledge, but to the realization of the meaning of life and universal values. When the *Doctrine of the Mean* speaks of "fearing what one has not heard" 恐懼乎其所不聞, it means fearing muddling through life without being able to "hear the Way"—the equivalent of wasting one's life—a serious thing indeed! The character for "sage," *sheng* 聖, includes the "ear" radical, 耳, suggesting that sageliness resides in "hearing the way" in order to know the will of Heaven, which is the rationalization of shamanism's "connecting Heaven and humans" 溝通天人. Clearly, China's notion of "hearing the Way" is quite different from the Western idea of "knowing the truth." The latter develops into epistemology, the former into pure "ontology," for it emphasizes practical physical action as its aim, rather than the knowledge of the object—including God as an object of knowledge. In sum, in light of the troubles of life and the fear of death, how could truth be found in knowledge! The search for transcendence in the face of the troubles of life and fear of death constitutes religion; choosing no life in the light of these troubles and fears is Buddhism; choosing contentment, acceptance, and the resonance of deep emotion is Confucianism.

4.9. 子曰:「士志於道, 而恥惡衣惡食者, 未足與議也。」

Confucius said, "For an intellectual to set his mind on seeking truth, but still be ashamed of coarse clothing or plain food—this type of person is not worth seeking out for a discussion."

Comments: To translate the word *shi* 士 as "intellectual" seems perfectly apt. A *shi* not only has knowledge and culture but is also a person with a "sense of mission"—precisely the definition of an "intellectual." But in today's life, it is not expected that someone who has knowledge and culture would have a sense of mission; this is where traditional society differs from modern society. Furthermore, in today's surging tide of commercialism, it is even more difficult to find someone who holds office out of a sense of mission, and is not ashamed of coarse clothing or plain food. In sum, one cannot expect that everyone will have the religious morality of a sense of mission. In the early twentieth century, Liang Qichao (梁啓超 1873–1929) made the distinction between "personal virtue" and "public virtue," which probably corresponds to what we are calling "religious morality" and "social morality." Thus, today the term "intellectual" may have a subjective or an objective meaning: objectively, it is someone who has culture and knowledge; subjectively, it is a knowledgeable person with the above-mentioned sense of responsibility. The term is quite complex; in its original sense, as conceived by Isaiah Berlin, Turgenev and other liberals may be called intellectuals, while Tolstoy, Dostoevsky, and others who emphasize religion and morality, or oppose contemporary Western culture, and so on, cannot be considered intellectuals. In this way, the term "intellectual" also bears a certain "modern tendency," that is, it reflects the faith, taste, and concepts of the modern era.

4.10. 子曰：「君子之於天下也，無適也，無莫也，義之與比。」

Confucius said, "The noble person treats all sorts of things in the world without either hostility or admiration, but takes only appropriateness and reasonableness as the standard of judgment."

Comments: This passage has had many different interpretations. The present translation seems to have some application to the present day, while still helping to explain [the notion of] pragmatic reason. For we often see that for many people, if they do not blindly reject certain things, they blindly hanker after them, or [in other words] they reject or admire based on their own likes and dislikes, with these responses often arising from ignorance or lack of rationality. This passage also brings up another important concept in Confucianism, that is, "appropriateness" or "reasonableness" (*yi* 義).[5] Is this a core Confucianism concept? What is the core idea or concept of Confucianism? Commentators are divided on the answer to this question. Some believe it is ritual (*li*) (Fingarette); some humaneness (*ren*) (Schwartz); some "the way, virtue, humaneness, appropriateness (*yi*), and ritual" (Chen Daqi 陳大齊); some "the way, virtue, humaneness, and ritual" (Wei Zhengtong 韋政通). There are those who emphasize the Way (Liu Shuxian 劉述先), and those who emphasize rightness or reasonableness (*yi*), seeing it as even more important than humaneness (Liu Dianjue 劉殿爵), and so on. In this reading, I follow the **old understanding in which ritual and humaneness are the core of Confucianism, with human culture (ritual) on equal footing with human nature (humaneness), and the latter coming as the effect of the former (Xunzi), and also governing the former (Mencius).** All the other concepts either derive from or are subordinate to these. If we regard *yi* as purely rational, then the Way and virtue are superrational, transcending even human culture and human nature, and none of them is a central focal point in Confucianism.

4.11. 子曰：「君子懷德，小人懷土；君子懷刑，小人懷惠。」

Confucius said, "The noble person takes care of virtue and government; the petty person takes care of his fields and land. The noble person cares about standards, the petty person cares about whether his profits are adequate or not."

Comments: "Noble person" (*junzi*) and "petty person" (*xiaoren*) here refer to the ruler, officials, and ordinary commoners. Commoners only care about their own land and life—this is as it should be. Their position is not the same, so their cares and what they pay attention to are not the same either—this is to be expected; and in these things it is not appropriate to speak in terms of low or high standards of morality to explain the difference between the noble person and the petty person.

One of China's big problems is that it only has a concept of "punishment" (*xing* 刑), and lacks a modern concept of law (*fa* 法). In the *Zuo zhuan* (sixth year of Duke Zhao[6]) it says, "When there was disorder in the Xia government, they created the 'Punishments of Yu.' When there was disorder in the Shang government, they created the 'Punishments of Tang.' When there was disorder in the Zhou government, they composed the 'Nine Punishments.'"[7] Anything connected with "virtue" or "morality" (*de* 德) is "punishment," not "law," and thus government regulations and social morality are only related to "punishment" (penalties against those who do not follow the ritual system). All of these are questions that "one who governs others"—that is, the "noble person"—is supposed to worry about, and not anything that the ordinary commoner particularly cares about. Ancient China had only "ritual," designed to uphold the hierarchical order of clan society, and the "punishments" that developed afterward; it lacked any "law" based upon the foundation of the rights of common man. So-called lawyers were criminal lawyers openly serving autocratic rulers, who could well be called "punishers."

This passage has the same meaning as 4.16, "The noble person understands ritual and righteousness, the petty person understands profit and loss."

4.12. 子曰: 「放於利而行, 多怨。」

Confucius said, "To rely only on profit in carrying things out is to incur a lot of resentment."

Notes: *Zhu Xi notes: Master Cheng says, "To desire profit for oneself is sure to harm others, and thus, much resentment [will follow]."*

Comments: Here again we see the phenomenon of the breakup of clan society. Because of the corrosive and eroding effect of money upon all things, traditional society began to disintegrate, and resentment became very widespread. Is this not the case also today? But in the midst of this grumbling, society develops and advances—this is why I always speak of "the antinomy of historicism and moralism." There is no way around it: society is constantly, tragically advancing. Although complaining is useless, it does have a positive side—it can serve to provide checks and balances. As I point out at various points in this book, beginning with the salt and iron debates of the Han dynasty, when literature of the able and virtuous expressed indignation against and lashed out at officials who "relied on profit in carrying things out," and continuing in the similar thoughts and attitudes of later Confucians, complaint played a very important role in judging the over-accumulation of authoritarian imperial power. Within this antinomy, therefore, how to grasp or handle the appropriate "proper measure" (*du* 度) has been one of the crucial things pushing society to develop. This is why, in the Chinese Confucian notion of "outer kingship," there was often the idea of the "mutual alternation of Confucianism and Legalism." I believe that the "mutual alternation of Confucianism and Legalism" (outer kingship) and the "mutual complementarity of Confucianism and Daoism" (inner sageliness) represent the two major aspects of the development of Confucianism. And these two aspects, in turn, are in a relationship of mutual complementarity and mutual supplementation with each other. Only in this way was it possible to construct the splendid complexity of the Confucian landscape. To explain Confucianism as a purely moral metaphysics is too one-sided and narrow.

Incidentally, the word *fang* 放 can be read as either "relying on" or "indulging," and either is possible here.

4.13. 子曰：「能以禮讓為國乎？何有？不能以禮讓為國，如禮何？」

Confucius said, "If one can use the ritual system and deference to govern the country, what could be the problem? If one cannot use the ritual system and deference to govern the country, then what is the ritual system for?"

Comments: The word "deference" (*rang* 讓) here is very important. It is one of the concrete contents of, and an important key to "ritual." The *Zuozhuan*, in the thirteenth year of Duke Xiang notes, "'Deference' is the pillar of ritual"; and in the second year of Duke Zhao, "Loyalty and faithfulness are the vessels of ritual; humility and deference are the ancestors of ritual." Another passage (tenth year of Duke Zhao) says, "Deference is the lord of virtue (*de* 德)." Why? Xunzi put it well: "What is the origin of ritual? I reply: man is born with desires. If his desires are not satisfied for him, he cannot but seek some means to satisfy them himself. If there are no limits and degrees to his seeking, then he will inevitably fall to wrangling with other men. From wrangling comes disorder and from disorder comes exhaustion. The ancient kings hated such disorder, and therefore they established ritual principles in order to curb it" (*Xunzi* 19.1).[8] "Among the beasts there are fathers and sons, yet not the familial affection between fathers and sons; there are male and female, and yet not the separation between men and women. In the Way of being human there is nothing without distinctions, and among distinctions, none is greater than hierarchical division, and among hierarchical divisions, none is greater than ritual" (*Xunzi* 5.5). "Why is [man] able to organize himself in society? Because he sets up hierarchical divisions. And how is he able to set up hierarchical divisions? Because he has a sense of duty (*yi* 義)" (*Xunzi* 9.19).[9] The use of external authority to implement a ritual system within the community is "duty" or "righteousness" (*yi* 義) (justice, equity, fairness). It encompasses the use of banishment (banishment from one's clan or tribe would have been a very serious penalty at the time), punishment, and execution to implement and support a ritual system in which "each receives his due," all in order to quell conflict and maintain the community. Deference is "ritual" or "duty" that is cultivated in both an individual's inner and outer being (primarily "outward" behavior, and only then "inner" cultivation or education). At the inner level, it means paying attention to the control of one's moods and desires (as, e.g., in the control of the appetite learned in childhood), developing a love for others as oneself, and the willingness to yield to others. Externally, from the point of view of behavior and action, demeanor, and posture, one should pay attention to temperance, yielding, modesty, refinement and courtesy. **Notions like "hierarchical divisions," "deference," "duty," and so on, originally were all in service of maintaining the hierarchical structure and social order of the clan system, but later they morphed into individual morality, governing the Chinese people's ways of being human and carrying out tasks,** and became something that one was expected to study from an early age. The story of Kong Rong giving the bigger pears to his brothers (孔融讓梨) is well known from ancient times. On the other hand, there has never been much place in the Chinese tradition for things like "blowing your own horn," showing off, acting the hero, relying on one's own courage (*ping yonggan* 浿勇敢), being proud of oneself, enjoying making a display of oneself, being self-satisfied, and so on. In this way, "deference" became, both internally and externally, an important element of and concrete means toward the formation of the psychological emotions and humanistic culture. Its downside is that it can turn into hypocrisy and weakness. Especially in the competitively-motivated modern society of this historical moment, how to attain individual fulfillment, while also preserving the beauty of this type of traditional virtue, is a problem.

4.14. 子曰: 「不患無位, 患所以立; 不患莫己知, 求為可知也。」

Confucius said, "Do not worry about having no position; what you should worry about is how to fulfill your duty to the utmost in the position you have. Do not worry about others not knowing you; rather, work hard, and others will come to know it."

Notes: *Zhu Xi notes:* "Suo yi li 所以立" *["something to stand in/on"] means how to stand in one's position. Liu Baonan* 劉寶楠 *quotes from Xunzi (6.14): "The well-bred man [*junzi*] can make himself honorable, but he cannot ensure that others will honor him. He can make himself trustworthy, but cannot ensure that others will trust him. He can make himself useful, but cannot ensure that others will employ him. And so, the gentleman is ashamed of not being cultivated; he is not ashamed of being maligned. He is ashamed of not being trustworthy; he is not ashamed of not being trusted. He is ashamed of being incapable; he is not ashamed of not being employed. Thus, he is not tempted by good reputation, nor is he intimidated by slander. He follows the Way as he goes, strictly keeping himself correct, and he does not deviate from it for the sake of material goods. Such a one is called the true gentleman [*junzi*]."*[10]

Comments: Private morality and public morality are the same in the end—there is no difference.

4.15. 子曰: 「參乎! 吾道一以貫之。」曾子曰: 「唯。」子出。門人問曰: 「何謂也?」曾子曰: 「夫子之道, 忠恕而已矣。」

Confucius said, "Ah, Zeng Shen, my thought and behavior are strung together into a unity." Zengzi said, "It is."

After Confucius had walked away, the other disciples asked, "What did that mean?" Zengzi said, "What the teacher strives for is nothing more than loyalty and consideration."

Notes: *Cheng Shude quotes Ruan Yuan's* 阮元 *(1764–1849) "Yanjing shi ji"* 揅經室集*: The term* guan *["string together" or "thread up"] appears three times in the "Analects": [here] in the Zengzi reference to "strung together into a unity;" in the Zigong reference to "thread them all together into a unity" ["Analects" 15.3]; and in Minzi Qian's reference to "the way it was"* 仍舊貫 *[in "Analects" 11.14]. What these three occurrences convey should not differ.* Guan *means a way of acting. Jiao Xun* 焦循 *(1763–1820) notes in "Diao gu lou ji":* Guan *means "through"* (tong 通)*. Thus it is said, [the Dao] "unites the divine virtues, and imitates the conditions of the ten thousand things"* 通神明之德, 類萬物之情.[11]

Qian Mu notes: Zengzi said, "The master's way is nothing more than loyalty and consideration." Afterward Mencius said, "The way of Yao and Shun is nothing more than filiality and fraternal duty." This is precisely where one can see their school of thought. But to say that the "Analects" as a whole speaks only of filiality, fraternal duty, loyalty and consideration, in the end will fall short of the whole truth.

Comments: This is a very famous passage, and has a great variety of readings, some even entering upon the mystical. The key lies in the meaning of "strung together into a unity." Some read this as referring to a Chan type of sudden enlightenment or secret transmission. Others regard it as a basic principle or concept that unites all things (as in Wang Bi's commentary). In the present reading, I take this to refer to [what one] practices or carries out (Zhu Xi comes close to this when he notes, "doing one's utmost is loyalty; extending oneself is called consideration"). For neither "loyalty" nor "consideration" refer to conceptual knowledge, but rather to the basic sense and principles of how to act as a human being, how to treat others and oneself. In this respect, they are examples of pragmatic reason. Furthermore, when the *Rites of Zhou* remarks that "consideration pleases the heart" 如心曰恕, while "loyalty concentrates the heart" 中心曰忠, these both have to do with the psychological emotions.[12] Clearly, these have to do with moral feelings and standards of behavior, absolute and universal, so that they can "string together into a unity" everything everywhere. One could also say that what "strings together into a unity" is humaneness (*ren*). This also works. Qian Mu's broad-minded explanation is from the perspective of a historian, and in places resembles Ye Shi 葉適 (1150–1223) and Kang Youwei: they were not satisfied with the fact that Zengzi and the schools associated with Zisi, Mencius, and the Song-Ming Neo-Confucians were interested only in the "inner sageliness" of filiality, fraternity, loyalty, and consideration, and went so far as to use these to sum up the *Analects*.

Is it possible, then, to explain this "loyalty" and "consideration" with which all is "strung together in a unity" as, respectively, "private religious morality" and "public social morality"? The former indicates the individual's unconditional, absolute obedience to the gods of heaven and earth, and to rulers, fathers, and elders; the latter refers to basic standards that uphold society as a whole in managing interpersonal relationships. The word for consideration, *shu* 恕, appears only twice in the *Analects*, the other being 15.24 ("That would be consideration [shu 恕]: what you do not want, do not give [or do] to others"), which could do perfectly as the foundational standard of "public social morality." The word for loyalty, *zhong* 忠, appears sixteen times in the *Analects*, much more frequently than *shu*, probably because at the time public social and private religious morality would often have been addressed together; beginning in ancient times, the private religious aspect would have been superior to all others, and was often mixed with ethics and government, as if they were the same thing, so that (public) social morality was always contained, absorbed, or swallowed up by (private) religious morality.

Let us return to the question of whether this passage touches upon the mystical. I believe that following the rationalization of shamanism or witchcraft, there remained within Confucianism and Daoism two major characteristics. The first is an emphasis on the position and power of humans, from the references in the *Book of Changes* to "participation with Heaven and Earth" 與天地參, to the Song Neo-Confucian idea of "establishing the ultimate humanity" 立人極. The other is mystical experience, particularly among Daoists, though also among Confucians, as in terms like "sincerity," "reverence," and so on, none of which are purely rational but rather involve a mysterious union of emotion and reason. Later, after the reception of Buddhism, the same strain developed into Chan Buddhism.

4.16. 子曰：「君子喻於義，小人喻於利。」

Confucius said, "The noble person understands ritual and righteousness, the petty person understands profit and loss."

Notes: *Cheng Shude quotes Jiao Xun's "Diaogu louji": If one is a commoner, then lacking constant harvests what follows is an inconstant mind. The petty person understands profit, but because the petty person understands profit, in order to govern petty people, one must use what they regard as profit in order to profit them. Thus the "Book of Changes" regards it as profitable for the people to show confidence in the noble person.*[13] *If the noble person can inspire the confidence of the petty person, then the petty person later will be influenced by the noble person. The petty person obtains profit, then can pursue duty [*yi 義*], while the noble person makes it his duty to profit the whole world.*

Comments: This passage is another important one; a major crux of Song-Ming Neo-Confucianism is the saying that "the distinction between righteousness or duty [*yi*] and profit [*li*] is what distinguishes man from beast." The opposition between noble person and petty person has thus become an absolute moral concept. "Profit" is human desire, and must be "extinguished" in order to preserve the Heavenly Principle (ritual and righteousness). I do not follow this reading here. Rather, I prefer to follow Jiao Xun's reading, quoted above. This is more in keeping with Confucius's notion of "make them numerous, enrich them, educate them" (*Analects* 13.9). Confucius emphasizes humaneness and ritual, Mencius humaneness and duty or righteousness [*yi* 義]. Righteousness or duty [*yi*] is the same as ceremony [*yi* 儀], which originated in the idea of keeping the rhythm in shamanistic dance, and later developed into the abstract and universalized notion of "ritual" "appropriateness." But ritual (*li*) and righteousness or duty (*yi*, i.e., *yi* 宜 ["appropriateness"]) cannot be completely without relationship with "profit" (*li*)—just as with the noble person and the petty person, "without petty people it would be impossible to cultivate a noble person" (see *Mencius* III.A.3).[14] Therefore, Confucius was not against speaking about "profit," but did so only rarely (*Analects* 9.1).

4.17. 子曰：「見賢思齊焉，見不賢而內自省也。」

Confucius said, "When one sees a good person, one should think how to emulate him; when one sees a bad person, one should reflect on one's self."

Notes: *Liu Baonan quotes Xunzi's "Xiu shen"* 修身 *chapter: "When you observe goodness in others, then inspect yourself, desirous of cultivating it. When you observe badness in others, then examine yourself, fearful of discovering it."*[15] *This is the meaning of this passage.*

Comments: [One should] always be unceasingly "advancing in virtue and cultivating enterprise," "examining oneself" (*Analects* 1.4), diligent, conscientious, and cautious, constantly seeking to perfect goodness. This is the self-cultivation of private religious morality. But not everyone can be expected to do this—it has no direct connection to the social system or social order.

4.18. 子曰:「事父母幾諫。見志不從, 又敬不違, 勞而不怨。」

Confucius said, "In serving one's parents, remonstrate with them gently and repeatedly. If they do not listen to you, continue to respect them and do not defy them; although you may be grieved, do not complain."

Notes: *Cheng Shude quotes the "Tan Gong"* 檀弓 *chapter of the "Liji": In serving one's father, one should hide [his faults] and not offend [against his authority]; by "hide" it means one should not broadcast his mistakes; by "not offend" it means one should not offend him by admonishing him to his face. The "Qu li"* 曲禮 *chapter of the "Liji" says, If after three attempts to admonish them, they do not listen, then obey them with weeping and tears.*

Comments: In the modern period, this is even more difficult to carry out. In traditional China, the relationship between father and son was foundational, and quite different from any other relationship. How one handled this relationship, how one cultivated the filial emotion of *xiao* (孝 filiality), is the very beginning of the Way of being human that Confucianism regards as primary. The rest of the social order grows out of and develops from this. Among animals, there is mother-love for offspring, but China's Five Relationships center on the love between father and son, not mother and son; what is taught is "the father's love and the son's filiality," emphasizing the feeling of "love" of parents (and particularly fathers) for sons and daughters. Therefore on the one hand the passage advocates admonishment, and on the other hand it emphasizes not doing injury to the emotions. In the Notes above, the words "hide" and "not offend" refer to the situation in which the parents have made a mistake;

in the process of admonishing them, one should not cause them to lose face before oneself or other family members. This is very concrete and realistic teaching. Of course, this reflects a sort of psychological internalization of the patriarchy of clan society. How this should be treated, understood, and "creatively transformed" today is a problem, especially in the face of Christianity's teaching that one must go against one's father in order to follow Christ ("A man's enemies shall be those of his own household" [Matthew 10:36]), and after Freud's challenging "father complex" teaching.

4.19. 子曰: 「父母在, 不遠遊。遊必有方。」

Confucius said, "While your parents are alive, do not travel afar. If you do travel, you must have a definite direction."

Comments: Today, there are some who no longer adopt this teaching, while some still follow it; because we have fast means of transportation such as airplanes and automobiles, although we may travel far (in terms of geographical position), we are not far (in that return time has become shorter). Actually, what is important here is that when Confucius spoke of humaneness or filiality, he was very concrete. For example, in this passage what is emphasized is not that one should not travel, but that one should not cause parents to miss one excessively (since when traveling afar it is difficult to see one another), or to worry overmuch (as directionless wandering is likely to cause one's parents to be uneasy). This type of concrete cultivation of the children's love for parents, that is, filiality and humaneness, **is the concrete cultivation of the emotions of human nature**, rather than a simple aphorism on how to conduct oneself in the world. **It refers to the concrete shaping of the emotions, rather than abstract conceptual ideals,** and what is important about it is one's emotional attitude as someone's child. Can China's youth carry on this beautiful moral tradition?

4.20. 子曰: 「三年無改於父之道, 可謂孝矣。

Confucius said, "If someone can maintain his father's work and deeds unchanged for three years, that person can be called a filial son."

Comments: See 1.11.

4.21. 子曰：「父母之年，不可不知也。一則以喜，一則以懼。」

Confucius said, "One cannot not know the age of one's parents, on the one hand to rejoice, on the other hand to fear."

Comments: Here again, we see the same concreteness. "Rejoice" because despite their increased years they continue to remain healthy; "fear" because as their years increase, they decline and approach death. I must say, this is painstakingly detailed psychological description and teaching. **Parents usually can remember their children's ages; how many people today remember the ages of their parents?**

4.22. 子曰：「古者言之不出，恥躬之不逮也。」

Confucius said, "That the ancients did not take speech lightly showed their shame at possibly being unable to live up to [what they said]."

Notes: *Zhu Xi notes: Fan* 范 *[Zuyu* 祖禹 *(1041–1098)] said: People will only speak lightly of what they [do not intend to] carry out; speaking of it is like doing it, and doing it like speaking of it; thus it is not easy for people to let something come out of their mouths.*

Comments: Zhu Xi's commentary is very interesting here. Today, it is very common for people to be unashamed to talk big, to say something and not carry it out, or to have their actions not match their speech. These are all questions of "private morality" (religious morality). In a democratic society, every politician engages in bragging in order to attract votes. But "private morality" can affect "public morality," and despite all our commercialism and advertising, in the final analysis, people still have more trust in relatively honest politicians or business people. "Private morality" and "public morality" can mutually penetrate, overlap, and transform each other. One should both pay attention to the distinction between them, and observe their connectedness.

4.23. 子曰：「以約失之者，鮮矣。」

Confucius said, "Those who err on the side of self-restraint are few indeed."

Comments: Chinese people tend to restrain themselves too much because of this, and this has done great damage to human nature. Of course, this saying of Confucius is not wrong, in that it makes sense in general.

4.24. 子曰:「君子欲訥於言, 而敏於行。」

Confucius said, "The noble person will speak less, and do more."

Notes: *Zhu Xi notes: Master Xie [Xie Liangzuo 謝良佐 (1050–1103)] notes: Simply speaking is easy, therefore one must restrict it; to rise and act is difficult, therefore one must be nimble at it.*

Comments: In the *Analects*, Confucius often opposes flattery and deceitful speech, appreciating instead being "simple" and "slow to speak" (*mu ne* 木訥) (13.27), and the like. This would seem to be quite different from today's Western philosophical idea of language as homeland (*jiayuan* 家園), as the foundation of being human. Perhaps this reflects the difference between "In the beginning was the Word" (John 1.1) and "In the beginning was the Act" (the Dao) 太出有為 (道). The Dao means the path. In Confucianism, the first thing is action, behavior, and furthermore, one moves from the Way of humanity to the Way of Heaven. When the former appears, the latter shines forth. Goethe (in *Faust*) says that it is not "in the beginning was the Word," nor "in the beginning was the Power," nor again "in the beginning was the Thought," but rather "in the beginning was the Act." This would seem to be very close to Chinese philosophy in that it claims there is "something" that is higher than and transcends language. This thing is neither language, nor thought, nor power, but human (or, in *Faust*, perhaps divine) action: practice, behavior, activity. Throughout the *Analects* is found the viewpoint that action is superior to words. Only in this way can interior and surface be unified, language and action be in agreement, so that a healthy human nature can be formed—this is the foundational spirit of Confucianism, and precisely what differentiates it from pure philosophy. General philosophy does not make these demands; it is only religion that demands that behavior must match doctrine. In Confucianism, this develops into the deep philosophical proposition of "effort as substance" 工夫即本體 with which the Song-Ming Neo-Confucians all used to warn themselves that words and action should be unified. But this has not necessarily extended to the thought of modern, present-day New Confucians, who have turned Confucianism into a purely speculative philosophy of the classroom, causing it to lose its original pseudo-religious character.

4.25. 子曰:「德不孤, 必有鄰。」

Confucius said, "The person of virtue will not be alone, but people will certainly draw near to him."

Comments: It will not be necessary to have a "friend come from afar" (1.1), for there are companions of the truth nearby. This is both a felt belief and an actual experience. Clearly, **"virtue" has a socio-pragmatic character.**

4.26. 子游曰:「事君數, 斯辱矣, 朋友數, 斯疏矣。」

Ziyou said, "In serving a ruler, if one is too pedantic, one will be disgraced. In dealing with one's friends, if one is too pedantic, one will encounter distance."

Comments: Clearly, according to classical Confucianism, the ruler and his ministers will be like friends in some ways, but must retain some degree of independence. Although ministers must offer well-intentioned sincere advice to their ruler, they must know when to stop, and must not insist. This is quite different from later generations' idea of "the loyal minister does not fear disgrace," or the practice of "remonstrating unto death." This distinction arises from the difference between ancient clan society and the later unified autocratic imperial domain. Actually, even your good friend will not always be patient with hearing your opinions; how much more so your ruler? Despite your every good intention and persistence in humaneness and righteousness, it may be to no avail and leave you in disgrace. Hegel might have laughed at talk of these types of experiences as simple aphorisms about how to live in society, but actually they contain deep truths about human life, that is, how to concretely maintain individual independence, and the importance of human dignity. Although Confucianism was never able to develop a philosophical theory such as Kant's "humanity as an end-in-itself," from the beginning it included elements of this type of thought. It should be able to serve as an important resource in the construction of a public social morality for today. *Analects* 12.23 is similar.

Book 5

5.1. 子謂公冶長:「可妻也。雖在縲絏之中, 非其罪也」。以其子妻之。

Confucius said of Gongye Chang: "One could marry one's daughter to him. Although he has been imprisoned, it was not his fault." And he gave his daughter to him in marriage.

Comments: Confucius did not choose a person based on temporary glory or shame; even today this belongs to what is not easy to put into practice.

5.2. 子謂南容:「邦有道, 不廢; 邦無道, 免於刑戮。」以其兄之子妻之。

Confucius said of Nan Rong, "If the state has a good government, he will not be overlooked; if the state's government is bad, he will not be detained or killed." He gave his own niece to him in marriage.

Comments: This is more secure, more safe than the case of Gongye Chang, therefore he gives not his own daughter but his niece to him in marriage. To put others before oneself is an aspect of private religious morality, and also the meaning of "ritual deference." It is a pity that girls of the time were not allowed to make their own choices.

5.3. 子謂子賤:「君子哉若人! 魯無君子者, 斯焉取斯?」

Confucius evaluated Zijian, saying, "A noble person, this man! If it is said that in Lu there are no noble people, how could he acquire these qualities?"

Comments: This is to say, good character is obtained from one's environment and education. **The crux of the entire *Analects* and the whole of Confucianism is its emphasis on education and the establishment of human nature.** It is precisely because of this emphasis on education and the establishment of human nature that we have the problem of cultural-psychological formation.

5.4. 子貢問曰：「賜也何如？」子曰：「女，器也。」曰：「何器也？」曰：「瑚璉也。」

Zigong asked Confucius, "What do you think of me?" Confucius said, "You are a kind of vessel." He asked, "What kind of vessel?" Confucius answered, "A jade vessel for worshipping a god."

Comments: Here there is both censure and praise, as well as humor. It is censure, because his abilities have not yet been adequately developed (see the passage that says "The noble person is not a tool" [2.12]). It is praise, because his ability has attained the height of refinement and profound nobility. All of this is spoken in the language of humor.

5.5. 或曰：「雍也，仁而不佞。」子曰：「焉用佞？禦人以口給，屢憎於人。不知其仁，焉用佞？」

Someone said, "Yong has humaneness and virtue, but he does not know how to speak." Confucius said, "Why should he need to know how to speak? Even if he could argue on and on, it would make people disgusted. Although I do not know whether or not Yong really has humaneness and virtue, why should he need to know how to speak?"

Comments: Here again we see how Confucius despised flattery (*ning* 佞), a love of speech, or the speaking of fine words. Probably at the time it may also have referred to talking a blue streak, or too much empty talk.

5.6. 子使漆雕開仕。對曰：「吾斯之未能信。」子說。

Confucius wanted Qidiao Kai to go take an official position. He answered, "I do not yet have confidence in this." Confucius was very happy.

Notes: *Kang Youwei comments: Because of his lack of courage or confidence in himself, Master Qidiao was unwilling to go after a position, that is, his learning was great and his ambition transcendent, but he was not content with small accomplishments and did not want to pursue hasty success.*

Comments: Confucius was happy with his humility and deference. Kang Youwei's note has a bit of the flavor of a minister speaking of himself through his comments on others.

5.7. 子曰:「道不行, 乘桴浮于海。從我者其由與?」子路聞之喜。子曰:「由也好勇過我, 無所取材。」

Confucius said, "If what I advocate were not being put into practice, and I took a raft and put out to float on the sea, probably Zilu would follow me." Zilu heard this and was extremely happy. Confucius said, "Zilu has more daring than I, it is just that he does not know how to shape or tailor himself."

Comments: Some follow ancient commentators and translate the last clause as "There is nothing to be praised here" (Yang Bojun), or "There is no way to draw useful material from this" 沒處去弄到這些木材 (Qian Mu).[1] In Confucius's many evaluations of or teachings for Zilu, he always faults him for his rudeness, wanting him to learn not to rely on hot-blooded courage; this is similar to saying that he should prune himself, or restrain himself. The line could also be translated as "His courage exceeds mine, too bad he has not had the opportunity to express it," in which case the statement becomes a completely positive one, which also does not seem to be appropriate. Zilu can also be seen as a precursor to the later "knights" (*xia* 俠), as his personality and characteristics seem to be close to such figures.

Here we see an aspect of the Daoist (or eremitic) in Confucius and Confucianism. Even as late a figure as Su Shi has the famous lines, "How I wish to sail away in my little skiff / And, high on the waters, live out the rest of my life!" 小舟從此逝, 江海寄余生.[2] But it is difficult to live on the seas, and most recluses retreated to mountains or wilderness areas, near the water's edge. The fishermen and woodcutters found in later poetry and landscape painting often shared the same delights as the Confucians (scholars) in little grass huts. **These figures together with nature (landscape) seem to represent or symbolize eternity. These are symbols of ultimate reality for Chinese people.**

5.8. 孟武伯問:「子路仁乎?」子曰:「不知也。」又問。子曰:「由也, 千乘之國, 可使治其賦也, 不知其仁也。」「求也何如?」子曰:「求也, 千室之邑, 百乘之家, 可使為之宰也, 不知其仁也。」「赤也何如?」子曰:「赤也, 束帶立於朝, 可使與賓客言也, 不知其仁也。」

Meng Wubo asked Confucius, "Is Zilu humane?" Confucius said, "I do not know." He asked again. Confucius said, "As for Zilu, a country of a thousand chariots can put him in charge of their soldiery and military administration. I do not know whether he is humane or not."

"What about Ran Qiu?" Confucius said, "Ran Qiu could be put in charge of the administration and general management of an area of a thousand households, or a clan with a hundred chariots. I do not know if he is humane or not."

"And what about Zihua [Gongxi Chi]?" Confucius said, "Zihua can put on the ceremonial robes, serve at court, and be put in charge of foreign affairs. I do not know whether he is humane or not."

Comments: This Meng Wubo, in asking about these three famous disciples of Confucius, most likely wanted to choose one from among them to serve as an official. He asked about humaneness because Confucius usually made it the subject of his teaching and [considered it] the standard for being human. Confucius's reply demonstrates and emphasizes the fact that humaneness is not like certain types of talent or ability and that by distinguishing it from talent and ability, we can observe the true significance of humaneness as psychological substance.

5.9. 子謂子貢曰:「女與回也孰愈?」對曰:「賜也何敢望回。回也聞一以知十, 賜也聞一以知二。」子曰:「弗如也! 吾與女弗如也。」

Confucius said to Zigong, "Who is superior, you or Yan Hui?" Zigong answered, saying, "How can I compare with Yan Hui? He hears about one thing, and from it deduces ten; I hear about one thing, and from it deduce two." Confucius said, "It's true that you cannot compare with him—you and I both cannot compare with him!"

Comments: In order to make it reflect positively on Confucius, many commentators have translated the last line as "I allow (or agree with) you, that you cannot compare with him." But is this not an exceedingly awkward reading? Actually, Han Yu said long ago, "A disciple need not be inferior to his teacher, nor a teacher more worthy than his disciple." Liu Fenglu in his *Lunyu shuhe* comments, "The Master himself said he was unequal to Yan Yuan [Yan Hui]." Furthermore, here we have these self-deprecatory, deferential words of Confucius himself.

The word *zhi* 知 here may be *zhi* 智, or wisdom, which was originally one of the "five virtues" 五德 (humaneness, righteousness, ritual propriety, wisdom, trustworthiness 仁義禮智信). Humaneness and wisdom often come up together in the *Analects*, but later philosophers have given little development to wisdom, up to the modern period, when under Western influence, thinkers like Wang Tao 王韜 (1828–1897), Kang Youwei, and Sun Yatsen attempted to penetrate the subject. Sun Yatsen emphasized, "Knowledge [*zhi* 知] is difficult, action easy," and Kang Youwei also emphasized wisdom (*zhi* 智). Wang Tao said, "The world sees humaneness, righteousness, ritual propriety, wisdom, and trustworthiness as the five virtues, [but] I think there is only one virtue, and that is wisdom [*zhi* 智]." Before them, Dai Zhen had attempted to explain Confucianism from an epistemological standpoint (see *Mengzi zi yi shu zheng* 孟子字義疏証), but his views were thoroughly overpowered by the ethical tradition that took humaneness as its core or substance.

5.10. 宰予晝寢。子曰：「朽木不可雕也，糞土之牆不可杇也，於予與何誅。」子曰：「始吾於人也，聽其言而信其行；今吾於人也，聽其言而觀其行。於予與改是。」

Zai Wo was taking a long nap during the daytime. Confucius said, "Rotten wood cannot be carved, and dung walls cannot be patterned with a trowel. What is there to blame Zai Wo for?" Again he said, "In the beginning, I would listen to people's words and trust their actions; today I still listen to their words, but I observe their actions. It is Zai Wo who has changed me."

Comments: Zai Wo was a famous disciple of Confucius, known for his speaking ability; this is the reason for Confucius's second comment here. Apparently, Zai Wo was smart but not diligent enough, was talented but paid little attention to cultivation. For these reasons he received repeated severe rebukes from Confucius. But not only did Confucius tolerate and accept him, he even strongly praised him. Only someone who does not rigidly apply a single standard in evaluating people can be a mentor or leader.

After the *Analects*, many famous classics taught using either argument (Mencius), exaggerated parables (Zhuangzi), abstruse mysteries (Laozi), exactitude (Xunzi, Hanfeizi), or unbridled expression (Qu Yuan), and so on. It seems they less and less started from the concrete situations of daily life or everyday living to express deep truths. The much later *Shishuo xinyu* (*New Tales of the World*) was dedicated to vain accounts of the elegant and talented, while the various Song and Ming "Jia xun" ("Family Instructions") were rigidly pedantic; none of these could come close to the *Analects*.

Confucianism has always emphasized diligence and strongly opposed laziness, and the *Analects* repeatedly scolds people for such things as "eat[ing] their fill all day long and [not applying] their minds to anything" (17.22), to the point that Kang Youwei made the "prohibition of laziness" one of his "Four Great Prohibitions." This active, enterprising spirit of continuous striving has become a sort of deep-seated cultural-psychological formation, that is, the emotio-rational structure of the spirit of tenacity. This is an important element of what has allowed the Chinese people to endure so long despite great suffering, and is also a cultural element in the success of thousands of overseas Chinese who have pioneered through great difficulty in various places, even if they may have been unconscious of Confucianism or Confucius. Actually, what great harm is there in sleeping in the daytime? Many people in the tropics have the habit of taking long naps in the daytime. For this reason, Wang Chong believes this passage to be unfair to Zai Wo, saying that Confucius "blames him for a small fault as if it were a major mistake—how can one serve such a person" (*Lunheng* 論衡, "Questioning Confucius" 問孔). This is why some commentators have argued that sleeping during the day is "against the Way of Heaven," and not a small fault at all, to explain why Confucius scolded him for it.

5.11. 子曰:「吾未見剛者。」或對曰:「申棖。」子曰:「棖也慾, 焉得剛?」

Confucius said, "I have not seen a firm and unyielding person." Someone said, "Shen Cheng." Confucius said, "His desires are many, how can he be firm and unyielding?"

Comments: "To have no desires makes one firm and unyielding" (無欲則剛) has become a traditional proverb, with which people like to exhort themselves and one another. To be "firm and unyielding" (*gang* 剛) does not refer to vigor or courage, but to an inner strength that has to do with moral will. It is what I quoted from Mencius in a previous passage: "He cannot be led into excesses when wealthy and honored or deflected from his purpose when poor and obscure, nor can he be made to bow before superior force" (III.B.2).[3] If one has excessive desires or is led by desires, it will be easy for him to yield and he will not be firm. The one who is "firm and unyielding" will not bend or flinch; there is no strength he cannot break and no refusal he cannot overcome. Clearly, what is spoken of here is the formation of the moral will. **Moral will and moral strength are expressed in sensuous behavior and practice. They incorporate and indeed reside in this kind of "solidification of reason," that is, the absolute mastery and dominion of the rational over the sensory (including "desire"). This is the root of the moral sense.** Whether it constitutes an external, transcendent absolute law, or is an inner "emergence of conscience," it is characterized by this "firm and unyielding" quality.

5.12. 子貢曰:「我不欲人之加諸我也, 吾亦欲無加諸人。」子曰:「賜也, 非爾所及也。」

Zigong said, "I do not wish others to impose anything on me, nor do I wish to impose on others." Confucius said, "Zigong, this is not something you are able to do."

Notes: *Zhu Xi notes: This is speaking of what the humane person does, which cannot be forced; this is why the Master regards Zigong as unable to attain it.*

Comments: This passage has many different interpretations. It should be read in concert with the passage that says, "What you do not want yourself, do not force upon others" (*Analects* 12.2). [Both] seem more appropriate to social contract theory, and can have quite universal application today—they can become the foundation of modern law or government. The reason [Zigong] was "unable to do it," from our point of view today, is because due to the trinity of religion, ethics, and government, the unity of public and private, and the way emotion was entangled with reason at that time, there was [as yet] no way for rationalization to happen. What is worth emphasizing is that what Zigong and others like him sought was this type of concrete principle of fairness and justice—or in other words, a public morality. This was quite different from the individual, subjective cultivation and human-oriented private religious morality sought by Yan Hui and Zengzi. When Zigong asks, "Is there one word that one can practice one's whole life," Confucius's answer was also the same: "That would be 'consideration' (*shu* 恕): what you do not want, do not give [or do] to others" (*Analects* 15.24). Zhu Xi's comment follows the tradition, and precisely takes these two types of morality that should be distinguished and speaks of them as one; it should not be accepted.

5.13. 子貢曰:「夫子之文章, 可得而聞也; 夫子之言性與天道, 不可得而聞也。」

Zigong said, "The Master's teachings on the *Books of Poetry* and *Documents*, the *Rites* and *Music*, and other ancient writings, we are allowed to listen to. The Master's teachings on human nature and the Way of Heaven, we are not allowed to listen to!"

Comments: This passage has many different interpretations, and has always presented difficulties and questions. Actually, it can be explained very simply: Confucius is careful, in speaking of great topics, to seldom use big words. As I have already discussed above, Confucius emphasizes beginning from the near-at-hand and real, from concrete words and behaviors; this is what causes his disciple to utter this praise. It is not that he does not address these things, but that he does not do so directly. All philosophers love to discuss great, deep topics—even today this is the case. They talk about Being, "transcendence," "authentic existence," "having vital living existence," and so on, and give little thought to everyday life. **Actually, without this "inauthentic" everyday life, with its putting on of clothes and eating of food, where would that unfathomable "authentic" "being" come from?** This is what I often speak of as the fact that "how to live" comes before "the meaning of life," and such questions. Confucius very seldom taught on these great topics, preferring to teach more on all kinds of concrete [things like] "humaneness," "ritual," and "the Way in everyday relationships." These are the true "nature and mandate of Heaven." But later Confucians often mistakenly thought that Confucius and his closest disciples had some sort of secret mind-to-mind transmission or mysterious learning. It is said that Xiong Shili scolded Feng Youlan, slapping the table and saying that "conscience" is not a supposition; Mou Zongsan, who was standing by, experienced a sudden enlightenment, in what had a bit of the flavor of a "mind-to-mind transmission" (*xinchuan* 心傳) of Confucian orthodoxy. Relying on direct individual experience and denying the importance of linguistic proofs can very easily tend toward non-rational religion. The present is not an era of Chan *koans*. Even if it adopts poetic language or even a Chan *koan*, philosophy always requires a kind of common language with which to express its rational realizations, insights, and transmissions; this is probably exactly how Confucianism differs from religion and yet also from Western-style philosophy, as well as from poetry or literature, while still retaining its philosophical, rational content.

5.14. 子路有聞, 未之能行, 唯恐有聞。

When Zilu had come to know one truth, but had not yet been able to put it into practice, he feared lest he should come to know a second one.

Comments: This vividly expresses Zilu's eagerness for integrity and boldness in putting into practice what he learned. In the *Analects*, Zilu's rash courage, Zigong's quick intelligence, Zengzi's cautious slowness, Zai Wo's sharp eccentricity, and so on, all seem to be quite distinctly drawn. This is why in the introduction to this book I argue that the figurative character of the *Analects* is stronger than that of many other classics.

5.15. 子貢問曰: 「孔文子何以謂之文也? 」子曰: 「敏而好學, 不恥下問, 是以謂之文也。」

Zigong asked, "On what basis was Master Kong Wen conferred the nickname 'Wen' [refined, civilized]?" Confucius said, "He is diligent at his work and loves to study, and he is not ashamed to ask questions and advice everywhere; this is why he was conferred the nickname 'Wen.'"

Comments: The word *xia* 下 in the phrase *xia wen* 下問 [meaning literally "ask below"; here translated "ask questions and advice everywhere"] can refer to someone whose position, status, or level of knowledge is lower than one's own. The phrase *bu chi xia wen* 不恥下問 has become proverbial; it is the principle that "what you don't know, you don't know." One should not conceal oneself, or refrain from asking questions based on a fear of losing face or status. This is a genuine type of refinement, and actually an excellent sort of psyche or habit to have. Asking questions in this manner is still useful today.

5.16. 子謂子產, 「有君子之道四焉: 其行己也恭, 其事上也敬, 其養民也惠, 其使民也義。」

Confucius evaluated Zichan, saying, "He has four aspects of a noble person's virtuous action: in attitude and behavior he is modest and serious; in service to his lord he is solemn and respectful; in nurturing the common people he is bountiful; in working the common people he is equitable and proper."

Comments: This passage addresses both "instruction" (private religious morality) and "administration" (public social morality), both "self-cultivation" and "governing the state" together. Actually the two are not necessarily connected, as we see from the example of Guan Zhong in the *Analects*.

5.17. 子曰: 「晏平仲善與人交, 久而敬之。」

Confucius said, "Yan Pingzhong is good at making friends with people; even if the relationship goes on for a very long time, he maintains the same respect as always."

Comments: To make friends and be able to maintain the friendship over the long term is not easy. We often see that too much closeness can lead to sudden falling out and becoming enemies, while being too distant can lead gradually to the relationship's complete dissolution. The old saying goes, "The noble person's friendship is as clear as water." Although it may be as clear as water, yet if one were to taste it, it would have a flavor, and probably it can only be accomplished by relying not only on the strength of friendly feeling, but also on the long-term mutual respect and esteem. This is not only the path to making friends, but also where the characteristic of the human feeling of friendship itself lies. The difference between friendship and love lies in the fact that the former is drawn-out and light, while the latter is intense and easily broken; they have different psychological requirements, and involve different psychological emotions. Commentators differ about whether the passage is saying that Yan Pingzhong respects others, or that others respect him; both readings are possible. Relatively speaking, it seems more apt to regard Yan Pingzhong's respect for others as what makes him good at making friends.

5.18. 子曰：「臧文仲居蔡，山節藻梲，何如其知也？」

Confucius said, "Zang Wenzhong kept a great ceremonial tortoise, and worshipped it with the decorations of the ancestral temple; how can this be considered intelligent?"

Comments: This type of superstition is the first respect in which he is unwise; violating the ritual system is the second. It is also clear that those who were called wise by their contemporaries may not have been wise. Was the ceremonial tortoise an example of shamanism, or primitive religion? The *Book of Documents* ("Da gao" ["Great Announcement"] chapter) refers to "the great precious tortoise [shell] left me by the King of Tranquility [Ning Wang]," and on painted pottery we find images of the tortoise. China's ancient shamanism did not take the path of a religion that worshipped an object (and perhaps the reason Confucius did not approve of Zang Wenzhong's type of worship is because it was tending in this direction), but rather was rationalized and combined with history and government to form a "shamanistic-historical culture." The result of this was the *Book of Changes*. The "Bu shi" ("Divination") chapter of the *Lunheng* says, "Zilu asked Confucius, 'One can obtain omens from the shoulder of a pig or the foreleg of a goat, and one can obtain numbers from the reed of a rough potato[4] or from angelica[5] greens; why then should I inquire using milfoil stalks or tortoise shells?' Confucius said, 'Not so. One must take things according to their names. *Shi* [milfoil 蓍] is said like *shi* [desire 耆], while *gui* [tortoise] is said like *gui* [to return]. To resolve a doubt, one must inquire about the desiring and the returning.'"[6] As when he explains the ideas of the "emperor with four faces," or "three hundred years" (see below), Confucius gives a rationalized explanation for why milfoil stalks and tortoise shells are used in divination—they are simply symbols of the experience of our elders. In addition, there are similar instances, such as when Confucius commends King Zhao of Chu for "not sacrificing" and deciding not to obey the answer obtained through divination (see *Zuozhuan*, year 6 of Duke Ai), and so on. This tradition led Xunzi to clearly state, "Those who are good at the *Changes* do not make a show of divining with it."[7] The *Book of Changes* was originally a divination text, but actually contains many historical facts and recounts many stories of experience, the function of which was still to cause people to influence objective reality and act upon objects. It has a very strong subjective volitional and dynamic quality, in marked contrast to the prostration, prayer, or willing subjection to the object that characterizes religious worship. This is an important point in the understanding of Chinese culture, and the historical basis for my emphasis on "this-worldliness," "emotion-as-substance," "pragmatic reason," and the "culture of delight." Zang Wenzhong was a very famous figure of the Spring and Autumn period, about whom the historical details have been lost, so that we do not know many details about him.

5.19. 子張問曰:「令尹子文三仕為令尹, 無喜色; 三已之, 無慍色。舊令尹之政, 必以告新令尹。何如?」子曰:「忠矣。」曰:「仁矣乎?」曰:「未知, 焉得仁?」「崔子弒齊君, 陳文子有馬十乘, 棄而違之。至於他邦, 則曰:『猶吾大夫崔子也。』違之。之一邦, 則又曰:『猶吾大夫崔子也。』違之。何如?」子曰:「清矣。」曰:「仁矣乎?」曰:「未知。焉得仁?」

Zizhang asked, "The chief minister Ziwen served as chief minister many times, and never displayed a joyful countenance; he was relieved of duty many times, without displaying an expression of resentment. He was sure to share with his successor the policies pursued during his term. What do you think?" Confucius said, "He was loyal enough." "Can he be said to be humane (*ren*)?" "I don't know. How can this be considered humane?"

Zizhang asked again, "Cui Zhu killed the ruler of the state of Qi. Chen Wenzi was a person who had ten chariots, abandoned them and left the state of Qi. When he arrived in another country, he said, 'This is about the same as Cui Zhu in my own country,' and left again. When he arrived in yet another country, he again said, 'This is about the same as Cui Zhu in my own country,' and left again. What do you think?" Confucius said, "He is pure enough." "Can he be said to be humane?" "I do not know. How can this be considered humane?"

Comments: This passage again emphasizes the fact that "humaneness" (*ren*) is an inner emotional substance, and not something that any outward behavior or quality can stand in for or replace. This "humaneness" is not limited to any kind of experiential phenomenon. Hume and Adam Smith and others also regarded "sympathy" as the impetus for and origin of morality; they differ from Confucianism in that "sympathy" is simply a sort of experienced psychology, while the "humaneness" of Confucianism bears a kind of "substantial" quality associated with the "participation with Heaven and Earth" (*yu tiandi can* 與天地參). Having originated in primitive shamanism, "humaneness" encompasses the universe and ties everything up together; it can be far or near, both easy to reach and difficult to attain, and this is why it can seem quite mysterious. This tradition continued through Kang Youwei and Tan Sitong's use of "electricity" and "ether" to explain humaneness: it is substance, it is life, and it is emotion.

5.20. 季文子三思而後行。子聞之, 曰: 「再, 斯可矣。」

Ji Wenzi thought three times before acting. When Confucius heard of it, he said, "Twice is probably enough."

Notes: *Cheng Shude quotes Huan Maoyong's* 宦懋庸 *(1842–1892) "Lunyu ji": The one who thinks about something three times, especially applying too much worldly wisdom, will be overly cautious. For a filial and righteous knight of staunch integrity, no matter how many his talents and abilities, must show an indomitable spirit in the moment if he is to succeed. From ancient times to today, there are many who regret for a lifetime a mistake born of second-guessing.*

Comments: This probably refers to some particular circumstance, in which Confucius suspects he is being overly cautious or failing to avoid timidity. Generally speaking, Confucius always emphasized caution in action. The phrase "think three times before acting" became a proverbial expression in later years, to encourage caution in action, but "twice is probably enough" is even better; too much thought can easily lead to an excessively detailed evaluation of pros and cons, and contrary to expectation, to error. As Huan Maoyong very truly noted above, "From ancient times to today, there are many who regret for a lifetime a mistake born of second-guessing." For one who "thinks three times" is actually more hesitant and indecisive. The point is to be "sagacious and resolute," for "he who hesitates is lost." This is neither ethics nor epistemology, but the rationalization of everyday experience and the manifestation of pragmatic reason.

5.21. 子曰:「甯武子邦有道則知, 邦無道則愚。其知可及也, 其愚不可及也。

Confucius said, "When the government was clean, Ning Wuzi was smart; when the government was in darkness, he was stupid. His smartness can be attained, but his stupidity is difficult to equal."

Comments: Confucius definitely had the active, enterprising, and unyielding side that "knows something is not possible, yet goes and does it" 知其不可而為之 (14.38). At the same time he repeatedly displays a self-preserving, self-protecting side, as when he says (in 5.7) "I took a raft and put out to float on the sea," or (in 7.11) "when not made use of, to gather oneself up," or again (in 15.7) "he hid himself away," and so on. Clearly, this has similarities with Daoism. In the *Inner Chapters* Zhuangzi frequently evokes Yan Hui to expand upon and develop this aspect, giving it a metaphysical-philosophical treatment; in this respect the *Zhuangzi* differs greatly from the *Laozi*, with its military strategy and Daoist-Legalist statecraft. There are two aspects to the unity between Confucianism and Daoism. One is the way in which Confucianism and Laozi and the Daoist-Legalists adopted from each other, supplemented each other, mutually interpenetrated and intermingled, and in the end finally formed what I have called the age-old "mutual alternation of Confucianism and Legalism," in which Confucianism played yang to the Daoists' yin in government and statecraft. The other is the way in which Confucianism, Zhuangzi, and eventually Buddhism mutually supplemented each other in the pursuit of the perfection of human personality, in what I have called "Confucian-Daoist mutual complementarity." The latter term I have already spoken much of; the previous term, not nearly enough. For example, the close continuity and interconnectedness among military strategists, Daoists and Legalists, and their great importance in furthering the process of rationalization of ancient shamanism, and so on, are all extremely crucial topics. I say "crucial," because they played a very important role in determining the shape of China's ancient culture.

5.22. 子在陳曰:「歸與! 歸與! 吾黨之小子狂簡, 斐然成章, 不知所以裁之。」

When Confucius was in the state of Chen, he said, "Let's return, let's return. This group of disciples in my home country have ambition, ability, method, and literary talent. I really do not know how to shape or cultivate them anymore."

Comments: In the state of Chen, Confucius suffered difficulties, even to the point of having nothing to eat; therefore he expresses this lament, saying it would be better to return home, where he has many things to do; why should he stay here and suffer mistreatment? The term *kuang jian* 狂簡 is here translated as having far-reaching ambition, capability, and talent.

5.23. 子曰:「伯夷、叔齊不念舊惡, 怨是用希。」

Confucius said, "Bo Yi and Shu Qi did not remember their past enemies, therefore their resentments were also few."

Comments: The idea of "not keeping a record of old wrongs" is not only a popular aphorism but also a traditional principle followed by the Chinese people. Emphasizing reconciliation, mediation, and compromise, letting bygones be bygones, not getting entangled in the past, avoiding revenge—these quite possibly result from hundreds and thousands of years of clan society's historical experience of attacking one's enemies and exterminating whole tribes. But it has also been very helpful to everyday relationships and the preservation of the race. For this reason, Chinese views of justice always have an eye toward "harmony"—emphasizing its practical effectiveness and results—rather than any imperative to judge between right and wrong in order to produce justice by means of punishment. For in a "he said, she said" sort of world, in which arguments abound, judgment is not easy, and severe punishments are not necessarily effective in the long term. Thus the emphasis on turning from evil and following the good, "fix it and be done with it." **This viewpoint has ancient origins in communal rather than individual contractual relations.** How to blend this spirit with the modern rule of law (based upon contracts between supposedly independent individuals) is a question that will require a good deal of "Chinese application of Western substance 西體中用,"[8] and "transformative creation."

Ye Shi in his *Xixue jiyan* 習學記言 comments, "What Confucius commends Bo Yi and Shu Qi for is that while they have the same resentments as is common, their ability to find joy in themselves and nothing to resent is quite uncommon." This reading starts from the feelings and cultivation of the individual (Bo Yi and Shu Qi). This reading is also plausible.

5.24. 子曰:「孰謂微生高直? 或乞醯焉, 乞諸其鄰而與之。」

Confucius said, "Who says this Weisheng Gao is forthright? Someone asked him to borrow a bit of vinegar, and he asked a neighbor for some to give him."

Comments: The fact that a debate about even such subtle immorality as this has been recorded makes it seem as if Confucius's every word was truth. It is also interesting to compare this passage to the hypocrisy of some of today's politicians and "good people."

5.25. 子曰:「巧言、令色、足恭, 左丘明恥之, 丘亦恥之。匿怨而友其人, 左丘明恥之, 丘亦恥之。」

Confucius said, "Honeyed words, affectation, and obsequiousness—Zuo Qiuming thought all of these shameful, and so do I. Hiding one's personal dislike and pretending to make friends with someone on the surface was something Zuo Qiuming thought shameful, and so do I."

Comments: Here we enter into the contradictions between ethics and politics. In politics, "Hiding one's personal dislike and pretending to make friends with someone on the surface" is common practice, without which there would be no politics to speak of. There was a common saying in the Cultural Revolution: "In politics there is no honesty to speak of" 搞政治無誠實可言.

5.26. 顏淵、季路侍。子曰:「盍各言爾志?」子路曰:「願車馬、衣輕裘, 與朋友共。敝之而無憾。」顏淵曰:「願無伐善, 無施勞。」子路曰:「願聞子之志。」子曰:「老者安之, 朋友信之, 少者懷之。」

Yan Hui and Zilu were with Confucius. Confucius said, "How about if each of you says something about his aspirations?"

Zilu said, "I would like to be able to allow my friends to use my chariot, horses, or expensive furs, and even if they damaged them, to have no regrets."

Yan Hui said, "I would like to not brag about my good points, and not make a show of my accomplishments."

Zilu said, "I'd like to hear the Teacher's aspirations."

Confucius said, "To assure that those of the older generation are secure, those of the generation of my friends are confident, and those of the younger generation show solicitude."

Notes: *Zhu Xi notes: To care for the aged with serenity, to treat friends with trust, and to care for the young with tenderness. Another reading takes "peace" or "serenity" to refer to making me peaceful or calm; trust to refer to trusting me; and care to refer to caring for me. This is also plausible.*

Comments: Zilu's answer again displays his emphasis on keeping his word, his loyalty, and his solemn and fervent heroic spirit. In Yan Hui's answer we see the familiar humility, prudence, and self-cultivation. Confucius's answer is particularly well known. To translate the last phrase, as "To care for the younger generation" is also possible.

5.27. 子曰:「已矣乎! 吾未見能見其過而內自訟者也。」

Confucius said, "Ah, I give up! I see no one who can recognize his own faults and have an inner sense of self-reproach!"

Comments: Together with Zengzi's comment about "every day I examine myself many times" (1.4), this could perhaps be stretched into a

Confucian "penitent consciousness." But what Confucians teach is the idea that "there is no greater joy for me than to find, on self-examination, that I am true to myself,"[9] meaning that the result of this type of inner self-examination and self-reproach is "pleasure." In other words, one moves from "clarity" or "understanding" (*ming* 明) to "honesty" or "sincerity" (*cheng* 誠) (*Zhongyong*), or from "fully realizing one's heart" (*jinxin* 盡心) and "knowing one's nature" (*zhixing* 知性) to "knowing Heaven" (*zhitian* 知天) (*Mencius* VII.A.1), and finally to "participation with Heaven and Earth."[10] This kind of Confucian philosophy of inner self-examination and self-reproach is still built upon the formation and pursuit of positive emotions, and thus is different from the suffering consciousness and deep sense of sinfulness associated with repentance toward God.

The *Zhongyong* says, "Sincerity (*cheng* 誠) is the Way of Heaven. Honesty toward others (*chengzhi* 誠之) is the Way of humanity." This word *cheng* is often used and difficult to explain. From Song-Ming Neo-Confucians through modern New Confucians, commentators have explained it as a basic moral nature, the so-called Heavenly Principle (*tian li* 天理) or "conscience" (*liangzhi* 良知). Actually, the term originated from a type of psychological-emotional state in shamanistic ritual, and was later elevated and rationalized, so that it should be understood as emotion-as-substance. After this, it developed into what I call an "emotional cosmology." It is both humaneness and love. And as I have said repeatedly above, **what gives Heaven and Earth, the universe, and the substance of existence an affirmative emotional character (sincerity and humaneness) is thus connected to the human world.** Only in this way can it both transcend everyday experience and at the same time reside in an individual's inner self, and thus construct a culture of delight that is characterized by pragmatic reason. Although it [may involve] "repentance," it is distinct from either guilt or shame.

5.28. 子曰:「十室之邑, 必有忠信如丘者焉, 不如丘之好學也。」

Confucius said, "In a small place of ten families, there will definitely be found one person who is as honest and reliable as I, but perhaps not one like me in love of study."

Comments: Here again we see an emphasis upon "study." "Study" of course includes the study of documents, history, knowledge, and all kinds of skills, but more than that, it also refers to the life-attitude and tenacious spirit of actively putting what one has learned into practice. It is an active thing, from start to finish, and certainly does not stop at a passive honesty or trustworthiness of character.

Book 6

6.1. 子曰：「雍也可使南面。」

Confucius said, "This Ran Yong could be an official."

Notes: *Yang Bojun notes: Whether the Son of Heaven, the feudal lords, or a high-ranking official, when he would appear in his official capacity he would always take the south-facing position. See Wang Yinzhi's "Jingyi shuwen"* 經義述聞.[1]

Comments: There is nothing to be said.

6.2. 仲弓問子桑伯子，子曰：「可也簡。」仲弓曰：「居敬而行簡，以臨其民，不亦可乎？居簡而行簡，無乃大簡乎？」子曰：「雍之言然。」

Ran Yong asked, "How about this man Zisang Bozi?" Confucius said, "He could do; he is straightforward and concise."

Ran Yong said, "To be solemn on the inside, and straightforward and concise in managing affairs—this way of governing the people is acceptable. To be relaxed on the inside, and simple in carrying out affairs—isn't this to be too simple?" Confucius said, "What you say is quite right."

Notes: *Zhu Xi notes: That is to say, if one manages oneself with dignity and respect, then there will be an inner ruler governing oneself with strictness; if in this way one behaves in a straightforward and simple manner toward the people, one's affairs will not be confusing and the people will not be in turmoil; this is why it is acceptable. But if one starts by dealing with oneself with simplicity, then there will be no inner ruler, and one will be lax in governing oneself.*[2]

Comments: Zhu Xi also says, "Recently I feel that the use of this word 'respect' (*jing* 敬) is important, from start to finish, for the true study of the sages."[3] If the term "respect" is so important, what exactly does it mean? According to Zhu Xi, "Respect is nothing more than the word *wei* 畏 ('fear,' or 'reverence')."[4] "Caution and reverent circumspection is *jing*."[5] Inwardly, "*Jing* means concentration" (*Lunyu jizhu*); "Occupy your position with great concentration, as responding to God 潛心以居, 對越上帝."[6] Outwardly, it means "making one's clothing correct, making one's attitude and gaze respectful. . . . The placement of one's feet must be solemn, the position of one's hands reverent." And, "On going out, one must be honest; in undertaking affairs, [one must act] in accordance with what is permitted" 出門必實, 承事如容.[7] The rites set great store by respect. Of course, this moves from inner (heart) to include outer (behavior, appearance). As I have expressed repeatedly in this work, *jing* ("respect") originated from a kind of shamanistic ceremony, and thus bears a religious emotional attitude. This is why it is "nothing more than the word *wei* ('fear')." Fear of what? Zhu Xi notes above, "as responding to God." Although Chinese thinkers, including Zhu Xi, would never have affirmed the existence of an anthropomorphic god, yet they did not reject but rather actively cultivated this sort of religious emotion and attitude: **There is a kind of universal feeling of reverence for the world and everything in it, and for the substance of humanity. This is what makes it possible for Confucianism, which is not a religion, to exercise a religious function and have a religious effect.** Of course, the term does still have its origins in shamanistic activities; *jing*, *cheng* ("sincerity"), *zhuang* 莊 ("gravity") and *wei* ("fear/reverence") all share this origin.

6.3. 哀公問: 「弟子孰為好學? 」孔子對曰: 「有顏回者好學, 不遷怒, 不貳過。不幸短命死矣! 今也則亡, 未聞好學者也。」

Duke Ai asked Confucius, "Of your disciples, which one loves learning?" Confucius answered, saying, "There was one called Yan Hui who loved learning. He would not become angry with others, and would not repeat the same type of mistake, but unfortunately he died early. Now there is no one, I have heard of none who love learning."

Notes: *Zhu Xi notes: According to Master Cheng [Yi] . . . when one acts, the seven emotions come out, namely joy, anger, sorrow, fear, love, hatred,* *and desire. The more the emotions blaze, the more one damages one's nature. Therefore, the one who studies controls his emotions and causes them to be unified inside him; he simply rectifies his mind and cultivates his nature.*

Comments: Here again, clearly, "love of learning" refers to practical behavior and inner cultivation. When one has a fault, the phenomenon of blaming others and losing one's temper (or taking one's anger out on others) is quite common still to this day. Zhu Xi's and Cheng Yi's comments emphasize the cultivation of the mind-nature (*xinxing*), excluding emotion, with the "seven emotions and six desires" standing in opposition to the cultivation of the mind-nature; and the rejection of the emotions, as if they were only something to be controlled and even destroyed. But this is incorrect. Appropriate control, having the seven emotions in check, is well and good; but Cheng Yi and Zhu Xi as well as the mainstream of all of Song-Ming Neo-Confucianism create an opposition between nature and the emotions, advocating the destruction of the emotions in order to preserve nature. But this "nature" is utterly devoid of content. This idea obviously originated with the commentators [and not Confucius]. The following comments by Yuan Mei 袁枚 (1716–1797) are very interesting:

> When Master Zhu [Xi] was in Nan'an, he would hear the bell of the temple, and he would be terrified and say, let us then get up, for this mind cannot be retained. What was the mind that he was unsure he would be able to retain? What was the mind that he lost as he went along? When Confucius heard the music of Shao, his mind followed the Shao [music] so that for three months he forgot the taste of meat; this was surely [a case of] not being able to grasp hold of or retain [the mind]. Luo Congyan 羅從顏 (1072–1135) taught people to recognize the atmosphere in which joy, anger, sorrow, or happiness has not yet manifested itself. We may ask, when the jade was still in the stone, or the sound still in the bell, without turning it over or striking it, how should one study or seek it? When Confucius heard Ziyou sing and play on stringed instruments (*Analects* 17.4), he was happy; when he chanced upon the place of someone's funeral, he was sad. When he had not yet become happy or sad, [it was as if] having not yet heard the sages, he still "heard and became enlightened." Zhou Maoshu [Zhou Dunyi 周敦頤

1017–1073] would not clear the weeds outside his window, saying they were like the life and vitality of his home. Li Yuan 李沅 was unwilling to clear away an herb or tear down a railing, saying, "Would I by this action affect a moment of my life?" He must have been aware that sweeping up is the job of the disciple, and [yet] with each new day he went on making inscriptions on soup bowls. Presumably it is the way of the sages that the grass should clear itself away, and the railing should replace itself. Both of these are explanations of this teaching.[8]

6.4. 子華使於齊，冉子為其母請粟。子曰：「與之釜。」請益。曰：「與之庾。」冉子與之粟五秉。子曰：「赤之適齊也，乘肥馬，衣輕裘。吾聞之也，君子周急不繼富。」

When Zihua was sent as an envoy to the state of Qi, Ran You asked for some millet for Zihua's mother. Confucius said, "Give her six measures." Ran You asked for a little more. Confucius said, "Give her sixteen measures." But Ran You gave her eighty measures.

Confucius said, "Zihua left for the state of Qi in a chariot pulled by sleek horses, and wearing an expensive coat of skins. I have heard it said that the noble person helps the needy, and does not add riches to the wealthy."

Comments: Qing scholars have extensively investigated exactly how many pounds or measures of grain the three terms used in the passage (*fu* 釜, *yu* 庾, and *bing* 秉) refer to. This is of very little importance, however, and here I have simply taken the broad meaning. The final phrase could also be translated with the saying, "Only send charcoal when it is snowing, and do not embroider flowers on brocade."

6.5. 原思為之宰，與之粟九百，辭。子曰：「毋！以與爾鄰里鄉黨乎！」

Yuan Si was made a local official, and was given nine hundred measures of millet, but he did not accept it. Confucius said, "Don't act like this—you could distribute it to your neighbors and countrymen!"

Comments: Let the reader not misunderstand this passage to suggest that people were going to Confucius for food. These two passages record Confucius's conversations with his disciples about receiving a salary. The point is not the amount, but the principle. The previous passage emphasizes receiving less, while this passage endorses receiving more.

6.6. 子謂仲弓曰:「犂牛之子騂且角, 雖欲勿用, 山川其舍諸?」

The Master said of Ran Yong, "The calf of a brindle ox grows up with a golden red coat, and horns. Not to use it [for sacrifice]—would the gods and spirits approve?"[9]

Comments: Against the background of the hereditary system of clan nobility, Confucius is unusual in advocating that one not inquire as to status at birth or family history, but only elevate the worthy. This shows that Confucius did not hold with convention or old rites and rituals in every matter.

6.7. 子曰:「回也, 其心三月不違仁, 其餘則日月至焉而已矣。」

Confucius said, "As for Yan Hui, he can go without violating humaneness or virtue over the long haul. The others can only do it for one or two days, or once every one or two months."

Comments: "Humaneness" here seems to refer to a consummate human psychological attitude that has a sort of mystical quality. Is this the idea of "what Confucius and Yan Hui took pleasure in," the state in which "joy, anger, sorrow, and happiness have not yet arisen" ("how my parents looked before they had me"), that Song-Ming Neo-Confucianism preached after the absorption of Buddhism? The state that can also be called a "peak experience" (Abraham Maslow), usually involving the grasping of something in a moment, a fleeting experience that is difficult to sustain over a long period of time, and thus is similar to the sense of "eternity in a moment" in Chan Buddhism? Song-Ming Neo-Confucians often used the discussion of "Yan Hui's love of learning" to describe this point. This "love" of course is not to take pleasure in poverty per se; rather, poverty and such things could not detract from this psychological state of his. The fact that Confucianism does not see poverty as anything to take pleasure in sets it apart from some religions, which see poverty, suffering, or difficulty as a manifestation of the will of God, and thus something in which a person can rejoice, so that adherents may purposely seek out suffering or abuse their own bodies in order to attain salvation or transcendence. This element is absent in Confucianism. Its highest realm is attained in this mystical pleasure of the "unity between Heaven and humans." Because it neglects this type of "pleasure," Yuan Mei's criticism of the Neo-Confucians, quoted above, seems frivolous and shallow. But the Neo-Confucians draw a sharp distinction between this type of "pleasure" and "joy, anger, sorrow, and happiness," emphasizing that one must drive out these kinds of secular emotions (the "seven emotions") in order to attain this "perfect pleasure." This is why they distinguish between "nature" and "emotion," and between what has "arisen" and what has "not yet arisen." This clearly bears the influence of Buddhism. Today our job seems to be **to recognize both the existence of this type of mystical religious peak experience and psychological attitude or realm of life, and at the same time the fact that this state need not be sharply opposed to or absolutely divorced from secular emotion. This is a key point,** as it bears upon the relationship between the "rectification of the seven emotions" 七情之正 and the "pleasure of Heaven and humans" 天人之樂.

6.8. 季康子問:「仲由可使從政也與?」子曰:「由也果, 於從政乎何有?」曰:「賜也, 可使從政也與?」曰:「賜也達, 於從政乎何有?」曰:「求也, 可使從政也與?」曰:「求也藝, 於從政乎何有?」

Ji Kangzi asked Confucius, "Could Zilu govern?" Confucius said, "Zilu is decisive; what difficulty would he have in governing?"

"Could Zigong govern?" Confucius said, "Zigong's understanding is extensive; what difficulty would he have in governing?"

"Could Ran You govern?" Confucius said, "Ran You has many talents and abilities; what difficulty would he have in governing?"

Comments: Clearly, in governing, the important thing is talent and ability, and not the cultivation of one's inner nature or "inner sageliness." In this respect, Confucius differs from the Cheng-Zhu school.

6.9. 季氏使閔子騫為費宰。閔子騫曰:「善為我辭焉。如有復我者, 則吾必在汶上矣。」

The head of the Ji clan wanted Min Ziqian to assume the position of the head official of the land of Fei. Min Ziqian said, "Please properly decline on my behalf! If they come to seek me again, I will have to flee abroad."

Comments: He expresses his determination to refuse.

6.10. 伯牛有疾, 子問之, 自牖執其手, 曰:「亡之, 命矣夫! 斯人也而有斯疾也! 斯人也而有斯疾也!」

Boniu was sick, and Confucius went to inquire after him. From outside the window, he took his hand, saying, "There is nothing to be done, it is truly fate! That this kind of man should have such an illness! That this kind of man should have such an illness!"

Comments: There are a number of explanations for why Confucius took his hand "from outside the window," rather than entering the house to see him, some saying it was a "bad illness" (perhaps contagious?), and so on, but none of this is important. What is important is that Confucius is not a founder of a religion or an immortal; he cannot make the blind see or heal the sick. All he can do is sigh at the inconstancy of fate; this is life. Thus the Confucian's obligation is to "do one's utmost and obey the will [or fate] of Heaven." "Fate" is chance; it is neither fatalism nor divine will. No matter how hard one works, there will always be all kinds of unavoidable and unforeseeable chance circumstances. Life is always like this, and there is nothing one can do but sigh deeply in response. Because chance is unpredictable, we sigh at "fate." So, clearly, "fate" is not rational; because it is related to "*qi*," it is difficult for people to express their feelings about it. In our birth, our experiences—in our very existence in this life—none of these are without the element of chance. Sayings like "Heaven is inscrutable," "fate is unpredictable," and the idea that one must struggle in life, "knowing it may be impossible but doing it anyway," along with the sorrowful feelings and suffering consciousness of humaneness—all these are indispensable elements of [China's] culture of delight.

6.11. 子曰：「賢哉回也！一簞食，一瓢飲，在陋巷。人不堪其憂，回也不改其樂。賢哉回也！」

Confucius said, "He really had sagely virtue, Yan Hui did. A bowl of rice, a gourd of water, living in a beaten-up old alley—others could not have endured such anxieties, but Yan Hui never lost his joy. He really had sagely virtue, Yan Hui did."

Comments: In an earlier passage [6.7], we already encountered this idea of "what Confucius and Yan Hui took pleasure in." The Mawangdui silk text entitled *Wuxing pian* (*On the Five Elements*) states, "For a noble person, if he does not have inner worries, he will not have inner wisdom, and if he does not have inner wisdom, he will not have inner joy. If he does not have inner joy, he will not be at peace; if not at peace, he will not be happy; and if not happy, he will not be virtuous." "Happiness" here is not unemotional or unrelated to the psyche—it is still a type of happiness, **but this happiness has already passed through morality to attain to a stable, supermoral state of mind.** "Worries," here, are clearly not ordinary worries, but instead can be understood to refer to Heidegger's "fear (of death)" or "anxiety (about life)." But if "worry" refers only to worry about "death," then from a Confucian point of view, it is overly vague and meaningless. There are many varieties of "death," perhaps united only by the sense of a biological ending; to fear this requires only the consciousness or foresight of an animal. Thus for Confucians, worry and fear must have more concrete content. The *Han shi wai zhuan* says, "The noble person has three worries: not knowing, can one not worry about this? Having knowledge and not studying, can one not worry about this? Studying and not putting into practice, can one not worry about this?" The Song Confucian Fan Zhongyan 范仲淹 (989–1052) said, "When living in the loftiness of the imperial court, one worries about one's people; when situated far away [in retirement] on the rivers and lakes, one worries about one's ruler. Thus one worries when put forward, and worries when held back." Clearly, **for Confucians, worry, anxiety, and fear all have to do with this human life, and bear this specific content.** Therefore, one thinks "worriedly," one studies "worriedly," and only in this way attains to "wisdom" and "pleasure" ("To study and frequently put into practice, is this not happiness?" [*Analects* 1.1]), and finally to the realm of "joy." In other words, one "knows it" (knowledge), "loves it" (morality), and "enjoys it" (aesthetics).

6.12. 冉求曰:「非不說子之道, 力不足也。」子曰:「力不足者, 中道而廢。今女畫。」

Ran You said, "It is not that I would not like to follow your thought and teaching, but that my strength is not adequate." Confucius said, "If your strength is not adequate, you will stop halfway down the road. What you are doing now is drawing a line and refusing to get on the road."

Comments: There are still many today who would use lack of strength as an excuse for laziness. This seems to be about the importance of will ("At fifteen I made up my mind to study" [*Analects* 2.4]).

6.13. 子謂子夏曰:「女為君子儒, 無為小人儒。」

Confucius said to Zixia, "You should be a scholar for officials, not a magician for the people."

Comments: There are, again, many readings of the phrases in the original, "a noble person's (or ruler's) scholar" 君子儒, and "a petty person's scholar" 小人儒. In my humble opinion it is actually referring to the distinction between the "Greater Tradition" (the rationalization of shamanistic-historical culture) and the "Lesser Tradition" (of popular shamanism). For the explanation, see my other writings, which I will not repeat here.

6.14. 子游為武城宰。子曰:「女得人焉爾乎?」曰:「有澹臺滅明者, 行不由徑。非公事, 未嘗至於偃之室也。」

Ziyou was minister of the Wucheng area. Confucius asked him, "Have you found any talented people?" Ziyou answered, "There is a man called Tantai Mieming, he never takes shortcuts in his work; and if it not a public matter, he never comes to my office."

Comments: This passage would seem to be addressed to those today who "take shortcuts and use the 'back door.'" After two thousand years it is still useful—clearly this is an issue with a long history. It is so difficult to depend upon individual moral training to uphold justice for society!

6.15. 子曰:「孟之反不伐, 奔而殿。將入門, 策其馬, 曰:『非敢後也, 馬不進也。』」

Confucius said, "Meng Zifan does not boast about himself. In defeat, when everyone was fleeing, he defended the rear all alone, then when entering the city spurred his horse on, saying 'It was not that I was courageous in defending the rear, it was that my horse was not fast enough.' "

Comments: The emphasis is on modesty. Perhaps a bit excessively so?

6.16. 子曰:「不有祝鮀之佞而有宋朝之美, 難乎免於今之世矣!」

Confucius said, "In this society today, if one does not have either the sharp tongue and smooth talk of Zhu Tuo or the beautiful appearance of Song Chao, I'm afraid it is very hard to get anything done."

Notes: *Cheng Shude quotes Fan Ning: Zhu Tuo used flattery to gain favor with Duke Ling; Song Chao used his good looks to gain the affections of Nanzi. In a state that lacks the Way, these are both admitted.*

Comments: Confucius's lament is also one we are familiar with still today. Confucius's complaint, Lu Xun's sighs—they are as fresh now as then, and this is why these texts are still read despite their age. *Mian* (免) [in the last line] should be understood to mean industrious serving.

6.17. 子曰:「誰能出不由戶? 何莫由斯道也?」

Confucius said, "Who can go out except by the main gate? Why do people not follow this path?"

Comments: The main gate, of course, opens onto the main road and not onto a small alley. The point of this is to say that the Confucian teaching—this learning or education that applies from home to state, from inner to outer—is a self-evident path that everyone should take, and that is easy to take.

6.18. 子曰:「質勝文則野, 文勝質則史。文質彬彬, 然後君子。」

Confucius said, "When basic nature supersedes cultural refinement, the result is rough and boorish. When cultural refinement supersedes basic nature, the result is rigid and stiff. When basic nature and cultural refinement are melded together and in balance, that is when you get a noble person."

Notes: *Zhu Xi quotes Yang Shi* 楊時 *(1053–1135): . . . rather than stiffness, I would prefer rough and boorish.*

Comments: The word *wen* 文 here refers to all kinds of etiquette and ceremony. Today, some people are very bold and unrestrained, their words are frank and tend toward coarseness; while others are courteous and polite, speaking a mouthful of somber seriousness, and tending toward rigidity. Even the outward appearance of a thoroughly noble person is difficult to attain, much more so the inner balance of nature and refinement. *Wen* may also refer to a kind of formalism or textualism—a bunch of rules, conventions, ornaments, and seeming beauty that in the end is unbearably empty and stale. Zhu Xi's note above is correct: it would be better to err on the side of rude nature, which has vitality and life, than on the side of dead staleness or empty ornament. Whether in human life or in work, this is always the case. Today many pursue the opposite course, setting great store by "cultural refinement." Can you see a lot of fashionable contemporary writing here?

China's pathway out of shamanism did not separate religion (emotion and faith) from science (thought and reason), but rather melded reason into emotion, creating a unity between reason and the emotions. Thus this passage may also serve as an appropriate context to mention the fact that it was neither blind, confused insistence nor pure, cold logical reasoning that finally formed the tradition of "pragmatic reason" and the "culture of delight" that constructed China's "this-worldly" (human) cosmology. "Basic nature" is emotion, while "cultural refinement" (*wen*) is reason. For basic nature to supersede cultural refinement comes very close to the animal but has the advantage of vitality; for cultural refinement to supersede basic nature becomes like a machine, and is more terrifying. Confucius makes "ritual" and "humaneness" his central categories, and this is precisely where his greatest achievement lies: in this way people are made into neither animals nor machines.

6.19. 子曰：「人之生也直，罔之生也幸而免。」

Confucius said, "A person should live with integrity; those who live crookedly are very lucky just to avoid disaster."

Comments: Life is short, and how to live it is worth thinking about.

6.20. 子曰：「知之者不如好之者，好之者不如樂之者。」

Confucius said, "The one who knows it is not as good as the one who likes it; the one who likes it is not as good as the one who takes pleasure in it."

Notes: *Zhu Xi quotes Master Yin Tun* 尹焞 *(1071–1142): The one who knows it, knows that there is [such a thing as] this Way. The one who loves it, loves it without having obtained it. The one who takes pleasure in it, has obtained it and takes pleasure in it. . . . Zhang Jingfu* 張敬夫 *[Zhang Shi* 張栻 *1133–1181] says: This is speaking of the "ancients who studied"—is this not why they pushed themselves and did not rest?*

Comments: Zhu Xi's comment is very good. These three, knowing, liking, and taking pleasure in, can be seen as mutually reflective of the three levels in the passage, "The *Songs* inspire a person, the ritual system establishes a person, and music perfects a person" (*Analects* 8.8). These levels speak of psychological states, all of which are oriented toward *yue* or *le* 樂—the highest level or realm, both in the sense of music (*yinyue* 音樂) and in the sense of happiness (*kuaile* 快樂). This realm is related to religion, because God's existence is not an epistemological question, nor merely an ethical question, but in the final analysis more an emotional and aesthetic question. What I have elsewhere spoken of as "aesthetic metaphysics" or "aesthetic theology" is just this. Mencius spoke of this when he said, "He is the same stream as Heaven above and Earth below" 上下與天地同流 (*Mencius* VII.A.13),[10] as did Zhuangzi when he spoke of "the enjoyment that is no enjoyment is Heavenly enjoyment" 無樂之樂，是為天樂.[11] This is the same religious quality of Confucianism that I have spoken of many times above, as well as what Confucians refer to when they say, "In ancient times, scholars were trying to improve themselves" 古之學者為己 (*Analects* 14.24). **It is an experiential, emotional thing, and not something that has to do with**

deliberative thought, knowledge, or will (knowing it, liking it); for this reason, it is not something that can be attained through analytical language or concepts, or the categories or principles of argument. This "emotion" or "pleasure" does not constitute a lower level aesthetic feeling (as Kierkegaard would have it), but rather is a substantive perception that incorporates both the reason and the will.

The reason this perception is called "pleasure" has to do with the special character of Chinese culture. Life is difficult, and there is no external power (god) on which to depend; people must rely purely on their own hard work to participate in nature and unify Heaven and humans. Due to the optimism fostered through this self-reliance, they [are able to] struggle against difficulties and continue to exist. Modern scholars often criticize Chinese tradition for being less deep than Western pessimism, little realizing that Western tradition has an omniscient and omnipotent god for its backdrop, so that although humans may be insignificant, they are not without a bulwark or support. Since China lacks this backdrop, there is no alternative but to struggle forward, being confident in oneself, and because of this lack of support, the seemingly extreme exaggeration of achieving "participation with Heaven and Earth" actually means they endure greater hardship and suffering than those who enjoy such support. One must approach Chinese thought from this direction in order to understand that the air of cheerfulness put on by its "culture of delight" hides the depths of a hundredfold sorrows.

6.21. 子曰:「中人以上, 可以語上也; 中人以下, 不可以語上也。」

Confucius said, "One can speak of the higher level with people of a higher than middle level; one cannot speak of the higher level with people of a lower than middle level."

Notes: *Zhu Xi notes: This speaks of how, in teaching people, one should speak according to their level, so that one's words may easily find entrance, and not fall into the fault of skipping over important steps.*

Comments: Proceeding in an orderly manner, step by step, is an educational approach; one must teach students in accordance with their aptitude, and not restrict oneself to any one approach.

6.22. 樊遲問知。子曰:「務民之義, 敬鬼神而遠之, 可謂知矣。」問仁。曰:「仁者先難而後獲, 可謂仁矣。」

Fan Chi asked how one could be wise. Confucius said, "Do your best to treat the people with appropriateness and reasonableness, and respect the gods and spirits while keeping a distance from them; this is what can be called wisdom."

Comments: Above I have already discussed how the attitude of "respecting the gods and spirits while keeping a distance from them," neither affirming nor denying the existence of gods and spirits—nor even questioning, doubting, or thinking about them—is a typically Chinese type of wisdom. This is because questioning, doubting, and thinking all involve the use of rational argument, and it is very difficult to use rational argument to either prove or disprove the existence of God or spirits. Since this is so, why should one either blindly believe in God or spirits, or forcefully reject them based upon science? Xunzi said, "If stars fall or trees groan, the people of the state are filled with fear and say, 'What is this?' I say: it is nothing. These are simply rarely occurring things among the changes in Heaven and Earth and the transformations of yin and yang. To marvel at them is permissible, but to fear them is wrong."[12] "Rarely occurring things," because of their rarity, naturally cause many to marvel, but there is no need to fear them or allow them to obstruct any human affairs. Today, scholars often speak of Xunzi's atheism, but actually this is simply an example of pragmatic reason and has nothing to do with materialism or idealism. We also see here that wisdom (*zhi* 智) and knowledge (*zhi* 知) for the Confucians had to do not only with understanding and knowledge (*renshi* 認識), but also with behaviors, attitudes, and states of mind.

This passage is probably addressing the fact that those in government usually do not care about the life or death of the people, and have a superstitious belief in respecting gods and spirits, or restrain the people's custom of worshipping the spirits. [Confucius's] answers are all given with respect to those who govern.

6.23. 子曰:「知者樂水, 仁者樂山; 知者動, 仁者靜; 知者樂, 仁者壽。」

Confucius said, "The intelligent person likes water, the humane person likes mountains. The intelligent person acts, the humane person is still. The intelligent person is always happy, the humane person lives long."

Comments: Using a comparison with mountains and water to describe humaneness and wisdom is very smart and extremely apt. "Humaneness," the highest realm of life, is like a mountain in its dependability, stability, solidity, and permanence. Wisdom, meaning study, planning, and thought, is like water in its agility, quickness, movement, and adaptability. The reason truly intelligent people are often happy is not just because they can readily solve all kinds of problems, but also because they understand the direction and meaning of human life. "Humaneness," then, seems to go even a level higher, beyond happiness or unhappiness (see above). His (or her) state of mind is so calm, peaceful, and unchanging that it becomes timeless time (longevity). "Liking water" or "liking mountains" is a type of "naturalization of humans."

The "naturalization of humans" has many levels of meaning. For example, various sports activities can allow one to escape social alienation (although today some competitive sports have been seriously alienated from society), and by developing the strength and abilities of an individual, the limbs, and the body produce enjoyment and pleasure through a sense of accomplishment. This type of happiness is not a social happiness related to accomplishment or success, but rather a physical, bodily happiness that also brings with it psychological happiness. Secondly, there is the "liking mountains and liking water" that refers to a return to nature, thus avoiding all kinds of social alienation and repairing any sense of loss. It is simultaneously a state of mind and a kind of physical-psychological state. Thirdly, there is the unity and harmony with the rhythms of nature and the universe that people attain through *qigong*, yoga, and so on. In sum, the "naturalization of humans" causes people to recover and develop the natural human qualities and abilities that have been twisted or damaged by society or the collective, so that body, mind, and spirit meld with all of nature, even if sometimes only briefly, but very meaningfully in terms of one's experience of life.

To flow continuously (like water), and yet remain (like mountains). "Blossom by blossom they open then fall" 紛紛開且落[13]—both active and still; "The day waxes long, like almost a year" 日長如小年[14]—stillness containing movement. The circumstances of life are like mountains and water, and this image unites Heaven and humans. But is this morality? No, it is aesthetics: the host and the guest are one, humaneness and wisdom walk together; it is both religion and philosophy. **China's is not (Plato's) theory of correspondence with truth, or (Heidegger's) theory of unconcealment and revelation, but a non-essentialism in which substance and function have the same origin in "In the beginning was the Deed" 太初有為.**

6.24. 子曰：「齊一變，至於魯；魯一變，至於道。」

Confucius said, "With one change, the state of Qi could reach the state of Lu; with one change, the state of Lu could reach the ideal realm."

Comments: That is to say, the state of Lu is higher than the Qi, because Lu descends from the Zhou dynasty, and more deeply maintains or retains in latent form the Zhou ritual system and customs. "Change" [here] is a return to the way of the ancients, and demands a reform that turns the clock back, which in the end proved impossible. Not only was Confucius unable to put it into practice in the state of Lu, but in his "travels far and wide," no one listened to him. Not only was "inner sageliness" never able to produce "outer kingship," but the "outer kingship" Confucius advocated was utterly unworkable, as it would have required a return to the traditional clan system. Confucius was, in the final analysis, an educator and a thinker, not a statesman. But his "education" and "thought" exercised a tremendous effect upon the Chinese people, a much greater effect than that of any politics or statesman.

6.25. 子曰：「觚不觚，觚哉！觚哉！」

Confucius said, "A wine cup that does not look like a wine cup—what a wine cup! What a wine cup!"

Comments: These words, full of nostalgia and lament for the past, are often quoted in later literature. This type of analogical or metaphorical thought is a form of literary expression that is also a traditional Chinese form of thought. The fact that the metaphor and imagistic association (*bixing* 比興) of the *Book of Songs* could be made to serve such varied political explanations and uses from the Spring and Autumn period through the Han dynasty prominently demonstrates this characteristic and customary type of thought. It was not based upon logical reasoning, but upon this type of analogy. Confucius's statements like, "Now, finally, I can talk to you about the *Songs*" (*Analects* 3.8), and "If you do not study the *Songs*, you will not be able to speak" (*Analects* 16.13), all reflect this mode of thought. Of course, in this type of analogical thinking, particularity (dependence upon individual feeling, experience, or direct sensory perception) is very important, and the "use of beauty to awaken to truth" (using the aesthetic sense to directly intuit rational knowledge) that I have spoken of in my aesthetics is related to it. That humans have this mode of thought is what sets them apart from machines that are capable of logical reasoning.

6.26. 宰我問曰:「仁者, 雖告之曰:『井有仁焉。』其從之也?」子曰:「何為其然也? 君子可逝也, 不可陷也; 可欺也, 不可罔也。」

Zai Wo asked, "If a humane man is told that someone has fallen down into a well, would he go down into the well to save him?" Confucius said, "Why would he? He may be asked to go over and look, but cannot be trapped into going down into the well; he can be deceived, but cannot be made a fool of."

Comments: Zai Wo always liked to raise strange and penetrating questions, to make it difficult for the teacher, in very interesting ways that demonstrated his true intelligence. Confucius also answers him well, explaining that the "humane person" is not a fool who can be easily bullied or trapped. Because part of "humaneness" (*ren* 仁) is wisdom, it is an emotional-rational construction. Unfortunately, today most humane people are [simpleminded] honest people, who always seem to be cheated by others.

6.27. 子曰:「君子博學於文, 約之以禮, 亦可以弗畔矣夫!」

Confucius said, "The noble person broadly studies documents and ancient books, and uses the ritual system to control and command; in this way he can keep from going against the truth."

Comments: The phrase "control with ritual" 約之以禮 is usually understood or translated as "restrain and control" [oneself]; but I do not follow that reading here. It is better to understand it as "commanding." What is spoken of as "being established in ritual" means to use principle and regulations to command behavior, and to shape one's own work and humanity. "Ritual" here is not overelaborate formality, nor is it purely ceremonial form.

6.28. 子見南子，子路不說。夫子矢之曰：「予所否者，天厭之！天厭之！」

Confucius went to visit Nanzi, and Zilu was unhappy about it. Confucius swore an oath, saying, "If I have done anything wrong, let Heaven punish me! Let Heaven punish me!"

Comments: When Confucius was pressed to the point of being unable to do otherwise, he had to resort to swearing to Heaven in order to express himself, just as people do today—the expression is palpable. The Confucius of the *Analects* is full-blooded and lively, with a temper and faults. For example, although "when approached he is gentle" (即之也溫), he often scolded his disciples, and sometimes quite harshly ("his speech is correct and incisive" 其言也厲).[15] Yet he often cracked little jokes, and was nothing like the perfectly flawless and lifeless wooden statue that later generations would put in their shrines. Today, historians of philosophy often use this passage to demonstrate that since Confucius swore oaths to Heaven, he was certainly a deist, but this would seem to be in considerable contradiction with "Does Heaven speak?" (*Analects* 17.19). Actually, as I have said before, in the *Analects* as a whole Confucius displays an attitude of pragmatic reason that neither confirms nor denies Heaven, fate, or the gods and spirits. When Mozi criticized the Confucians for "[taking] Heaven not to be all-seeing and [taking] ghosts not to be divine,"[16] he was being quite accurate, and of course was drawing on Confucius. When this passage refers to Confucius swearing to Heaven, these are words spoken in the heat of emotion, and not adequate to prove or disprove anything.

"Nanzi" is said to have been the dissolute wife or consort of a ruler, an "immoral" person; Confucius visited her rather than avoiding her, causing even his closest disciples doubt and unhappiness. Clearly, Confucius is quite different from later fake moralists; he was not affected or pretentious, but had a high degree of adaptability.

6.29. 子曰:「中庸之為德也, 其至矣乎! 民鮮久矣。」

Confucius said, "The Mean [*zhongyong*] is the highest when it comes to humaneness and virtue. It is a long time since people had it."

Notes: *Zhu Xi notes:* Zhong *is what we name that which does not overstep but reaches everywhere.* Yong *means usual or ordinary. . . . Cheng Yi says: What is not bent is called* zhong; *what does not change is called* yong.

Comments: What is the "Mean" (*zhongyong* 中庸)? This is one of the fundamental categories of Confucianism. *Zhong* I will discuss later. Zhu Xi's note explains *yong* as *pingchang* 平常 ("ordinary"), and goes on to quote Cheng Yi, who said, "What does not change is called *yong*," and "*yong* is the fixed principle of all under heaven," [a definition] that continued in use through later generations. He Yan 何晏 (196–249) also annotates *yong* as *chang* (常 "constant"). But why should the "ordinary" be an unchanging "fixed principle of all under heaven"? Why is it so important? Chen Chun 陳淳 (1159–1223) explains, "**All that which in everyday life people commonly do and cannot abandon is normal and true.** The 'ordinary' (*pingchang*) is what has been done and not abandoned for thousands of years. For example, the eating of the five grains and the wearing of cottons and silks have not changed for thousands of years."[17] Contemporary scholar Xu Fuguan 徐復觀 (1904–1982) explains it even better:

> The so-called "Mean" (*yong* 庸) unites the ideas of "ordinary" and "use" (*yong* 用) to create new content. The *Shuowen* dictionary defines it thus: "*Yong* means use." And, "*Yong* refers to 'ordinary behavior.'" Thus, "ordinary behavior" actually refers to "behavior that has a universal and appropriate quality." "To behave in an ordinary way" means "in every time and place, to do all the things that one should or can do." . . . This shows that Confucius is demonstrating the "way of humanity" (that describes how people should go about being human) in the context of things every person can and should practice in their life and behavior. This is a major point on which Confucius's teaching decidedly parts ways with all religion and even with metaphysics.[18]

In actuality, this is precisely what I have spoken of as "pragmatic reason." *Yong* is "use"; *zhongyong* (the Mean) is pragmatic reason. It emphasizes the establishment of the right Way and timeless principles of human relations within the practices of everyday life—in a "Way of humanity" that is the "Way of Heaven." Although it is ordinary, it is the locus of the Way. This is why Confucius exclaims, "The Mean is the highest when it comes to humaneness and virtue." This is the highest place. The highest place is not in another world; it does not transcend this world. But why is it "a long time since people had it"? Perhaps this indicates that the people of the time were seeking beyond their reach, rather than emphasizing the truth that "the Way is in everyday life."

The Way of the Mean in today's society should also be sought in the everyday life of ordinary people, in modern existence. There is no need to overly emphasize elevated abstruse theories or the resources of the tradition. I strongly advocate the theory of "overlapping consensus" that John Rawls puts forward in his book *Political Liberalism*. I believe that this truly can enable modern legal-moral principles to be teased out of any cultural tradition and established in modern life. **Freedom, democracy, and social justice can all be derived from the organism of the modern life of common, ordinary people; there is no need to trace their source to Greek tradition or Christianity, and so on.** This is exactly identical to the theory of "Chinese application of Western substance" (*xiti zhongyong* 西體中用); the "substance" is modern life, and the cultural tradition plays only a secondary role. My emphasis in this book on the separation between public social morality and private religious morality is similar, as the latter at most plays only a regulative and not a constitutive function.

6.30. 子貢曰: 「如有博施於民而能濟眾, 何如? 可謂仁乎? 」子曰: 「何事於仁, 必也聖乎! 堯舜其猶病諸! 夫仁者, 己欲立而立人, 己欲達而達人。能近取譬, 可謂仁之方也已。」

Zigong said, "If one were to broadly benefit the people, and thus be able to universally succor the masses, what of that? Can such a person be called humane?" Confucius said, "Why only humane? This should be called sagely. Even Yao and Shun had difficulty accomplishing this. What we call humaneness means that when you want to stand up yourself, you help others stand; when you want to develop and grow, you help others to develop and grow. Starting from what is near at hand can be said to be the method for putting humaneness into practice."

Notes: *Zhu Xi notes: To extrapolate from oneself to others is the heart of humaneness. From this standpoint, one can see the continuous course of the Heavenly Principle. To describe the shape of humaneness, there is nothing more apt than this.*

Comments: Throughout the whole text of the *Analects*, humaneness is said to be greater and higher than other categories—greater and higher than ritual, justice, loyalty, trustworthiness, familial affection, gravity, reverence, respect, and so on. This is the only place where reference is made to the category of "sageliness" as even higher and greater. This demonstrates precisely that "humaneness" refers mostly to a psychological feeling and a spiritual realm, while "sageliness" includes external achievement and all objective success; this is what makes it greater than humaneness. In this passage we also see how Confucius emphasized the achievement of "broadly benefitting the people"; he was not interested in individual moral achievement, unlike the Buddhist-influenced Song-Ming Neo-Confucians. It also demonstrates how difficult it was even for figures like Yao and Shun to achieve the perfect ideal of "broadly benefitting the people." This is why Confucians always take as their goal "relative comfort" (*xiaokang* 小康) rather than thoughts of far-off utopias. This is typical of pragmatic reason, and can form the basis for something approaching the liberalism of English empiricism. The utopian society of the "peace of the whole world, [all like] one family, one person" 天下大同, 一家一人 is basically a co-opting into the teaching of Confucius and the Confucians of what was a Mohist ideal for the lower masses who were dissatisfied with the status quo and a Daoist ideal for upper class scholar-officials who were contemptuous of vulgarity and wished to escape from the world. Zhu Xi's explanation of how "standing oneself helps others to stand" also demonstrates that "humaneness" is psychological substance.

Book 7

7.1. 子曰：「述而不作，信而好古，竊比於我老彭。」

Confucius said, "In expounding rather than creating, and in trusting and loving the ancients, some have compared me with Old Peng."

Comments: Who is "Old Peng"? Explanations are many, various, and inconclusive. Some say it refers to Laozi, but this is not important. What is important are the four words "expounding rather than creating." Confucius dreams of the Duke of Zhou, emphasizes the ritual system, and trusts and loves the ancients; he is actually the stalwart transmitter and protector of the ancient clan tradition. Confucius was quite self-conscious about this. But in any "expounding" there is also creation, and when Confucius explained "ritual" using "humaneness," this was "creation." Actually Confucius "both expounded and created." What he expounded was ritual; what he created was humaneness. He created in order to expound, and in so doing transcended the expounding. After Confucius, the two categories of humaneness and ritual always occupied the central position. In general, although the tradition claimed that humaneness explains ritual, actually it used ritual to govern humaneness. Beginning with the statement in the "Record of Music" that [one should] "destroy human desire," Song-Ming Neo-Confucians replaced ritual with Principle or Heavenly Principle; this was the theory of Heavenly Principle and human desire that severely devalued and despised the emotion of love that is connected with desire, and that is the true, fundamental core of humaneness. In the modern period, humaneness and ritual stand in opposition; humaneness opposing ritual is in reality desire opposing Principle. This is naturalistic humanism: naturalness is human nature. Beginning from Li Zhi and Dai Zhen, these reached a peak in Kang Youwei and

Tan Sitong. The theory of emotion-as-substance that I advocate separates ritual from humaneness, and allows for the interaction of Principle and desire. As such, it constitutes a return to Confucius and inaugurates a fourth period of Confucianism.

7.2. 子曰:「默而識之, 學而不厭, 誨人不倦, 何有於我哉?」

Confucius said, "Silently remembering in the mind, studying without being satisfied, and advising others untiringly—what more is there for me to do?"

Comments: To "silently rehearse in one's mind" of course applies to all kinds of knowledge and skills. Later, with the influence of Buddhism, many philosophical treatises were written on this word "silent." Some said that because "substance has no sound or smell, Confucius stayed silent from start to finish" (Wang Fuzhi, *Du Sishu da quan shuo*). Others say, " 'Silently remembering in the mind' does not mean having a silent mouth, but having a silent mind. Having a silent mind means that the way of language and thought comes to an end, and the thoughts and plans of the mind are extinguished, and one is suddenly enlightened and brought into agreement with [the Way]" (Jiao Hong [1540–1620], *Bi cheng*); "This refers to a depth of self-understanding, a grasp of the will of Heaven and substance, as well as the true state of one's self—that is, naturally in a moment and not as a result of human arrangement—it is a profound steadiness and settled stillness; this is what it means to be able to be master of form and body" (Li Zhongfu [1501–?], *Sishu fanshen lu*); and so on. From the discussion of "the point at which joy, anger, sorrow or happiness have not yet broken out" in the *Doctrine of the Mean* to the Song Neo-Confucian emphasis on "quietude," "solitude," and "silence" in what gradually became a mystery that transcended emotions, these marked a great change from and elevation of Confucius's meaning, setting out a path based on "nature" or "Principle" as the substance.

Here I do not follow this reading. I believe that **based upon such passages as "Time and the seasons are just like this" 逝者如斯夫 (9.17), we can understand that Confucianism emphasizes action, behavior, strength, life, and being, as opposed to stillness, solitude, silence, emptiness, or nothingness. If we speak of substance, it must be found in the former and absolutely not in the latter; only in this way can we connect back up with the fundamentally "living,**

human" spirit embodied by the phrase, "In its capacity to produce and reproduce, we call it change" 生生之謂易.[1] Silence, solitude, stillness, emptiness, and nothingness simply serve as a type of experiential realm for an individual's life realization, to supplement and enrich the active, strong, and living substance. This is how Confucianism and Daoism (or Chan Buddhism) mutually supplement one another. It is precisely because Confucianism is not a speculative philosophy or an epistemology of analytical concepts that it can have this kind of ineffable "silence." Silence is an experience; though one's words and concepts should fail, still this mind remains.

How is it that someone would "study without being satisfied"? Because study would not be a means but an end in itself, namely self-cultivation. Is not this what we mean when we say, "live to old age, study to old age, improve oneself to old age"? In addition, this type of study should include study for its own sake, as in doing science for the joy of science. This is of extreme importance both today and for the future.

Confucius said, "I am on the same road as the scribes and [shamans] but end up differently" 吾與巫史同途而殊歸者也.[2] Confucius is the transmitter and rationalizer of the shamanistic-historical culture. The construction of China's pragmatic reason and culture of delight proceeded from shamanism to history to Confucianism, forming a cosmology and understanding of humanity that takes emotional psychology as its core; this is why it is important that we not go backward by any sort of mystical reading of this passage.

7.3. 子曰:「德之不脩, 學之不講, 聞義不能徙, 不善不能改, 是吾憂也。」

Confucius said, "Not to cultivate character; not to delve deeply in study; to know the truth but not put it into practice; to have faults without being able to correct them—these are what I worry about."

Notes: *Zhu Xi quotes Yin Tun* 尹焞 *(1071–1142): In virtue, one must cultivate oneself in order to become complete, and in study one must be thorough in order to understand; to see the good and be able to pursue it, or to spare no effort in correcting one's faults—these four things are important to practice every day.*

Comments: Zhu Xi's note is very good. "It renews everything daily: this is its glorious power" 日新之謂盛德 refers to the same thing.[3] It is only in this unceasing diligence and indefatigable industriousness that we find the concrete outworking of the Confucian view of human life.

7.4. 子之燕居, 申申如也, 夭夭如也。

When Confucius was able to stay home idle, he was at ease and content.

Comments: [Confucius] was not always "reviving the past to shake up the present" 作古振今, or wearing an uptight expression and acting the sage. The "hypocrites" of later generations often were exactly this way, to a nauseating extent. Even the high-minded ones like Cheng Hao would "see a tree and think of making a bridge," then blame themselves for it—thinking like this all the time, while in actuality making themselves hypocrites in thought. Another example is Liu Zongzhou's 劉宗周 (1578–1645) famous *Renpu* 人譜. If you do not believe me, go read it! The same spirit is apparent in those today who put on a stern expression and blame China for lacking a consciousness of sin, so that law is not upheld and democracy is difficult to enact. But the Chinese people's carefree, contented spirit, and the fact that they are not ashamed before Heaven or humans—this ability to be "at ease and content"—is a realm of life that is worthy of affirmation.

7.5. 子曰: 「甚矣吾衰也! 久矣吾不復夢見周公。」

Confucius said, "I have really gotten old! For a long time I haven't dreamed of the Duke of Zhou."

Comments: Again, there are two explanations: one is that his heart's intent has wasted away so that he does not dream; he knows that the revival of the Eastern Zhou and the old rites is impossible, therefore he does not dream. The other is that his intention remains, while his body wastes away; because of age, his strength is not adequate, and therefore he does not dream. The latter reading falls short, for "his fierce ambition still remained" 猛志固常在,[4] and "Ah but the times were against me" 時不利兮.[5] Confucius's deep lament is also tragic. While one lives, one should have dreams. As Kong Yingda 孔穎達 (574–648) remarked, "Zhuangzi believed in inaction, and taught stillness, inactivity, and freedom from worry; for this reason he said that the sage has no dreams. But although the sages differed in their insight, they were like other people in that they have the five emotions. Since they have the same five emotions, how can they be without dreams?" This is well said, for the five emotions are the foundation of humanity, and so is dreaming. To get rid of emotion or to have no dreams, no ideals, no aspirations, is to be like a dead man. **One must live out one's humanity in life, not death; since one cannot be without life, how can one be without dreams?**

7.6. 子曰: 「志於道, 據於德, 依於仁, 游於藝。」

Confucius said, "Let [your] aspiration be set upon the Way, be founded upon virtue, rely upon humaneness, and become adept at mastering the arts."

Notes: *Zhu Xi notes: Aspiration means the destination of the mind. . . . Virtue [de 德] means to get or obtain [de 得]; that is, to obtain the oneness of one's mind with the Way and not lose it. To rely upon [humaneness] means not to go against it. . . . To "wander" [you 游] means play or pleasure. The "arts" refer to being adept at ritual and musical ceremony, archery, charioteering, calligraphy, and mathematics, and practicing them every day without fail. Wander in them day and night, in order to expand the appeal of your writing.*

Comments: This is a more-or-less comprehensive outline of Confucius's educational ideas. For the word here translated "adept at mastering," *you* 游 [literally, "to wander"], Zhu Xi's annotation as meaning "play or pleasure" is inadequate (Yang Bojun's gloss, *youqi* 游憩 ["wander at leisure"], is the same). It should include the idea of being so well-practiced and adept at ritual, music, archery, charioteering, calligraphy, and mathematics (the so-called Six Arts) that one attains complete freedom, like a fish in water; that is, one obtains freedom and therefore happiness through a thorough mastery of the arts. This is a type of happiness that comes from "science for science's sake, art for art's sake."[6]

7.7. 子曰: 「自行束脩以上, 吾未嘗無誨焉。」

Confucius said, "Anyone fifteen years of age or older I have not turned away from teaching."

Notes: *Cheng Shude quotes the "Biography of Fu Zhan" in the "Book of the Later Han": The poet Du recommended Zhan as having been completely without fault or blemish from the time he wore a hairband. Note: "From the time he wore a hairband" means from fifteen years of age on. The "Biography of Yan Du" says: From when I wore the hairband. Note:* Shuxiu 束脩 *means a restraining ornamental band [worn in the hair]. Zheng Xuan notes in his commentary on the "Analects": This means fifteen years old and up.*

Comments: The term *shuxiu* ["restraining ornament"] is usually explained as meaning "ten bundles of dried meat,"[7] but in this reading I follow the Han dynasty classical masters [see Notes above]. This is also in keeping with Confucius's words, "At fifteen I set my mind upon study" (*Analects* 2.4), and the *Book of Documents* statement that "when he was fifteen he entered lower school." There are also those who read this as an ornamental article of clothing, or as restrained and polished behavior (Chen Daqi 陳大齊 in his *Lunyu yijie* 論語臆解, quoting Li Xian 李賢 and others). From the standpoint of age, Confucius's disciples were the age of high school or college students. Apparently Confucius did not teach early elementary students.

7.8. 子曰：「不憤不啟，不悱不發，舉一隅不以三隅反，則不復也。」
Confucius said, "Without stimulation, there can be no enlightenment, and without doubt there is no discovery. If someone points out one leg of a table, but does not know there are three other legs, I will have nothing more to say [about such a person]."

Comments: Is the table and its four legs an analytical proposition? Is Confucius bemoaning people's lack of basic ability to analyze and synthesize, or their lack of the simplest power of perception? I do not know. The emphasis of pragmatic reason is upon insight, intuition, and sudden awakening, all of which have a very concrete emotional quality, and not on abstract theoretical arguments, exhaustive explanations, or the process of reasoning. In Chinese culture, from poetic criticism to educational methods, the emphasis throughout is on "touching upon it and then stopping," or "not seeking to explain it completely." This carries through all the way to the "stick and shout" and instantaneous enlightenment of Chan Buddhism. In everything, this is regarded as the superior method: allowing those being educated to experience their own realizations and achieve personal insights, attaining real wisdom in a vivid and lively manner, rather than sinking to a formulaic, mechanistic frame of mind. Because logical proofs do not depart from either deductive or inductive reasoning, true scientific advances do not come from these types of methods, but from a seemingly ineffable "free imagination" or "free perception." The tendency today is to demean and raze the tradition at every turn while greatly praising Western methods, though at the same time literary and art criticism is obscure and tortuous, with "arguments" galore; yet these fall far short of the pithy [evaluations] of the ancients. Actually, what need is there for such slavish imitation? True communication and thinking exist in the realm of "without stimulation there can be no enlightenment," and not that of "the process of reasoning." Neither the Han and Tang commentarial traditions nor the recorded conversations of the Song and Ming created long treatises or logical arguments, and in no way do they conform to today's so-called academic norms or scholarly standards, yet they can still enlighten people's minds and bestow true wisdom. A thousand pages of abstruse words are not as good as "deciding a case based on one or two sentences" (*Analects* 12.12), and this is why I prefer to create this type of non-scholarly commentary rather than a long treatise. If there is just a small amount of meaning to be communicated, use just a small number of words; it is not necessary to force ourselves to imitate the length of grandma's foot-binding cloths.

Or we could say that this passage is not about knowledge, but about virtuous action. That is, when it comes to virtue one should be able to use one case to draw inferences about others, to use the narrow to govern the broad. This is how it can be "strung together into a unity" (*Analects* 4.15). This reading also works.

7.9. 子食於有喪者之側，未嘗飽也。

When Confucius was eating with the family of someone who had died, he would never eat his fill.

Comments: True.

7.10. 子于是日哭，則不歌。

If Confucius cried on a particular day, he would not then sing.

Comments: These two passages both describe how truth and sincerity must be sustained across a certain period of time in order for these to be truly human emotions. This is also the only way that one can establish and cultivate human emotions. An adult cannot just cry and then laugh like a small child; that would reflect an animalistic mood. It is only lines like these [of Su Shi's] that comprise truly human emotion:

I have not tried to remember
What is impossible to forget.
Your solitary grave is a thousand miles away,
No way to tell you my loneliness.
If we were to meet, you would not recognize me—
Face covered with dust,
Hair like frost.[8]

不思量，自難忘，千里孤墳，無處話淒涼。縱使相逢應不識，塵滿面，鬢如霜。

In these lines, because they are saturated with reason and memory, the emotion takes on an exquisite quality, and attains dignity and permanence. Arts and literature have played a tremendous role in this respect. This is precisely what I mean by cultural-psychological formation.

7.11. 子謂顏淵曰：「用之則行，舍之則藏，唯我與爾有是夫！」子路曰：「子行三軍，則誰與？」子曰：「暴虎馮河，死而無悔者，吾不與也。必也臨事而懼，好謀而成者也。」

Confucius said to Yan Hui: "When made use of, to get up and act; when not made use of, to gather oneself up—it is only you and I who are able to do this."

Zilu said, "If you were to lead an army, with whom would you do it?"

Confucius said, "One who fights a tiger with his bare hands, or crosses a river with only his legs, and has no regrets even should death result—with such a one I would never do it. It would definitely have to be someone who faces his duty with prudent fear, and accomplishes action through careful thought; (only with such a one would I do it)."

Comments: The question and the answer are both quite interesting. Zilu is jealous of Confucius's abundant praise of Yan Hui and so attempts to brag about his own courage; this is vividly apparent in the text. But Confucius stops him in his tracks once again, with the same old message: one cannot depend only upon courage.

7.12. 子曰:「富而可求也, 雖執鞭之士, 吾亦為之。如不可求, 從吾所好。」

Confucius said, "If wealth is something that can be sought and obtained, even if it means being someone who watches the door in the market, I would do it. If it is not, then it is better for me to do something I want to do."

Comments: Here again we see the idea that "fate determines life and death, Heaven determines wealth and rank." Becoming rich is a very fortuitous thing, not something that one can simply work hard to obtain. It is not like studying, or working on being a good person, in which as long as one works hard, one can always attain some level of success.

7.13. 子之所慎: 齊, 戰, 疾。

These are the things Confucius handled with great care: sacrifices, war, disease.

Comments: Clearly, Old Master Confucius took great care of his own body. This is even more clearly demonstrated in the meticulous discussions in Book 10 of eating, drinking, traveling, and lodging. Of course, this statement is directed at those who govern, so that disease refers to infectious disease among the people. *Qi* 齊 here is the same as *zhai* 斋 [meaning "fasting"].

7.14. 子在齊聞韶，三月不知肉味。曰：「不圖為樂之至於斯也！」

When Confucius was in the state of Qi, he heard the Shao music being played, and for a long time afterward lost his taste for meat, saying, "I never imagined that the joy of music could reach this level."

Notes: *Cheng Shude quotes Cai Jie* 蔡節 *in his [Southern Song] "Lunyu jishuo": Shao is a kind of dance music. Three months means a long period of time. Qian Mu explains: This refers to a kind of artistic frame of mind that the sage has. When Confucius says [in "Analects" 7.19], "When made use of he forgets to eat; he is often happy to the point of forgetting his worries," this is also a kind of artistic frame of mind. When morality flows together and melds with an artistic frame of mind, this attains to the height of the sagely realm.*

Comments: It is not likely that Confucius could really have [lost the taste for meat for] as long as "three months" [as the original text has it]. Therefore, Han Yu and Cheng Yi argue that the two characters "three months" 三月 were originally the character *yin* 音 (meaning "sound"). Zhu Xi [punctuates the passage so as to make it say] that Confucius studied the Shao music for three months. In ancient times, "three months" was used to generally refer to a long period of time and did not necessarily mean a literal three months. When the *Analects* says Yan Hui did not violate benevolence for "three months," this is also how it is meant. It is simply an exaggerated description. Qian Mu's note is better, pointing out that this refers to a realm of human life that unites morality and art.

The *Analects* speaks frequently about music, while the *Mencius* seldom does so. The *Analects* for the most part records concrete speech and action, while the *Mencius* gives free rein to unconstrained words and arguments. That only Confucius can be considered the "perfect sage and first teacher" is clear. Education or teaching is far from merely the transmission of knowledge, the discussion of arguments, or the practice of skills; instead, it consists in the shaping or molding of all of one's nature and character. This is why music (or "musical education") is important, for music has nothing to do with knowledge or skills, but directly affects the spirit and shapes a person's temperament. Although at that time, the ritual regulations had perhaps already lost their particularity, it was actually precisely in the teaching of these concrete manners, attitudes, behavior, and speech that the human emotio-rational structure could be established. The statements, "Without using a carpenter's square or compass one cannot make a square or circle" (*Mencius* IV.A.1), and "the ritual system establishes a person, and music perfects a person" (*Analects* 8.8), both have this meaning. **The actual content and specifics of the ritual or music can vary greatly with the time period and society, but the cultural-psychological "formal principle" of this pedagogical approach will always remain fresh,** for without human culture it is impossible to have human nature. This is why **Old Master Confucius emphasized that "to control oneself in order to conform to the ritual system is humaneness" (*Analects* 12.1); he taught humaneness without neglecting ritual.** Song Neo-Confucians lost this to some degree.

7.15. 冉有曰:「夫子為衛君乎?」子貢曰:「諾。吾將問之。」入, 曰:「伯夷、叔齊何人也?」曰:「古之賢人也。」曰:「怨乎?」曰:「求仁而得仁, 又何怨。」出, 曰:「夫子不為也。」

Ran You said, "Would the Master support the ruler of Wei?" Zigong said, "Okay, I will go ask him."

He went into Confucius's room and asked him, "What kind of men were Bo Yi and Shu Qi?" Confucius said, "They were sages of old." Zigong said, "Did they have complaints or regrets?" Confucius said, "What they sought was humaneness, and what they obtained was humaneness; what did they have to complain about or regret?"

When Zigong had come out again, he said, "The Teacher would not do it."

Notes: *Yang Bojun notes: The ruler of Wei refers to Duke Chu of Wei, called Zhe* 輒. *Zhe was the grandson of Duke Ling of Wei, and the son of Prince Kuaikui. Prince Kuaikui had offended the wife of Duke Ling of Wei, Nanzi, and had fled to the state of Jin. After Duke Ling died, Zhe was made ruler. Zhao Jianzi of the Jin sent Kuaikui back, in preparation for invading the state of Wei. The state of Wei resisted the Jin soldiers, and naturally refused the return of Kuaikui. Seen from the point of view of the father-son relationship between Kuaikui and Zhe, it appeared that father and son were contending for the position of ruler of Wei, exactly the opposite of the behavior of the brothers Bo Yi and Shu Qi, who each refused the throne in favor of the other, and in the end both renounced the position of ruler. This is why Zigong asks about them, in order to try to ascertain Confucius's attitude toward Duke Chu (Zhe). In praising Bo Yi and Shu Qi, Confucius is of course expressing disapproval of Duke Chu.*

Comments: This passage is impossible to understand without knowing the historical background, therefore I have reproduced Yang Bojun's note.

7.16. 子曰:「飯疏食飲水, 曲肱而枕之, 樂亦在其中矣。不義而富且貴, 於我如浮雲。」

Confucius said, "To eat coarse grain and drink fresh water, and to use the crook of my arm as a pillow, there is joy found in these. Position and wealth obtained in unrighteous ways, for me, is like clouds floating in the sky."

Comments: Clouds floating far off in the sky have nothing to do with me. What is "joy" *le* 樂? It is a kind of pseudo-religious psycho-emotional state. Above we have already talked about how it is higher than any material life or realm, and transcends wealth and poverty, rank and lowliness. The poetic and visual effect of this passage has caused people to linger over it and repeat it across the millennia. To say it refers to an aesthetic realm would be very apt.

The question becomes, what is the relationship between the "seven human feelings" and this type of "pleasure of Heaven and humans." In Neo-Confucianism, the two are clearly separated and even opposed to one another, and the former is regarded as an enemy. More recent, naturalistic views of human nature, in contrast, see the latter as outworn mystical pedantry, and disproportionately develop the former. Both of these miss the mark. "What Confucius and Yan Hui rejoiced in" undoubtedly refers to the "pleasure of Heaven and humans," that is, what Mencius called the joy of being "in the same stream as Heaven above and Earth below" (*Mencius* VII.A.13).[9] Yet this does not belittle or exclude the common pleasures of the "seven human emotions," as in what Mencius called the pleasure of "having the most talented pupils in the Empire" (*Mencius* VII.A.20), or "enjoyment by yourself" and "enjoyment in the company of many" (*Mencius* I.B.1), and so on.[10]

7.17. 子曰:「加我數年, 五十以學易, 可以無大過矣。」

Confucius said, "If you gave me a few more years of life, I would take fifty years to learn the *Book of Changes*, and then perhaps I would be able to be without major fault."

Comments: This is another passage that has many differing explanations, especially on the question of why "fifty" years? Zhu Xi argues that the characters for "fifty" (*wushi* 五十) should read "death" (*zu* 卒). Others argue they should read "me" (*wu* 吾). Qian Mu and some others argue that *yi* 易 (the *Changes*) should read *yi* 亦 (meaning "also"), so that the line would read, "Even if I had fifty more years to continue to study, I would only be able to avoid major faults." In the present reading, I rely upon Confucius's statement, "At fifty I knew the will of Heaven," suggesting that Confucius enjoyed the *Book of Changes* in his later years, and on the fact that the Mawangdui manuscripts have *yi* 易 (for the *Changes*) here. The *Book of Changes* is an ancient divination text, used for telling fortunes (today it is still used as such); it deals with human life, the manners and morals of the time, fate, and philosophy. It has its origins in prehistoric shamanism, and connects with historical experience as it moves toward rationalization. It embodies a sort of cosmology and view of life that is also full of mystical flavor. **In the Mawangdui manuscript version of the *Xicizhuan* (*Appended Phrases*) there is the phrase "The *Changes* has great constancy [*daheng* 大恆],"**[11] **which is much superior to the received edition, which reads "The *Changes* has the Supreme Polarity [太極 *taiji*]." *Heng* means constant. There is also the [explanation of the hexagram Qian in the received text that reads] "Heaven puts into motion strength, and the noble person uses it to strengthen himself without ceasing."** If Confucius's love for the *Changes* in his later years was sincere, there was a reason for it. The word *ji* 極, on the other hand, is difficult to explain or understand, and mistakes are abundant in the work of later Confucians, including all the Song-Ming Neo-Confucians, who added many meaningless arguments about *wuji* 無極 ("no polarity") and *taiji* 太極 ("Supreme Polarity").

7.18. 子所雅言，詩、書、執禮，皆雅言也。

Confucius often spoke of the *Book of Songs*, the *Book of Documents*, and how to observe and maintain the ritual system. All of these are "literary language" (*wenyan* 文言).[12]

Comments: The meaning of the phrase *yayan* 雅言 [here translated "often spoke of" and "literary language"] has been explained in many different ways but remains unclear. The greater number take it to refer to Chinese characters, that is, the written language. In my reading, this is a crucial issue. One of the main distinctives of China is the relationship between its written and spoken languages. I believe that China's written language does not constitute a record of or preservation of spoken language; rather, it arose independently, likely having its origins in the keeping of records by the tying of knots. For this reason, in the six categories of Chinese characters, there is the principle, "ideographs are primary."[13] The written language was first mastered by ancient shamans→rulers→aristocrats, and was both sacred and mystical. Later, due to its role in passing on experiences, historical facts, and the accomplishments of the ancestors, it became united with the spoken language, but never identical to it, with each always maintaining its oppositional, independent character. China's written language exercises a controlling, governing, and modeling function vis-à-vis the spoken language, and it is the written (characters) and not the (spoken) language that has taken on the important role of unifying and organizing society. This is a major distinctive of Chinese culture. The written language is the direct record and expression of "In the beginning was the Act" (see 17.19 below), and it has influenced or even determined the fundamental shape of Chinese thought. As such its importance is extreme. Its emphasis upon form and not sound, its extremely versatile yet also regular quality, and its inability to be phonetically transcribed or to submit to the imposition of a Western grammar are all thanks to this quality.

7.19. 葉公問孔子於子路, 子路不對。子曰: 「女奚不曰, 其為人也, 發憤忘食, 樂以忘憂, 不知老之將至云爾。」

The Duke of She asked Zilu, "What kind of person is Confucius?" Zilu did not answer. Confucius said, "Why didn't you say, 'When made use of he forgets to eat; he is often happy to the point of forgetting his worries; he is unaware of his own old age coming on,' and things like that?"

Comments: Zilu did not answer. It is difficult to answer, difficult to describe Confucius as a whole. Confucius's own answer, on the other hand, is vivid and unassuming. In just a few phrases, he paints the picture of a person who transcends the ordinary. This person has resolved the problem of "fear," and forgotten "the onset of old age," that is, the nearness of death. Confucius often discussed "joy" or "pleasure" (*yue/le* 樂), and praised Yan Hui for having "never lost his joy" (*Analects* 6.11). In later years, the Wang Yangming school would also say that "to study is to learn this pleasure" (學是學此樂), this "pleasure" being none other than "humaneness," that is, the realm of human life, and the spirit of human personality. Compared with those who think constantly about death—who, certain of the inevitability of death, therefore seek its fulfillment—it seems clear which is the higher road. Of course, **the origins of what is called "the pleasure of Confucius and Yan Hui" lies in the mystical experience of primitive shamanism, that is, the overwhelming joy of the unity of humans with all in the universe.**

As I have said many times above, in China we have "In the beginning was the Act," or "In the beginning was the Way" ([as in] walking).[14] **Because of "this Way," therefore, we have this *qing* (情)—meaning "situation or condition" (*qingkuang* 情況), "state," or "circumstances" (*qingjing* 情境), as in the *Book of Changes* phrase "to categorize the *conditions* of the ten-thousand things" 類萬物之情.**[15] **Due to objective "circumstances" or "states" (*qing* 情 and *jing* 境) there are subjective "feelings" (*qing* 情) (life's emotions), and realms (*jing* 境) (the realm of human life). This is the main thread of Chinese "philosophy."** All kinds of circumstances presented in Chinese literature and poetry, such as Tao Qian's poetry (including the poem set quoted in Book 1), are concrete expressions of these types of life emotions and the realm of human life. Wang Guowei's 王國維 (1877–1927) notion of the aesthetic realm (*jingjie* 境界) should also be understood from this standpoint. Thus, "circumstances" are not just moral but actually transcend morality; only then do they attain the "boundary between Heaven and humans." To explain "establish a mind for Heaven and Earth" [Zhang Zai 張載 (1020–1077)] as having to do with a moral mind, and to force "Heaven and Earth" to equal morality, would seem very elevating, while actually it is withering; this does not compare to the Chan school of Buddhism. Actually, the "mind" in "establishing a mind for Heaven and Earth" does not refer to morality or knowledge (reason), but to aesthetics. The flight of birds, the jumping of fish—these are full of life and vitality, and there is deep meaning in them. Young scholars always use Western pessimism to denounce the shallowness of Chinese tradition, insisting that depth can only be found in recognizing the omnipotence and omniscience of god and the inevitability of human sin, and thinking that taking what "should be" for what "is" is the arrogance of human reason, and the origin of utopianism. Actually, it was precisely because China did not have a belief in God that its tradition established this worldview of "enjoying life" and sought support in it, using it to seek progress. [As this view was] renewed day by day, and renewed again, this intensely optimistic way of approaching existence, life, and knowledge actually **brought what "should be" together with what "is," so that the human ability to "participate with Heaven and Earth" 參天地 and "assist in transformation and nurture" 贊化育 became a source of encouragement. Although it gives a high position to humanity, should that be reason to consider the sorrowful, bitter side and difficult situations of this kind of life philosophy second to a teaching that requires people to prostrate themselves before holy temples?** And this life philosophy in the end returns to a "joyful" psychological life, or human realm, attained by "becoming human" or "establishing sageliness"; this is why I oppose the anti-psychologism of this century.

7.20. 子曰:「我非生而知之者, 好古, 敏以求之者也。」

Confucius said, "I wasn't born with knowledge; rather, I obtained it through a love for antiquity and by diligent seeking."

Comments: The word *min* 敏 [here translated as "diligent"] occurs many times in the *Analects*, usually meaning "nimble" (*minjie* 敏捷), "clever" (*congmin* 聰敏), or "swift" (*jisu* 疾速). The *Shuowen* dictionary defines *min* as *ji* 疾 (fast). Chen Daqi 陳大齊 (1886–1983) says in *Lunyu yishuo* that this occurrence should not be glossed as "quickness" but as "doing one's best" (*minmian* 黽勉), and that "敏以求之 [the last phrase] should be taken to mean 'diligent seeking.'" We can follow this reading. Confucius many times declaims that he is what he is due to diligent study, **never once bragging about his intelligence or talent, let alone spreading any stories about miracles or supernatural enlightenment; he always emphasizes untiring study. This is one of the crucial points of Confucius and Confucianism,** and is the root of the Chinese virtue of modesty. When later Confucians exalted Confucius to the status of a "Heaven-sent sage," they greatly missed the mark. As for "loving antiquity," this means that he regarded the accumulation and study of historical experience as important and precious. Pragmatic reason is also historical reason.

7.21. 子不語怪, 力, 亂, 神。

Confucius did not speak of the strange, of violence, of rebellion, or of ghosts and spirits.

Comments: It is difficult to understand the "strange" and "ghosts and spirits," and there is nothing to be said about them, thus he does not discuss them. Similarly, violence and rebellion are not normal behavior, and not worth speaking of, thus he does not speak of them. The former practically determined the basic Confucian stance of refraining from discussion of or reliance upon anything mystical, miraculous, transcendent or magical—in short, anything non-rational. Consider this exchange from the "Virtue of the Five Emperors" chapter of the *Da Dai Liji* (Dai the Greater's *Li Ji*):

> Zai Wo asked Confucius [about a reference to] "the Yellow Emperor's three hundred years. Was the Yellow Emperor a man? Or not a man? How could he live to three hundred?" Confucius said, "Zai Wo! [The ages of] Yu, Tang, Wen, Wu, Cheng, and the Duke of Zhou could be found out. Not so this Yellow Emperor. How should we think of him? It is hard for the Master to say." Zai Wo said, "This is the reason I asked." Confucius said, "The Yellow Emperor . . . lived, and the people benefitted from him, for one hundred years; he died and the people feared his spirit for one hundred years; he perished [from memory] and the people used his teachings for one hundred years; thus they say three hundred years."

Confucius first avoids the question, then finally is forced to give a rationalized response, denying that a person could live for three hundred years. Elsewhere, we have Confucius's explanation of the saying, "The Yellow Emperor has four faces" to mean that the Yellow Emperor sent out officials to the four directions, and so on;[16] this demonstrates the same characteristic [unwillingness to consider the supernatural]. The paucity of ancient Chinese myths is at least partly a result of the purposeful deletion, revision, failure to discuss or record, or rationalization by Confucius and the Confucians. This also reflects the growing trend of bringing rationality into emotion, and avoiding non-rationalized emotion. The Chinese people love to speak of the unity of emotion and reason, and the intermingling or melding of reason and emotion, in which emotion and reason do not develop in absolute independence from each other; this is both a strength and a weakness of the culture.

7.22. 子曰:「三人行, 必有我師焉。擇其善者而從之, 其不善者而改之。」

Confucius said, "If three people walk together, there is sure to be one among them worthy of my emulation. I will choose his strengths to emulate, and when I see his faults, I will improve myself."

Notes: *Zhu Xi notes: Of the three walking together, one is myself. Of the other two, one is good and one bad, so that if I follow the goodness of the one and reform the bad of the other, both of them are my teachers. Mister Yin [Tun] says, "When one sees a good person, one should think how to emulate him; when one sees a bad person, one should reflect on one's self" [4.17], thus the good and the bad are both my teachers; is there any end to the progress one can make in progressing in goodness?*

Comments: This degree of humble love of learning is so very different from today's attitude of considering everyone beneath one. Why "three people"? Zhu Xi's comment is in line with *Analects* 4.17, "When one sees a good person, one should think how to emulate him; when one sees a bad person, one should reflect on one's self." But this is really overly rigid and even comical. Actually this passage means that even should there be only two people walking together, there would still be someone or something to learn from.

7.23. 子曰:「天生德於予, 桓魋其如予何?」

Confucius said, "Heaven above gave me moral character; what can Huan Tui do to me?"

Comments: This passage has often been taken to mean that Confucius bore some sort of mystical destiny or some kind of mystical "holiness," so that he had Heaven's protection and did not need to be afraid. Actually, this is just an ordinary expression of boldness. Why read it so literally, so as to make Confucius out to be a god? A sense of historical destiny borne of a sense of responsibility can lead one to believe that there is a kind of objective principle or law at work, and this is where this bold statement comes from—he is encouraging and emboldening himself, like the great fearlessness of Mencius when he said, "One goes forward even against men in the thousands."[17]

7.24. 子曰:「二三子以我為隱乎? 吾無隱乎爾。吾無行而不與二三子者, 是丘也。」

Confucius said, "Do you disciples think I am concealing anything? I have concealed nothing. There is nothing about which I am not open with you. This is how a certain Mr. Kong acts."

Comments: We have no way of knowing what the context of this passage was. In sum, Confucius explains that for a teacher, all of his words, actions, and thoughts can be open to his students; his knowledge, scholarship, morality, and writings can all be shared with them—nothing should be concealed. Perhaps at the time teachers seemed always to have some sort of divine secret that made people curious about them, and this is why Confucius's disciples might have asked this type of question in which the influence of the ancient shamanistic tradition is still evident. Actually, still today do we not hear people ask their teacher what their "secret" is, or what is the secret of their success?

7.25. 子以四教: 文, 行, 忠, 信。

Confucius instructed his disciples in four areas: literature, behavior, loyalty, and trustworthiness.

Notes: *Cheng Shude quotes Jin Lüxiang* 金履祥 *(1232–1303) in his "Lunyu jizhu kaozheng": Literature, behavior, loyalty, and trustworthiness—here the Master is teaching people the order of what comes first and last, what is shallow and what deep. Literature refers to the "Book of Songs," the "Book of Documents," and writings on the Six Arts, by which it is possible to examine the model of the Sages and plumb the plainness of reason. Thus one begins by teaching the knowledge of these. When one knows, one can act; what one knows firmly, one puts into action, thus he progresses to behavior. When one knows and can practice something, but is not yet true in one's intentions, then knowledge may sometimes tend to boasting, and action may come out as hypocrisy; thus he progresses further to loyalty and trustworthiness. Loyalty arises in the heart, and trustworthiness is the expression on the exterior. Master Cheng said that exerting oneself to the utmost is loyalty, while following one's duty without going back on it is called trustworthiness. In the world, there are certainly those who have sincere intentions but who in their affairs cannot* *always fully carry out their duties; therefore he finishes with trustworthiness. When one arrives at trustworthiness, every matter is accomplished and no application is improper. This is the order in which the Master teaches people, from first to last, shallow to deep; these are the four steps.*

Comments: "Moral behavior" should already include "loyalty" and "trustworthiness"—why then are these listed separately? Many Confucians across the centuries have offered many explanations, all a bit farfetched. Chen Tianxiang 陳天祥 (d. 1516) in his *Sishu bian yi* suggests that either "the disciples did not record [his statements] well" or something was "lost in transmission." The note above, which explains the list in terms of an order, from external to internal, from knowledge to emotion and the will, is quite painstakingly worked out and very apt.

7.26. 子曰:「聖人, 吾不得而見之矣; 得見君子者, 斯可矣。」子曰:「善人, 吾不得而見之矣; 得見有恆者, 斯可矣。亡而為有, 虛而為盈, 約而為泰, 難乎有恆矣。」

Confucius said, "A sage I have never seen; if I could see a noble person (*junzi*), that would be enough."

Confucius said, "A good person I have never seen; if I could see a person who could persist, that would be enough. To say one has what one does not have, to call emptiness full, or to make poverty pose as richness—these are very difficult to persist in."

Comments: Commentators for the most part take this to be speaking of individual personal integrity, but if we read it together with the passage, "If good people were to govern the affairs of the country for a hundred years" (*Analects* 13.11), it would seem to be speaking of those who govern. For someone who governs to treat lacking as having, or empty as full, or to say that although you are poor you are still rich—of course such a person will be unable to persist. Actually, many of the statements of the *Analects* are demands made of those who govern, but later Confucians explained them in terms of every person's morality or self-cultivation, and thus they are sometimes difficult to put into practice. There are also those who, because of the inconsistency of tone, question whether this passage contains mistakes or omissions.

7.27. 子釣而不綱，弋不射宿。

Confucius fished with a hook, but did not use a net. He shot birds, but not those perching or in their nests.

Comments: Older commentators often used this passage to speak about how "in taking things, one should practice economy," that is, do not kill needlessly or net fish indiscriminately; this is rational experience. What is emphasized here, though, is more the benevolent feelings.

7.28. 子曰：「蓋有不知而作之者，我無是也。多聞擇其善者而從之，多見而識之，知之次也。」

Confucius said, "There are those kinds of people who have no knowledge, yet act based on no foundation; I do not have this habit. I listen much, and choose the good from among what I hear to follow and put into practice. I see much, and remember. This is the order and process of knowledge."

Comments: The last phrase, "the order and process of knowledge," has been read differently, for example, as "This is a second level of knowledge" (Qian Mu) or "This is a close second to inborn knowing" (Yang Bojun). I do not agree with these. This passage should be read alongside "expounding rather than creating" (*Analects* 7.1) and similar passages that all express how much Confucius valued the experiences of the past and opposed acting in a vacuum; he valued study and practice and opposed the vain discussion of the abstruse.

7.29. 互鄉難與言，童子見，門人惑。子曰：「與其進也，不與其退也，唯何甚！人潔己以進，與其潔也，不保其往也。」

The people of Huxiang were very difficult to deal with, but Confucius received a youth from there. His disciples were very doubtful. Confucius said, "One should accept progress, not approve of backsliding. Why be so severe? If someone cleans himself up and seeks to progress, we should accept the present state of cleanliness; this is not to approve of his past."

Comments: This passage should be read alongside passages like "In teaching students, one should not make distinctions" (*Analects* 15.39). This means that people are all capable of being taught; any fault can be reformed. An emphasis on post-natal study, education, construction, formation—which all include the correcting of one's mistakes—is part of the basic spirit of Confucianism. What we call "human nature," the way of being human, good action, and good work all derive from this. Here we can also see Confucius's inclusive spirit: he always saw the best in people.

7.30. 子曰: 「仁遠乎哉? 我欲仁, 斯仁至矣。」

Confucius said, "Is humaneness very far or remote? If any person truly desires it, it will come."

Notes: *Zhu Xi says: Humaneness is a virtue of the mind; it is not external.*

Comments: Some take this to indicate a Chan type of sudden enlightenment, but that is not appropriate here. This should be read in connection with the passage, "If one truly and diligently sets one's heart on humaneness, one cannot do bad things" (*Analects* 4.4), which suggests that as long as one has the will or intention to cultivate benevolent feelings, one will be able to attain to it. I have already pointed out above how Zhu Xi, in taking this to refer to the mind-nature (*xin xing* 心性) and making morality the basic nature of humanity, its basic heart or substance, is making this overly abstract. This is also what Mou Zongsan vehemently attacked as "mere being without action" (存有而不活動).[18] The School of Mind associated with Lu Xiangshan and Wang Yangming takes it to yet a deeper level of internalization, emphasizing that humaneness and virtue are not external divine commands but that Heavenly Principle is within people's mind. Wang Yangming went so far as to say that "if you seek it in the heart-mind, that is wrong; although the words come from Confucius, we cannot affirm them" (*Wang Yangming quan ji*, *juan* 2). But what does this "heart-mind" refer to after all? There are three paths: one leads into Chan Buddhism, which emphasizes mystical experience; one returns to Heavenly Principle, the old familiar path of Cheng-Zhu [Neo-Confucianism]; one recognizes the difficulty of dividing the flesh from desire, and tends toward naturalistic humanism. None of these three paths is a through street; there is no way around but by re-interpreting the classics, to forge a new theory of an emotio-rational Mean.

7.31. 陳司敗問昭公知禮乎? 孔子曰: 「知禮。」孔子退, 揖巫馬期而進之, 曰: 「吾聞君子不黨, 君子亦黨乎? 君取於吳為同姓, 謂之吳孟子。君而知禮, 孰不知禮? 」巫馬期以告。子曰: 「丘也幸, 苟有過, 人必知之。」

Chen Sibai asked, "Does Duke Zhao [of Lu] understand ritual?" Confucius said, "He understands ritual."

When Confucius had left, Chen bowed to Wuma Qi, approached him, and said, "I have heard that the noble person is not partial. Could it be that in fact the noble person is partial? When he was in the state of Wu, Duke Zhao took a wife. They were of the same surname, [so] he called her Wu Mengzi (Eldest Daughter of Wu). If Duke Zhao understands ritual, who doesn't understand it?"

Wuma Qi reported this to Confucius. Confucius said, "I am very fortunate. If I should commit an error, others are sure to know it."

Notes: *Zhu Xi notes: Confucius cannot himself say something about his ruler's mistake, nor can he say that to take a wife of the same clan shows a knowledge of ritual, therefore he accepts his response as a mistake and does not deny it. . . . But in accepting that he has made a mistake, he still does not directly say what his mistake was; by acting as if he did not know about the Eldest Daughter, he can be a model for ten thousand generations.*

Comments: In ancient times, people of the same surname did not marry. Duke Zhao had gone against ritual, and naturally Confucius knew it. Zhu Xi's explanation above is the most elegant, demonstrating that Confucius knew how to speak, and was also quite "clever," so that he never directly said that his ruler did not know ritual; the scene is quite vivid.

7.32. 子與人歌而善, 必使反之, 而後和之。

If Confucius asked someone to sing, and he sang well, he would ask him to sing it again, and then would sing it himself.

Notes: *In the "Shiji," "Kongzi shi jia" chapter, it reads: [When he would] make someone sing, if he was good, then he would make him sing it again, then he would know it. Kang Youwei notes: The Song dynasty "sages" observed ritual very strictly . . . handing [music] over to actors and entertainers, as something that serious intellectuals [*shi 士*] would not do. Consequently, they led China to disparage singing, lost the delight in the human way that nurtures life, and went against the sagely way of rejoicing in life. They purported to respect Confucius but secretly followed Mozi. As a result, the way of humanity became barren, and the world could not bear it. . . . This was the mistake of Cheng-Zhu [Neo-Confucianism].*

Comments: This is a realistic sort of description. What is it for? Its meaning is as follows: **Music forms the emotions, and it is only by singing something several times that it can be solidly learned and become an emotional construction.** From ancient times to the present day, has it not been true that the rhythms and melodies, and so on, of a piece of music must be repeated many times? This is not only for the purpose of fully expressing the emotions, but also has to do with the construction of emotion [itself]. Kang Youwei's criticism of Cheng Yi and Zhu Xi is very correct. Above, I have already pointed out that if Mencius spoke very little of music, Cheng Yi and Zhu Xi did so even less. Actually, what Confucius gave attention to and studied in his day was precisely "ritual and music," not "mind" and "Principle." In this respect, Xunzi was closer to Confucius.

7.33. 子曰: 「文, 莫吾猶人也。躬行君子, 則吾未之有得。」

Confucius said, "In my study of the rites and documents, I am probably about the equal of other people; but when it comes to diligence in the practice [of what it takes] to become a noble person, I have not yet achieved it."

Notes: *Yang Bojun quotes the "Jing yi shu wen" 經義述聞:*[19] Mo 莫 *is probably a variant for* qi 其; *[the passage] means that in speech and writing I am equal to others.*

Comments: As before, this puts a very strong emphasis on practice.

7.34. 子曰:「若聖與仁,則吾豈敢?抑為之不厭,誨人不倦,則可謂云爾已矣。」公西華曰:「正唯弟子不能學也。」

Confucius said, "When it comes to 'sageliness' or 'humaneness,' I would not presume to those appellations. However, when it comes to diligence without flagging, teaching without tiring, this is all that can be said to be true [of me]." Gongxi Hua said, "This is exactly what we disciples cannot do."

Comments: The idea of being "unflagging in study, untiring in teaching" has come up many times already in the *Analects*. Yang Bojun in his commentary on this passage quotes Mencius II.A.2, where we find Zigong's view of the question: "Not to tire of learning is wisdom; not to weary of teaching is benevolence [*ren*, humaneness]. You must be a sage to be both wise and benevolent."[20] On the one hand, "If any person truly desires [humaneness], it will come" (7.30) suggests that humaneness is easy to attain. On the other hand, we have the statement here, "When it comes to 'sageliness' or 'humaneness,' I would not presume to those appellations" that suggests it is very difficult. Is this not a logical contradiction? Obviously, the theory of humaneness of Confucius and his disciples is not an analytical philosophy that seeks logical consistency; rather it is a theory of pragmatic reason that emphasizes behavior and practice, purports to cultivate the emotional nature, and emphasizes self-consciousness and constancy, and for this reason it is both difficult and easy. Here there is a distinction between intentionality and actuality.

Confucius several times refers to himself as "untiring" or "unflagging"—this is the tenacious spirit of the Chinese people's practical intentionality. Undaunted by setbacks, undeterred by difficulty, this is the path to success. Confucius is not at all like the Heaven-sent sages of various religions, who know without studying, and transcend this human realm. In addition, it must be said that the original meaning of this "sageliness or humaneness" should still be sought in the heights of mystical experiences, realms, and human personalities attained in shamanistic ceremonies, which although they had already become rationalized to some degree, Confucius did not feel he could be a successor to. Later, this level of primitive meaning would be completely lost.

7.35. 子疾病, 子路請禱。子曰: 「有諸? 」子路對曰: 「有之。誄曰: 『禱爾于上下神祇。』」子曰: 「丘之禱久矣。」

Confucius was sick, and Zilu wanted to go offer prayers. Confucius said, "Is there a basis for it?" Zilu said, "Yes. In the ancient documents it says, 'We prayed for you to Heaven and Earth, the gods and spirits.'" Confucius said, "I prayed long ago."

Comments: Confucius was opposed to doing this. **Confucius spoke of "Heaven" and "Fate," but never of "prayer"; contrary to many religions,** he never purposely entreated God or the gods or spirits for particular protection or help. If one fulfills one's role and duty, one can feel at ease and justified, and though one might meet great failure, one will have no regrets. As I discussed above, Confucianism advocated "doing the most humanly possible and obeying one's fate" and **did not put faith in chance, God's will, or miracles.** "Heaven's mandate" or "fate" is not something that people can control or manipulate. Although people can "participate with Heaven and Earth and assist in transformation and nurture," they have definite limits. If one hits against those limits and fails or is destroyed, one does not ask for undeserved grace or divine forgiveness; only thus is human dignity genuinely preserved.

7.36. 子曰: 「奢則不孫, 儉則固。與其不孫也, 寧固。」

Confucius said, "Extravagant people are not modest, frugal people are stubborn. Compared with being immodest, it is better to be stubborn."

Notes: *Yang Bojun quotes Huang Kan* 皇侃 *[of the Southern Dynasties]: The two things are both faults. If one immodestly piles up possessions, those possessions will certainly harm him; suddenly they are overturned—it can happen in a moment. If one stops at meanness, one will not attain sincerity (*cheng*), but [at least one] will not be overtaken by possessions.*

Comments: The above note speaks only from the point of view of external merit and fault, profit and loss, while it may be more interesting to consider the question of the psychological relationship between extravagance and pride (immodesty), and especially that between frugality and obstinacy. Confucius seems to be speaking from experience here, and in our daily life today we can often see the truth of this. Extravagance is often associated with pride and arrogance, and frugality and stubbornness are not often separated. The question the *Analects* raises here of this kind of concrete relationship and association within the psychology of human nature is worth continued investigation.

7.37. 子曰:「君子坦蕩蕩, 小人長戚戚。」

Confucius said, "The noble person is broad-minded; the petty person is always vexed."

Comments: The word *qiqi* 戚戚 may also be understood to mean "worried," "depressed," or "ill at ease." The phrase *tan dangdang* 坦蕩蕩 is usually glossed as "broad-minded." Here again, what the passage is speaking of is the relationship between psychology and conduct, and by placing conduct and action above psychological states, **it suggests a kind of realm of life that is precisely the Confucianism that I am trying to get across in this work.**

7.38. 子溫而厲, 威而不猛, 恭而安。

Confucius was warm and yet solemn, impressive and yet not violent, respectful and composed.

Comments: Here again we see the A ≠ A ± "proper measure" *du* 度 (of the Doctrine of the Mean), that is, what we today would call being good at exercising sound judgment or acting in proper measure. Of course, this is difficult. Yet it is not only in conduct, work, the ritual system, or playing music, but in every aspect of Chinese culture (including medicine, agriculture, military strategy, the arts, etc.) that the most attention is paid precisely to this sense of propriety. This sense comes entirely from the historical accumulation of experience, which is the reason China emphasizes history and experience, and stresses these ideas related to the "Mean" and proper measure. This may appear to be abstruse or mystical, but actually it is very ordinary, if difficult to grasp or put into practice. This is where the difficulty of pragmatic reason lies.

Book 8

8.1. 子曰:「泰伯, 其可謂至德也已矣! 三以天下讓, 民無得而稱焉。」

Confucius said, "Now Tai Bo, what he did could be said to be the ultimate in virtuous conduct. Three times he declined the position of ruler of the state. The ordinary people really did not know how to adequately praise him."

Notes: *Zhu Xi notes: Tai Bo was the eldest son of King Tai of Zhou.*

Comments: To what does this phrase *san rang* 三讓 (here "three times he declined") refer? And why did he decline? What value or meaning did this action have? Although there has been much historical research, the real situation is still very difficult to make clear. Therefore, we must depend on the literal meaning and read it to mean simply, "to yield or defer." Deference (*rang*) is an important ritual characteristic (see 4.13), and of course it could not have been easy to defer that highest position of leadership, for the "sage's great treasure is called position" 聖人之大寶曰位.[1] This is why the ordinary people would have been at a loss to explain this action or to praise it. Actually, this is just an expression of the democratic customs of the ancient clan system. In ancient Chinese documents there are many stories of running away or hiding to avoid the "position of sovereign," and most have historical basis; it was not like in later generations when people were scrambling for the "great treasure" of this position. For the leaders of ancient clans worked hard and endured difficulty; they had no special authority, but rather were true public servants, "working for the people" *wei renmin fuwu* 為人民服務. This is why in comparison to the realities of later ages, Confucians considered the ideal state or utopia to involve "returning to the flourishing of the Three Dynasties," for this period actually had a certain "democratic" flavor.

8.2. 子曰:「恭而無禮則勞, 慎而無禮則葸, 勇而無禮則亂, 直而無禮則絞。君子篤於親, 則民興於仁; 故舊不遺, 則民不偷。」

Confucius said, "Respectfulness without an understanding of ritual will tend toward weariness; prudence without an understanding of ritual will tend toward cowardliness; courage without an understanding of ritual will tend toward upheaval; frankness without an understanding of ritual will tend toward hurtfulness. When the noble person treats his relations with great kindness, the ordinary people will move toward humaneness; when he does not forsake his old friends, the human feeling among ordinary folks will not be lackluster."

Notes: *Yang Bojun quotes Wang Kaiyun* 王闓運 *(1833–1916) in his "Lunyu xun"* 論語訓*: This is speaking of how governing the people is a matter of the "tips and the roots." Respectfulness means giving respectful service, but if one taxes agriculture and sericulture and raises revenues for waterworks, without being restrained by ritual, this will weary the people. Prudence means modesty, frugality, and simplicity. Note that* 葸 (xi *"frightened") may be read as* 偲 (cai *or* si)*. One will inspire fear and will not be able to draw near to the people. If [the ruler] is courageous in his conduct, the people will also love boldness, and will easily rebel. If one is too straight-laced the people will not be able to endure it, like a cord that is tied in a knot.*

Comments: The meanings of the first and second parts of this passage are not connected. If one connects them, then they should be interpreted in the manner suggested by the note above, as both addressing how to "govern." The passage is also speaking strongly of the importance of ritual; in whatever human situation, whether government or simple human conduct, "if it is not regulated by or judged in accordance with ritual, then it will not work" (*Analects* 1.12). "Ritual" refers to all sorts of regulations and norms governing all kinds of governmental action, and at the same time is the measure of individual conduct, so that it does not become "wearisome," "cowardly," "rebellious" or "hurtful." The connection between the first and second halves of the passage can be seen as the relationship between *li* (ritual) and *ren* (humaneness), for "treating one's relations with kindness" belongs to the ritual system, while "moving toward humaneness" has to do with the emotions. The ritual system of the first half of the passage is just what restrains and regulates all kinds of emotional attitudes (like respect and prudence) or actions (like courage or frankness). This is why "ritual" can serve as a measure of civilization and rationality, and thus is the thing that regulates, forms, and establishes all kinds of inner emotions; that is, it is the locus of human nature. This is how we should explain why Confucius speaks repeatedly of being "established in ritual" (*Analects* 8.8) or "to control oneself in order to conform to the ritual system is humaneness" (*Analects* 12.1). Thus, the ethics of human relationships in the ritual system are not simply based on rational relationships, but reside more in the human feeling in which rationality is melded into the emotions. For in Chinese tradition, the "human warmth" that revolves around the relationship between members of the family is connected to rational, social relationships.

8.3. 曾子有疾, 召門弟子曰: 「啟予足! 啟予手! 《詩》云『戰戰兢兢, 如臨深淵, 如履薄冰。』而今而後, 吾知免夫! 小子! 」

When Zengzi was seriously ill, he called his disciples and said, "Arrange my feet, and arrange my hands. In the *Shijing* it says, 'Trembling, cautious, / As if standing on the brink of a bottomless gulf, / As if walking on thin ice' 戰戰兢兢、如臨深淵、如履薄冰.[2] From today on, I know I won't have to worry about this anymore, oh disciples!"

Notes: *Kang Youwei notes: The "Analects" was compiled by Zengzi's school, and Zengzi's teaching majored on keeping one's word. Here we see how on the point of death he . . . speaks about the way of the noble person, but it is still only in the rough [aspects] of countenance, appearance, and tenor of speech. And in [his concern about] positioning his hands and feet, he is simply trembling and cautious about guarding personal purity and avoiding censure. The collected sayings of Zengzi numbered eighteen chapters, and all had to do with personal restraint, honesty, and circumspection; this accords with Dai's notes that the* Zengzi *had ten chapters. Ye Shi of the Song's suggestion that Zengzi never heard Confucius [teach on the] Great Way was probably not very far off. . . . The disciples of Zengzi's school had this narrow aim for their learning, and considering that they held authority over the compilation* *and selection of the text . . . they must have made mistakes and introduced corruptions and rough approximations; they could not have fully captured the spirit of the teaching, to say nothing of passing it down to tens of thousands! But if Yan Hui, Zigong, Zimu [Shang Qu], Zizhang, and Zisi had compiled it, knowing their vast learning and depth of thought, [the text] would not have been this [shallow]. Furthermore, If Chong Gong, Ziyou, and Zixia had compiled it, knowing their subtlety with words to express great truths, [the text they produced] also would not have been this limited. . . . If the "Analects" had been compiled and selected only by Zengzi's disciples and those of his school, it would only have passed down preliminary remarks on keeping one's word, and would have included little on the Great Way of sageliness and humaneness, and Confucianism would not have become great. Therefore, the idea that the "Analects" is really the product of Zengzi's school is not adequate to account for all of Confucianism.*

Comments: The first line of the poem quoted, "Trembling, cautious" (*zhanzhan jingjing* 戰戰兢兢), is still used in the spoken language to this day, and so does not need to be translated [into modern Chinese]—on the contrary, translated it would lose its flavor. The word *qi* 啟 means "open," and we can speculate that here it means that he asks the disciples to open up and thus properly arrange his hands and feet. Older translations mostly have "see my feet, see my hands," but although they can manage to interpret it this way, this reading is forced, and one really does not understand what it means to say. In Wen Tianxiang's conception, "only when duty is fulfilled can humaneness be perfected," so that "whether today or tomorrow, there will be almost nothing to be ashamed of." [One moves from] the sense of responsibility (i.e., duty *yi* 義) to the sense of Heaven and Earth *tiandi gan* 天地感 (i.e., humaneness). "Trembling, cautious," carefully keeping it without fail, that is duty; "I know I won't have to worry about this anymore," finally freeing oneself, that is humaneness. Only when duty is performed to the utmost is humaneness complete. In this, Zengzi shows even more brilliance.

I have already discussed Kang Youwei's commentary in the introduction, and so I will not repeat it here. To summarize, what Yan Hui, Zengzi and others transmitted was a Confucian religious morality, which, through the development it underwent in Song-Ming Neo-Confucianism, became the *daotong* (Received Tradition) of Confucius, Mencius, Cheng Yi, Zhu Xi, Lu Jiuyuan, and Wang Yangming. When today's modern New Confucians call this the "quintessence" or the "lifeblood" of Chinese culture, this is taking it too far.

8.4. 曾子有疾，孟敬子問之。曾子言曰：「鳥之將死，其鳴也哀；人之將死，其言也善。君子所貴乎道者三：動容貌，斯遠暴慢矣；正顏色，斯近信矣；出辭氣，斯遠鄙倍矣。籩豆之事，則有司存。」

Zengzi was gravely ill, and Meng Jingzi went to see him. Zengzi said, "When a bird is dying, its call is mournful; when a person is dying, his speech is good. There are three items of etiquette cherished by the noble person: he gives attention to his appearance, and in this way avoids rudeness and lassitude; he makes his attitude correct, and in this way approaches trustworthiness and reliability; he pays attention to what he says, and in this way avoids vulgarity and mistakes. As for those details of the sacrifices, there are specialists to take care of those."

Comments: The word *dao* 道 ("way") here refers to the ritual system.[3] He Yan in his 集解 *Jijie* notes, "Zheng [Xuan] 鄭玄 (127–200) says that *dao* here refers to ritual." All of this is directed toward those who govern.

8.5. 曾子曰：「以能問於不能，以多問於寡；有若無，實若虛，犯而不校，昔者吾友嘗從事於斯矣。」

Zengzi said, "To have ability and yet consult those without ability; to be rich in knowledge and yet consult those without much knowledge; to have but appear not to have; to be full yet appear empty; to be violated, but not enter into a dispute—in the past I had a friend who was like this."

Comments: This passage has some aspects that are suggestive of Daoism, yet they are not the same. Scholars have all read this to be speaking of Yan Hui. It is no wonder the *Zhuangzi* so often refers to Yan Hui.

8.6. 曾子曰：「可以託六尺之孤，可以寄百里之命，臨大節而不可奪也。君子人與？君子人也。」

Zengzi said, "One can entrust a young prince to his care, or grant him the fate of a nation; in the face of a great crisis, he remains unchanged. Is this how a noble person acts? Of course it is."

Comments: Private religious morality appears in societal politics. This is why private morality should govern social morality.

8.7. 曾子曰:「士不可以不弘毅, 任重而道遠。仁以為己任, 不亦重乎? 死而後已, 不亦遠乎?」

Zengzi said, "An intellectual cannot but be grand and resolute, because his responsibilities are heavy and his road long. For to take humaneness as one's responsibility, is this not heavy? And to continue until death, is this not a long road?"

Comments: These several passages in a row all concern Zengzi. Zengzi is described as obsequious and "trembling, cautious"—obviously his is a religious morality. He seems rigid, obtuse, and awkward. Confucius even said of him, "[Zeng] Shen is dull" (*Analects* 11.18). But at the same time there are these moving, immortal words that are so full of feeling; this is precisely the characteristic of religiosity. **The religious school or religious aspect emphasizes strict demands and scrupulous obedience in small matters, but at the same time it also demands that, starting with small things in all kinds of ritual matters, one establish a strong character that is powerful and unyielding. The establishment of this strong character, as well as the possibility of various kinds of moral conduct, does not come from momentary boldness, or from a mood or whim, but is the result of a long-term honing that begins in small things.** There is a Chinese saying that expresses this: "Fervent pursuit of humaneness is easy, calmly facing death is hard" 慷慨從仁易, 從容就義難. Thus it is not [a matter of] the momentary feeling of bravery or heroism we see in "Draw the blade, what a thrill! / Its sharpness deserves this fine young head!"[4] 引刀成一快, 不負少年頭 (Wang Jingwei 汪精衛 [1883–1944]), but rather the attitude of "seeing death as a return" 視死如歸 that allows someone under a death sentence for three years to remain undaunted, as in "Among men it is called 'flood-like,' / Surging to fill all under the blue sky"[5] 於人曰浩然, 沛乎塞蒼冥 (Wen Tianxiang). This is what Zengzi was speaking of when he said, "An intellectual cannot but be grand and resolute, because his responsibilities are heavy and his road long," what Mencius was referring to when he said, "I excel at cultivating my 'flood-like' *qi*," and what Confucius called the unbending, unyielding, persevering, and resolute spirit of "It is only in the cold of winter that one knows the cypress and pine do not wither" (*Analects* 9.28). This kind of character or spirit has a religious quality and is characterized by religious emotion, and is worth advocating and encouraging. Even Kang Youwei, who, as we have mentioned, was critical of Zengzi, praised this passage as representing the "true Confucianism."

8.8. 子曰：「興於詩，立於禮。成於樂。」

Confucius said, "The *Songs* inspire a person, the ritual system establishes a person, and music perfects a person."

Comments: This is another very important passage. Being "established in ritual" has been addressed in many passages already, in a very objective manner. "Ritual" provides regulation of behavior, and objectively cultivates human nature and establishes human character, so as to provide people the qualifications for membership in the clan collective. The *Songs* inspire and enlighten the temperament, arouse the mind, and cause people to set out on the pathway toward human nature. Music causes people to attain the perfection of human nature (see 6.20, and my discussion in *The Chinese Aesthetic Tradition*).[6] Clearly, terms like "perfection" (*cheng* 成), "complete person" (*chengren* 成人), "study for [improving] oneself" (*wei ji zhi xue* 為己之學) (cf. *Analects* 14.24), and so on, are far from mere intellectual understanding, but rather have to do with the cultivation of the affections, that is, the shaping and growth of emotionality and intentionality. This is not something that can be attained through rational analysis or conceptual cognition, but must be directly learned through realization, recognition, or experience. Only through the melding of reason into the emotions, or the presence of reason in emotion, is this human emotion or realm of human life possible; this is why the passage says, "perfected in music."

As for "the *Songs* inspire a person," the *Songs* (poems) refer to thought, but not only conceptual thought—this is a "words not adequate to the meaning" (*yan bu jin yi* 言不盡意) kind of thought, and only for this reason can it arouse inspiration. Poetry must have the outer shell of thought (language, concepts), and yet this outer shell is both closed (having this thought, this meaning) and open (not limited to this thought or this meaning); this is what we mean by "writing not adequate to the words, words not adequate to the meaning" (*shu bu jin yan, yan bu jin yi* 書不盡言，言不盡意). This kind of thought starts with the individual and extends from there. The saying, "The *Songs* have no fixed interpretation" (*shi wu da gu* 詩無達詁) also refers to this. And all the range of human emotional experience, hardship, and suffering exist in this language-cum-psyche in which "words end but meaning does not end" (*yan jin yi wei jin* 言盡意未盡). This is traditional China's form of thought and language, as well as its form of living and being human. For this reason, the characteristics of Chinese thought are related to "poetry," namely, its tendency not to emphasize logical inference, deduction, or induction, or to stress grammar and syntax (in language), but instead to emphasize sensory association and analogical relationships—all these are related to this character. It has its origins in witchcraft (what James George Frazer [1854–1941] spoke of as the Law of Similarity and Law of Contagion).[7] This type of analogy has both emotional elements and experiential elements, and therefore has no fixed order and presents indistinct and polysemous states. It is characterized by non-linear relationships, and thus net-like intersectionality, as in "clouds follow the dragon, wind follows the tiger" (*yun cong long, feng cong hu* 雲從龍, 風從虎). Thus it is not purely rational, but rather aesthetic in form. My idea of "realizing truth through beauty" (*yi mei qi zhen* 以美啓真)[8] has a similar meaning. Direct, vague, polysemous, while also concise and precise. This form of thought is of course also related to the characteristics of Chinese characters. Chinese characters have their basis in "ideographs"; they use "compound ideographs" (the understanding of information) or "pictograms" (the memory of visual images) as their method; they use "phono-semantic compounds" to make a connection with language; and then they use phonetic loan characters and derivative cognates as means of supplementary development.

8.9. 子曰:「民可使由之, 不可使知之。」

Confucius said, "One can ask the people to follow, but one cannot necessarily ask them to understand why."

Notes: *Cheng Shude quotes Liu Kai's "Lunyu buzhu": "Pan Geng was moving the capital to Yin, but the none of the people wanted to do so; Pan Geng insisted upon doing it, giving the order over and over, and finally the people began to be forced to follow him. When Zi Chan* 子產 *[Gongsun Qiao* 公孫橋 *d. 522 BC] took charge of Zheng, he caused the capital and the remote areas each to have their proper regulations; the people of Zheng complained at first but later regarded him with favor. Thus it is possible to cause people to do something; but if you want to make them understand what you do, that is utterly impossible."*

Comments: These lines are, of course, denounced by today's moderns who advocate democracy. Kang Youwei changed the punctuation to read,

"If the people permit something, cause it to be followed; if [the people] do not permit it, cause it to be understood" 民可, 使由之; (民) 不可, 使知之; this is essentially to democratize Confucius. Actually, as the Note says above, this was not unusual in ancient times. The ancient idea of "democracy" (*minzhu* 民主) is precisely to "be a ruler for the people" 為民做主; "regarding the people as precious" 民為貴 means the same thing. It is not the modern view in which the people are in charge. Therefore, it is "for the people," but not "of the people" or "by the people." Today's notion of "serving the people" (*wei renmin fuwu* 為人民服務) is at most just "for the people" masquerading as "of the people." Among ancient sayings there is also "One may [allow] the people to join in the joys of success; one may not begin by considering something with them" 民可與樂成, 未可與慮始—all these refer to the same experience, and are nothing to think strange or wrong. Times change, and of course right and wrong for Confucius were not the same as the right and wrong of today.

8.10. 子曰: 「好勇疾貧, 亂也。人而不仁, 疾之已甚, 亂也。」

Confucius said, "Loving courage and despising poverty may produce a rebel; excessively hating those who are not humane may produce a rebel."

Comments: Speaking from experience, and employing dialectic, this passage shows the importance of leniency.

8.11. 子曰: 「如有周公之才之美, 使驕且吝, 其餘不足觀也已。」

Confucius said, "If you have the beautiful talents of the Duke of Zhou, but are proud and closed-minded, then there is nothing worth looking at."

Notes: *Liu Baonan quotes from the "Han shi wai zhuan" [juan 3]: When King Cheng allotted the state of Lu to Bo Qin, the Duke of Zhou admonished him, saying, "Go! And do not be proud of your fiefdom of the state of Lu. I am the son of King Wen, the younger brother of King Wu, and the uncle of King Cheng, and have dealings with the Son of Heaven himself—I do not occupy a negligible position in the world. Yet, every time I bathe, I have to stop and wrap up my hair three times, and at every meal I have to stop in the* *midst of eating three times, so anxious am I not to miss one worthy man in the world.*[9] *I have heard that those of virtuous action and ease who maintain these with respect thus obtain glory; those with large holdings of land who maintain these with frugality thus can hold them in peace; those with position and reputation who maintain these with humility thus obtain nobility; those who control large populations and military strength and maintain these with reverence thus obtain victory. The intelligent and talented who maintain these using ignorance thus attain goodness; those of vast knowledge and experience who maintain these by lowliness thus attain wisdom. These six are all the virtue of modesty."*

Cheng Shude quotes Hui Dong's "Jiu jing gu yi" [The ancient meaning of nine classics] commentary on the "Wu jing" chapter of the "Zhou shu" [Zhou History]: The Duke of Zhou said, "Neither be proud nor timid, [and you will be] timely and without cause [to regret]." This was the lifelong teaching of the Duke of Zhou, and the source of the abundance of his administration.

Comments: As the Notes above suggest, lack of pride was one of the Duke of Zhou's main virtues. The reason Confucius repeatedly emphasized humility and modesty was precisely in order to pass on this virtue of the Duke of Zhou's, seeing this as the content of "ritual." "Power corrupts, but absolute power corrupts absolutely" is a famous saying in the contemporary world, so the fact that the Duke of Zhou had absolute power, yet remained uncorrupt (or so it is believed), was due to this virtue of humility. And this virtue is unattainable, as is apparent from the fact that absolutely no later ruler was ever able to attain it, and two thousand years later all we have left is Confucius's praise. Those with virtue do not necessarily have position, and those with virtue who obtain position do not find it easy to retain their virtue. Some blame the evil of human nature, thus Xunzi's notion of "transforming nature and establishing deliberate effort" 化性起偽,[10] which seeks to institutionalize [virtue]. Later, Dong Zhongshu and others would bring in Daoism, Legalism, and yinyang thought, worldviews in which Heaven and humans are in mutual correspondence and interaction,[11] while at the system level providing for remonstrances, censors, and ministers to check [imperial] power and divide up authority. Making cultural officialdom superior to military leadership served to shore up central authority and the unity of the country, and so on, thus holding together the Chinese empire over two thousand years of continuity. This element is thus the "lifeblood" or the "quintessence" of Confucianism. In sum, [had China] relied purely on personal morality like that of the Duke of Zhou to ensure against the loss of governing authority, or on a blind quest to achieve to "outer kingship" through "inner sageliness," this would long ago have ended in illusion or myth. Huang Zongxi knew this, which is why he said "There is rule of law, and then there is ruling people" 有治法而後有治人; why should today's scholars continue to wallow in the past, and insist on making such forced interpretations?

8.12. 子曰:「三年學, 不至於穀, 不易得也。」

Confucius said, "For someone to have studied for three years, and still have no plan to serve in office—this is hard to come by."

Comments: "Study and excel, then take office" was the ancient system. The original purpose of "study" was to "serve in office"; this is why it says, "hard to come by." It was probably starting with Confucius that "study" first took on an individual quality, that is, study that was not necessarily for the purpose of holding office. The most important significance of the school associated with Zengzi lies here; this is something that Kang Youwei overlooked. Yan Hui and Zengzi both enjoyed "study" for its own sake.

8.13. 子曰:「篤信好學, 守死善道。危邦不入, 亂邦不居。天下有道則見, 無道則隱。邦有道, 貧且賤焉, 恥也; 邦無道, 富且貴焉, 恥也。」

Confucius said, "[Have] sincerity of faith and love of learning, regard death with seriousness and carry out the way of righteousness. Do not enter a dangerous country; leave a chaotic country. When there is peace in the world, come out to work, when there is no peace, hide yourself. When the state is good, poverty and lowly position are shameful; when the state is bad, riches and high position are shameful."

Comments: This is where the difference between Confucianism and Daoism lies. Because the difference between having the Way and not having the Way is meaningless for Daoists, it does not matter whether the government is good or bad, in any case one should "flee." Furthermore, they believe that "all crows are equally black," meaning there is no such thing as a good government, state, or world. When Confucians speak of retreating or hiding, it is in order to lie low and protect themselves, so that in the future, "in prominence he [can make] perfect the whole Empire as well."[12] Both Daoists and Confucians emphasize the importance of preserving one's life, and do not advocate casually "giving one's life." "Regarding death with seriousness" means that "death is heavier than Mt. Tai" 死有重於泰山 (as Sima Qian said).

8.14. 子曰:「不在其位, 不謀其政。」

Confucius said, "If you do not occupy that position, do not attempt to plan out its duties."

Comments: Why not? Firstly, it will be a futile effort. Secondly, you will avoid suspicion and avert disaster. Thirdly, see 14.26.

8.15. 子曰:「師摯之始, 關雎之亂, 洋洋乎! 盈耳哉。」

Confucius said, "When Grand Music Master Zhi began to perform, and came to the final chorus of the 'Ospreys,' what beautiful music filled the ears!"

Notes: *Zhu Xi notes: Master Zhi: the music master of Lu was named Zhi. Luan is the final portion of a piece.*

Comments: There are many explanations for the word *luan* 亂. I adopt the view that it means "the final chorus."

8.16. 子曰:「狂而不直, 侗而不愿, 悾悾而不信, 吾不知之矣。」

Confucius said, "[If someone is] presumptuous and not frank, ignorant and not honest, without ability and not trustworthy, I am not sure what should be done [with such a person]."

Comments: The latter could perhaps make up for the former faults, but when both faults are there, it is difficult to deal with. This is speaking from experience as well as phenomenological analysis, and would seem to apply still today.

8.17. 子曰:「學如不及, 猶恐失之。」

Confucius said, "Study as if afraid you will be unable to catch up, and also as if afraid of losing something."

Comments: Being both eager to pursue new knowledge and afraid of losing old wisdom, one must therefore look ahead and behind. One should study as if piloting a boat upstream: if you don't go forward, you will go backward.

8.18. 子曰:「巍巍乎! 舜禹之有天下也, 而不與焉。」

Confucius said, "Lofty indeed, the way that Shun and Yu obtained the world, without having gone looking for it."

Notes: *Zhu Xi notes: "Bu yu 不與" would appear to mean "be concerned with," so this is saying they did not take pleasure in position. Liu Baonan notes: This is praising Shun and Yu. It speaks of obtaining the world without seeking it oneself. The "Record of Mingdi" in the "Wei Zhi" [Chronicle of the Wei] quotes the "Biography of Xiandi," saying: "Confucius greatly praised the majestic and vast merits of Yao and Shun, believing that Yao's abdication of the throne to Shun was the virtuous action of a great sage."*

Comments: The two Notes provide different explanations. In ancient clan society, the leader should originally have been selected, but in actuality, both Shun and Yu may both have seized power. The record in the *Bamboo Annals* [quoted by Liu Baonan] seems to be reliable. Confucian idealization of democracy in clan society is expressed in this passage. Zhu Xi's note is incorrect.

8.19. 子曰:「大哉, 堯之為君也! 巍巍乎! 唯天為大, 唯堯則之。蕩蕩乎! 民無能名焉。巍巍乎! 其有成功也; 煥乎, 其有文章!」

Confucius said, "Great is Yao! Lofty is Heaven! Only Yao is able to imitate it! So vast, the people are not able to find words to praise him! So lofty, his achievements! So bright, the elegance of his ritual system!"

Comments: The important sentence here is "Only Yao is able to imitate it." This actually means that Yao is an intermediary, connecting Heaven with humans, and using Heaven as the model for his administration, in the sense of, "Does Heaven speak? The four seasons are set in motion, and the myriad things are born and grow" (17.19). Later notions of Heaven and humans reflecting each other, of the official system being modeled on Heaven, and of the unity between the order of the universe and the order of society (the order of political relations), and so on, all developed out of this. It says in the "Three Unities of the Way of Kings" in the *Chunqiu fanlu*, "Three strokes, connected at the center, we call 'King' (*wang* 王). The three strokes are Heaven, Earth, and humanity. What connects them at the center is what unifies their Way. The thing that takes Heaven, Earth, and humanity at their center and threads them up to unite them—if not the king, what other thing could do this? For this reason, the king takes only Heaven as his model, and by modeling its seasons, attains perfection." What in the end constructs this huge "one-world system (the universe—society—humanity)," began with the tradition of the shaman-king, who could ascend to Heaven and descend to earth. Yu, Tang, and King Wen were all great shamans; is this not even more the case when it comes to Yao and Shun? Thus, "Yao imitating Heaven," "Shun respectfully [sitting] in that seat [facing south]" (15.5), "govern[ing] like the North Star" (2.1)—are these not all traces of shamanism? [The ruler] sits facing south, and practices magical arts in accordance with astronomy. The way of governing among humans (the Way of humanity) is thus the Way of Heaven; Heaven and humans are unified and connected by means of the practice of shamanism. "The unity of Heaven and humans" has a very ancient origin that can be traced back to this. **Heaven does not speak, and yet the four seasons run their course and the myriad things are born—the so-called governing by non-action of Confucians refers to acting in accord with Heaven. Even Xunzi did not change this. "Heaven" in the hands of the Duke of Zhou and Confucius was continuously exorcised of its anthropomorphic elements and gradually grew closer to an objective (natural) "law," though it was not entirely the same. For it always maintained its religious character of "ruling in obscurity," which**

became something for feeling and faith to latch onto. No doubt the rationalization of witchcraft also became the source of the idea of "reaching the greatest height and brightness, and taking the Mean as one's Way" 極高明而道中庸.[13]

8.20. 舜有臣五人而天下治。武王曰: 「予有亂臣十人。」孔子曰: 「才難, 不其然乎? 唐虞之際, 於斯為盛。有婦人焉, 九人而已。三分天下有其二, 以服事殷。周之德, 其可謂至德也已矣。」

Shun had five ministers, and the world was at peace. King Wu of Zhou said, "I have ten able people." Confucius said, "Talent is hard to come by, isn't it so? From Yao and Shun up to the present time, it has been most abundant. Among these ten people, one was even a woman, so we should count this as only nine people. Having obtained two-thirds of the territory, but still continuing to serve the Yin dynasty, Zhou's virtuous action should truly be considered supreme."

Comments: The above several passages all have to do with how good ancient society was, how good its sage rulers and wise ministers were. When Confucius speaks of reviving the ancients, what he means by "ancient" is mid-to-late-stage clan society, which already had hierarchical order. By contrast, the "ancient" praised by Daoists and Mohists refers to the early stage of clan society, or even earlier. Confucius's "ancients" had a clearly developed system of rites and administration, but most important were their customary (or ceremonial) rules, the simplicity of their society, their purity of heart, the stability of their social order, and the relative rarity of struggles for power—these are what Confucius idealized, and what became the ideal world of Confucians.

8.21. 子曰: 「禹, 吾無間然矣。菲飲食, 而致孝乎鬼神; 惡衣服, 而致美乎黻冕; 卑宮室, 而盡力乎溝洫。禹, 吾無間然矣。」

Confucius said, "As for Yu, I have nothing to say [against him]: he ate very poorly, yet sacrificed richly to his ancestors; he dressed poorly, yet wore a splendid cap and gown for ritual occasions; he lived very poorly, yet exerted himself to the utmost in repairing the dikes and irrigation channels. As for Yu, I have nothing to say [against him]."

Comments: In sum, he did not think of himself, but served the people, including serving the clan's ancestors with solemnity. The "sacrifices" were always a major affair in ancient times. They were closely related to maintaining the existence and continuity of the clan, country, and people, as it was actually by way of these sacrificial ceremonies for the ancestors that the clan collective was unified and consolidated. This was the ancient custom, as well as the origin of shamanism. The Chinese people retained the tradition of sacrificing to the ancestors strongly over a long period of time, so that still today its influence is felt. It is here that the "pith," "lifeblood," and "received tradition" (*daotong* 道統) lies, not in idle talk of the "mind-nature" (*xinxing* 心性) of Song-Ming Neo-Confucians or modern-day New Confucians. Of course, this is also where the Chinese version of the union between church and state (i.e., what I call the trinity [*san he yi* 三合一] of ethics-government-religion) originates. How this can be deconstructed and reconstructed is a very important question for us today. The main duty of Confucianism lies here, and not in how to carry on Song-Ming Neo-Confucian theorizing about the mind-nature.

Book 9

9.1. 子罕言利, 與命, 與仁。

Confucius rarely discussed profit; he spoke of fate and commended humaneness.

Comments: The *Analects* actually does seldom speak of "profit," but it repeatedly speaks of "fate," and most often discusses "humaneness"—upwards of a hundred times. However, most commentators explain this passage to mean that he seldom speaks of profit, fate, or humaneness, which would seem quite out of keeping with the original text. There are even those who read this to mean he seldom spoke of the relationship between profit and fate and humaneness.

"Profit" (*li* 利) can encompass "material gain," "benefit," or "advantage," and although Confucius did not address it directly, he not infrequently addressed it indirectly. Later Confucians took this passage as a condemnation of commerce and forbade the discussion of "personal gain" or "profit." Yet Confucius praised Zigong for "often calculating correctly [in business/speculation]," and is not the injunction to "make them numerous" and "enrich them" (13.9) by extension speaking of a sort of "profit"? On this Confucius is not like Mencius.

"Fate" (*ming* 命) is very difficult to explain. What is fate? Usually it is understood to mean "destiny," "fatalism," or "determined by fate," things that imply an irresistible inevitability. I already discussed above that actually the opposite is true: fate (*ming*) means something fortuitous. Precisely because it is fortuitous, it is hard for people to anticipate, grasp, understand, or control; this is why it elicits sighs of resignation. If it were truly an inevitability, law, or trend, people could understand it and come to terms with it and there would be no need for this sort of feeling. The mysterious character of fate lies in its fortuitous nature, its chance character, which transcends human ability to understand or imagine. Any fortuitous or chance event has its causes, but since it is not the result of an inevitable principle, people have trouble using rational logic or experience to explain it, and instead turn to magic, divination, or other non-rational means in hopes of understanding it.

But because people are used to investigating and understanding things based upon the rational principles that govern real life, they often see fortuitous events as inevitable, and chance as fate. When fate is understood as Heaven's intent, then "fate" becomes "the will of Heaven" (*tianming* 天命). This "will of Heaven" refers to what is ordered or mandated by Heaven above, and thus it evolves into something that governs people, that controls and orders their life (including both collective and individual life); it becomes a sort of force, trend, or belief. But as to what it actually is, if we do not attribute it to the intention or power of an anthropomorphic god, it should be understood as an "objective trend." In sum, it becomes the object of people's fear, obedience, reverence, and worship. Some people turn it into a basis for action, for issuing orders; others receive it, prostrating themselves in submission to it, as in the saying "Be happy in poverty and content in the Way." From ancient times until today, it seems it has always been like this.

Therefore, it would seem that what we can do today is to get rid of this alien power that controls people and stop seeing fate as inevitability, but rather understand it as chance, **emphasizing that one should do one's utmost to understand and grasp chance, in order to establish one's own destiny. Out of chance events, one should establish what is inevitable, and out of chance events grasp hold of life. Proceeding with initiative, one should open up the future, rather than waiting for, accepting, and resigning oneself to all sorts of chance events.** This is what it means to grasp one's own destiny and to defeat so-called fatalism. **Only this is truly "knowing one's destiny" or "establishing one's fate." Only this is true subjectivity.**[1] **This is the case for the whole human race, collectively and individually.**

For an individual to be born and find him or herself on this earth is very random. The existence of the human race, the existence of the world, is also like this. For this reason, to insist on asking "What is it?" or "Why is it?" is meaningless and difficult to answer. Actually this is a "false question," which is better left unasked. **It is better to ask: Since this world exists, and there is existence and human life, how should**

we act? How should we live? Based upon what should we live and act? As I have said above, Confucius always gave a "how-to" answer to the "what is" questions. Therefore he also seldom discussed "fate," but often discussed "humaneness." What fate is, is difficult to know; what humaneness is, on the other hand, is possible to do. As I have said above, Confucians are not concerned about "what" but about "how."

This is true not only of Confucians, but also of Daoists. The five thousand words of the *Laozi* cannot be understood from an ontological or existential standpoint (unfortunately this can be said of [the work of] most scholars). The *Laozi* was originally concerned with military strategy. What it means by the Dao, or the "Way," is what we commonly speak of as "how to do" something. **The phrase "ingenious tactics depend on careful thought" (運用之妙, 存乎一心) is certainly true; though there may be principles, there are no rules. Therefore, "The Dao that can be spoken of is not the constant Dao" (*Laozi*). If the Way can be explained in words, it is no longer the Way. And only with "no desires" (or "purposelessness") can one objectively view the marvels of how things behave; "having desires" (or "purposiveness"), one can subjectively grasp the essence (and boundaries) of things, and so on.[2] These are all examples of the active analysis of pragmatic reason, not contemplative cosmology or ontology.**

The reason that Chinese culture and philosophy emphasize becoming over being, function over substance, the human over the divine (the spiritual is also fully subordinate to human affairs) can all be seen to reflect this spirit of "knowing fate."

9.2. 達巷黨人曰:「大哉孔子! 博學而無所成名。」子聞之, 謂門弟子曰:「吾何執? 執御乎? 執射乎? 吾執御矣。」

A man from the Daxiang area said, "That great Confucius, his learning is broad, but he hasn't made a name for himself through any specialty." Confucius heard it, and said to his disciples, "Which should I pursue? Should I pursue charioteering or archery? I think charioteering will do."

Notes: *Zhu Xi says:* Zhi 執 *[to hold, grasp, stick to] means to specialize. Archery and charioteering are each one of the Arts, and the one who drives a chariot is a slave, so those who specialize in this are lowly. Confucius is* *saying, "So you want to make me choose a specialty to be famous for? Then I will choose charioteering."*

Comments: This passage, like the previous one, is difficult to interpret. The traditional commentaries all insist on reading it according to its literal meaning. Should one be a "generalist" or a "specialist"? Philosophers and thinkers are usually not specialists, and therefore Confucius sighs and says that in that case, he will be the lowest possible specialist. "Of the Six Arts, none is more coarse than archery and charioteering, and charioteering is coarser than archery" (Li Guangdi 李光地, *Lunyu Liji*)—this agrees with Zhu Xi. In today's China, where "thought is taking a back seat and scholarship is proliferating" 思想告退而學問方滋, "Should I pursue charioteering or archery?" Better to not "make a name for oneself" and leave it at that.

9.3. 子曰:「麻冕, 禮也; 今也純, 儉。吾從眾。拜下, 禮也; 今拜乎上, 泰也。雖違眾, 吾從下。」

Confucius said, "Using hemp to weave one's hats accords with ritual; today they use silk. This is simpler, and I follow the practice. To bow at the bottom of the steps accords with ritual; today they have begun to do it at the top of the steps. This is proud, so even though it is against the common practice, I continue to advocate the bottom of the steps."

Comments: Confucius upheld some aspects of ritual practice, and did not uphold others. Thus he was both "constant" 經 (*jing*, principled), and "adaptable" 權 (*quan*, flexible). From the present example, **what belongs to principle and must be upheld are mostly those behaviors and actions that directly affect the inner emotions; those that need not be upheld are mostly purely external ceremonial regulations.** As reflected in the statement "You cherish the sheep, I cherish the ritual" (3.17), neglecting the sacrificial rites would directly affect the inner emotions and the actions of filial piety, therefore they must be maintained. On the other hand, the passage "In ritual, simplicity and economy are better than elaborate extravagance. In matters of mourning, true sorrow is better than grand ceremonies" (3.4) demonstrates that in general, purely external, formal rites are not so important. It is clear to see that Confucianism originally took the psychological emotions as the foundation.

9.4. 子絕四: 毋意, 毋必, 毋固, 毋我。

Confucius absolutely avoided four faults: he did not make wild guesses, was not arbitrary, was not stubborn, and was not self-important.

Comments: What is the "self" [or "I" 我]? This is the biggest question. What is the "reality" or the "meaning" of a living individual's "self"? When Camus said suicide was the fundamental philosophical problem, this is what he meant, namely, What is the meaning of my life? Why must I live? Postmodern theory believes that the self consists of broken fragments, that there is no unified self, that the "I" is simply the present moment, and thus it is meaningless to try to answer the question "What is the self?" In this view, people become close to animals, for animals do not need a consciousness of self, they do not need the categories of cause and effect, they do not need to think about the future or the past. Their immediate "existence" involves nothing more than unthinking, irrational desires, impulses, and instincts. Does humanity, by way of this anti-alienation, anti-mechanistic anti-rationalism, finally go the way of animals? **But are humans just animals? Is the "self" actually fragmentary? These questions deserve further thought.** Confucius's notion of "lack of self" (*wu wo* 無我) is very far from this indeed. That he "was not self-important" includes both the idea that he does not think the truth lies in his own hands and the idea that he does not make his own loss or gain into principles or standards.

9.5. 子畏於匡。曰: 「文王既沒, 文不在茲乎? 天之將喪斯文也, 後死者不得與於斯文也; 天之未喪斯文也, 匡人其如予何? 」

Confucius was held captive in the land of Kuang. He said, "King Wen of Zhou is already dead, and does not culture reside here where I am? If Heaven above really wants to destroy culture, then those who come after will have no way to have this culture. If Heaven above does not wish to destroy culture, then what can the people of Kuang do to me?"

Comments: Does the Chinese phrase *hou si zhe* 後死者 ("those who die after") refer to Confucius himself? Or those who come after Confucius? I read it as the latter. Confucius regards it as his duty to transmit the Way, that is, to preserve and pass on the "Way of the Former Kings." This is what today we would call a sense of cultural or historical responsibility.

Some take the discussion of "Heaven" in this passage to demonstrate that Confucius was a theist. Because the passage hints that Heaven intends for this culture to be preserved, Heaven must have a will and personhood. Actually, Confucius is quite vague in what he says on these points, including in this passage; he is not at all clear. What he is clear on seems to be simply endowing the universe with an emotional coloring that warmly affirms life. This has been the tradition, from the *Book of Changes*, Dong Zhongshu, and the Song-Ming Neo-Confucians, with their view that reason does not depart from *qi* nor conscience from the senses, to Kang Youwei and Tan Sitong's insistence that electricity is humaneness, or that ether (*yitai* 以太) is humaneness, and so on: it is a view of humanity and the cosmos as suffused with emotion. Cheng Hao 程顥 (1032–1085) used a medical definition of "numbness" to explain the Confucian idea of humaneness, similarly to how Tan Sitong's stated that "humaneness is equal to 'not blocked' [*tong* 通]"—both had this kind of philosophy infused with emotion. Confucius transformed the fervor of primitive shamanistic "feeling" into the rational "feeling" of this philosophy, which encompasses what it means to be human (benefiting others and helping the people), human personality (individual autonomy), a sense of historical responsibility (faithfulness), and so on, and certainly was far from being limited to simple knowledge. It still encompasses knowledge, however, and therefore we also have the later concepts of the unity of knowledge and action, investigating things in order to perfect knowledge, and other doctrines.

9.6. 太宰問於子貢曰:「夫子聖者與? 何其多能也?」子貢曰:「固天縱之將聖, 又多能也。」子聞之, 曰:「大宰知我乎! 吾少也賤, 故多能鄙事。君子多乎哉? 不多也。」

The Grand Minister asked Zigong, "Is your teacher a sage? Why is he so varied in his talents and abilities?" Zigong answered, "It is Heaven that wanted him to be a sage, and furthermore gave him many talents and abilities."

Confucius heard this and said, "Does the Grand Minister know? As a youth I was poor, and so learned all kinds of skills. Does a noble person need this many skills? He does not."

Comments: The last line could also be translated, "Are these skills too many for a noble person? They are not too many." The passage emphasizes the fact that abilities are attained through learning, versus the idea of a "Heaven-sent sage"; this is very different from all kinds of founders of religions.

9.7. 牢曰:「子云,『吾不試, 故藝』。」

Lao said, "The Master has said, 'It is because I was not serving as an official that I learned so many skills.'"

Comments: As this passage so closely follows upon the previous one, the two should be combined into one, both of which address the questions of Confucius's technical skills and abilities.

9.8. 子曰:「吾有知乎哉? 無知也。有鄙夫問於我, 空空如也, 我叩其兩端而竭焉。」

Confucius said, "Do I have knowledge? I do not. There was a man from the country who asked me questions, and I had no knowledge [of how to answer], so I turned the matter over in my mind and investigated it inside and out, from start to finish, until I finally arrived at a result."

Notes: *Zhu Xi notes:* Kou 叩 *means "to start." The* liang duan 兩端 *means the "two ends." It means the beginning and end, roots and branches, top and bottom, finer and coarser points.*

Comments: Perhaps this is close to the Socratic method of seeking the truth by asking questions. Zhu Xi's note lacks the pairing "inside and out," which should be added. The Chinese phrase "*kongkong* 空空" (here translated "I had no knowledge") is sometimes understood to mean "honest-looking."

9.9. 子曰:「鳳鳥不至, 河不出圖, 吾已矣夫!」

Confucius said, "The phoenix does not fly out, and the Yellow River does not display images of auspicious signs; there is nothing I can do."

Comments: This should not be understood to demonstrate Confucius's belief in some sort of mysticism, but rather should be read in light of the last line, that is, as an inner feeling of pessimistic lament. The

Analects records numerous instances of this type of pessimistic mood. It is nothing unusual, simply a typical human feeling. The last line can also be translated as "This life of mine is over."

9.10. 子見齊衰者、冕衣裳者與瞽者, 見之, 雖少必作; 過之, 必趨。

If Confucius saw people dressed in mourning, wearing the ritual sacrificial cap, or blind, when he met them, even if they were young, Confucius would stand up; or if he passed them, he would always pass them quickly, with quiet steps, bowing at the waist.

Notes: *Zhu Xi quotes Yin Tun: This is the sincerity of the sage; inner and outer are one.*

Comments: This demonstrates respectfulness. Again, the emphasis is on a certain emotional attitude, what Zhu Xi's note rightly calls the unity of inner and outer. It is extremely important that a society has the support of this type of interpersonal consideration and relational emotion. Thus, even though it is an individual attitude, it can serve a social function. "The character of the common people will be deeply faithful and honest" (*Analects* 1.9) also relies on this.

9.11. 顏淵喟然歎曰: 「仰之彌高, 鑽之彌堅; 瞻之在前, 忽焉在後。夫子循循然善誘人, 博我以文, 約我以禮。欲罷不能, 既竭吾才, 如有所立卓爾。雖欲從之, 末由也已。」

Yan Hui sighed deeply, and said, "The more I look up at it, the higher it seems; the more I dig into it, the more impenetrable it seems to be. I see it before me, and suddenly it is behind me. The Teacher is good at leading along one step at a time, enriching me with his breadth of knowledge, regulating me with the solemnity of his ritual system, so that though I might want to quit, it is impossible to do so. He fully unearths my abilities, so that it seems I can stand very, very tall; but when I want to continue following him forward, again I feel I do not know how to proceed."

Notes: *Qian Mu notes in "Lunyu xin jie": Only the Way of Confucius, although it is so lofty and deep as to seem unattainable, is also simply within* *people's natures. It lies in the changing of one's countenance; in the duties of eating, drinking, waking, residing, social intercourse, giving and receiving [gifts]; the relations between ruler and minister, father and son, husband and wife and brothers; whether to go or stay, separate from or follow, refuse or receive, accept or reject. It extends to the conduct of governing affairs, and the attention to ceremonial detail. If one carefully reads the "Analects," the Way of Confucius is completely contained in it; as it says: "There is nothing about which I am not open with you. This is how a certain Mr. Kong acts" [7.24]. If one does not forsake its core, one will be able to see its exterior manifestation. There is another kind of way that cannot be fathomed or deduced, so that people are unable to seek it out or investigate it. Scholars who thoroughly study the "Analects" can see Confucius's Way; it is truly unassuming and close to us. And if we pay careful attention to this passage it will become clear that it is precisely in this unassuming, near-to-hand character that we find its depth and unattainability. Even the sagely Yan Hui had this lament.*

Comments: Qian Mu's commentary is excellent; this is the meaning of the saying "The Way is found in everyday relationships" 道在倫常日用之中. What Yan Hui says constitutes the highest possible praise on the part of a student for a teacher: it is the sense of awe for the teacher whose features and character are like those of a mystical dragon of which we can see the head but not the tail, which the student can seek but not attain. The characteristics of Confucius's teaching of Yan Hui go far beyond the educational goals and scope of "When study is complete, hold office" (*Analects* 19.13) to encompass the pursuit of and aspiration toward the perfection of the human personality and the human realm. This is the religious aspect of Confucian morality. It plays the pseudo-religious role of saving the soul and ridding it of the worldly and vulgar. Being this kind of teacher was what won Confucius this kind of lofty imagistic description that borders on mysticism. The short phrase "Though I might want to quit, it is impossible to do so" demonstrates the attitude of continuously going deeper in study.

9.12. 子疾病, 子路使門人為臣。病閒, 曰: 「久矣哉! 由之行詐也, 無臣而為有臣。吾誰欺? 欺天乎? 且予與其死於臣之手也, 無寧死於二三子之手乎? 且予縱不得大葬, 予死於道路乎? 」

Confucius was very ill, and Zilu wanted the disciples to act as retainers. Later, when Confucius was somewhat less ill, he said, "For too long, Zilu has cheated me! I am not qualified to have retainers, yet to my surprise I have them; who am I cheating? Heaven? Furthermore, rather than die among some so-called retainers, I would prefer to die among you disciples. Even if I could not be given a grand funeral, surely I would not be thrown out onto the street?"

Notes: *Zhu Xi notes: The Master had already lost his position and had no retainers. Zilu, in desiring to have retainers to handle his burial, meant to honor him as a sage.*

*Liu Baonan notes: The Master had served as Minister of Justice of the state of Lu, a high post. Now Zilu in his respect for Confucius wants to give him the burial of a high official, so he makes the disciples into retainers in order to help to manage it. For an official's death to be handled by an official was in accord with ritual. For the Master to want to die in the presence of his disciples indicates that his feeling for his disciples is more intimate. This why the Huang Commentary says, As in the three relationships, when speaking of the sacrifices offered by one's relations, ministers would not be as good as disciples. And it says, In the rituals governing ministers, there is provision [*yang 養*] and there is positioning [*fang 方*]; since there is positioning, there is separation; there is no positioning for the disciples, and lacking positioning, it is more intimate.*

Comments: Liu Baonan's commentary is correct in saying that the disciples were closer than any retainers. It is not simply a matter of strict adherence to ritual, but more a matter of familial affection. "Heaven, Earth, country, family, teacher" are clearly all objects of feeling, worship, and reverence.

9.13. 子貢曰: 「有美玉於斯, 韞櫝而藏諸? 求善賈而沽諸? 」子曰: 「沽之哉! 沽之哉! 我待賈者也。」

Zigong said, "Here is a piece of beautiful jade. Should I keep it safe, hiding it in a cabinet? Or should I find a knowledgeable customer to whom to sell it?" Confucius said, "Sell it, sell it! I await the customer."

Comments: Confucius constantly keeps "outer kingship" in mind, comparing himself to a good product that is for sale. In this respect he is far from the Confucius of Song-Ming Neo-Confucian interpretations.

9.14. 子欲居九夷。或曰:「陋, 如之何! 」子曰:「君子居之, 何陋之有? 」

Confucius wanted to go live in an undeveloped area. Someone said, "What will you do about how backward it is there?" Confucius said, "If a noble person goes to live there, can it still be backward?"

Notes: *Liu Baonan cites Mencius: "A gentleman transforms where he passes, and works wonders where he abides."[3] This is why if a noble person lives [somewhere], [the locals] can transform their old customs, and grow accustomed to the rites."*

Comments: The character *lou* 陋 is understood to mean "crude." Qian Mu glosses it as "culturally unenlightened," which in any case means bad, uncultured, uncomfortable, inconvenient, and so forth. Thus the translation, "backward." Why does Confucius wish to go there? Is it not likely due to his great discontent with the fact that in all his travels around the various states, he finds no one to make use of him in the more civilized states of the central plains?

9.15. 子曰:「吾自衛反魯, 然後樂正, 雅頌各得其所。」

Confucius said, "When I returned from the state of Wei to Lu, I ordered and regulated their music. The 'Hymns' (*ya* 雅) and 'Eulogies' (*song* 頌) were each accorded their proper places."

Comments: Here again we see the emphasis upon music. Originally, music preceded the rites, in the source of all spiritual culture, that is, the shamanistic music and dance of the ancients. Only later was the ritual system divided off. After the emergence of the ritual system, "music" became a part of the "rites." (See the first chapter of my *The Chinese Aesthetic Tradition* [*Huaxia meixue*].) For Confucius to have "revised the *Songs* and the *Documents* and corrected the *Rites* and *Music*" would have been a big job. The "Hymns" and "Eulogies" were both "temple songs" directly related to the sacrifices and other important ceremonies. To say that they were accorded their proper position was to demonstrate that one was carrying on the work of the Duke of Zhou in "systematizing the rites and establishing music," and thus preserving the traditional ritual system. This, of course, was precisely what Confucius both wanted to and had to do. Confucius's role as an educator and thinker is inseparable from his preservation of the traditional ritual system by making it into a pseudo-religious spiritual enterprise. As a result, "musical religion" was not actually continued or passed on, and its importance was nearly lost, as it was gradually ritualized or turned into entertainment. This belongs to the inevitability of historical development; because of its gradual distancing from ancient shamanistic ceremony and its increasing rationalization, society began to be preserved by ritual precepts and no longer relied upon primitive music and dance. This is why, after all, Confucius speaks so much more of the ritual system than of music.

9.16子曰: 「出則事公卿, 入則事父兄, 喪事不敢不勉, 不為酒困, 何有於我哉? 」

Confucius said, "Abroad, I serve officials and superiors; returning, I serve father and elder brothers. If there are funereal matters to attend to, I dare not stint. I am not addicted to wine or greedy for drink—what other strong points have I?"

Comments: The phrase "I dare not stint" means that I must self-legislate and apply the utmost effort. Morality is always the application of reason to constrain, fetter, and lead the emotions, commonly involving the triumph of reason in the "struggle between reason and desire." This "struggle" starts out self-conscious (as in "I dare not stint") and gradually becomes "unself-conscious." The beginning of virtue is this "struggle between reason and desire" (morality); the endpoint is the "melding of reason and desire," "emotion" (aesthetics).

9.17. 子在川上, 曰: 「逝者如斯夫! 不舍昼夜。」

Confucius, standing on the riverbank, said, "Time and the seasons are just like this! They keep flowing on, day and night."

Comments: This is probably the most important philosophical statement in the entire work. Confucian philosophy emphasizes practice and is based upon action, in keeping with the [action of the] universe; this is what is meant by the phrases "The movement of Heaven is full of power" (天行健) and "The CREATIVE works sublime success, / Furthering through perseverance" (乾，元亨利貞).[4] In this respect it is thus distinct from all philosophies or religions that are based upon "stillness." Song Neo-Confucian slogans like the "unity of action and stillness" (動靜如一) or "both active and still" (亦動亦靜) are unavoidably influenced by the Buddhist emphasis on stillness. The contribution of Xiong Shili 熊十力 (1885–1968) in the modern period was precisely in his renewed emphasis on the substance of "motion" (*dong* 動). What "time and seasons are just like" [in this passage] is "motion." His argument relates particularly to the fact that it is only in the emotions that time can interact with substance or reality. This is a lament for time and refers to people's inner time. External time that takes the clock as its symbol and standard is an objective, social product that serves the demands of pragmatic human activity and communal existence. It is a different sort of space for human activity, an external form of utilitarian, practical action. It arose out of the social practices of the labor of production, and was created by the activity of the use of tools (see my *Pipan zhexue de pipan* [*A Critique of Critical Philosophy*]). Humankind needs this type of pragmatic, spatialized time in order to plan for the future and sum up the past. The time of what Kant called the "inner sense" still belongs to and serves this; it is but a perceptual form of knowledge. This type of form is the internalization of reason. But "true" time exists only in the emotional experience of the individual. This type of "time" lacks any kind of independent fixed extent; its length is the length of psychological experience. As Schiller has said, "We are no more in time; rather, time is in us with its entire never-ending succession" (*Aesthetic Letters*).[5]

History, as a phenomenon of time, only becomes substance (or final reality) in emotional experience. This is also where emotion-as-substance differs from techno-social substance: techno-social substance is measured by the external time of historical progression, because techno-social substance is created, regulated, and constrained through collective human practice. In the long river of history, the individual really is, as Hegel puts it, often sacrificed to the ruse of reason and has no real freedom to speak of. (Before the increase of free time and the advent of the "kingdom of freedom," this was the reality.) Only in emotional time is it any different. Here, people can find "truth," freedom, eternity, and home. This is where the final human reality resides, and what Tao Qian spoke of in his poem: "There flocks of birds rejoice to find lodging, / and I too cling with love to my cottage" 众鳥欣有托，吾亦愛吾廬.[6]

In the objectified emotional object, that is, nature or works of art, people can behold the self, experience existence, and affirm life. This is home, and this is substance—the ultimate meaning of human life and the universe. Here, **past, present, and future are truly melded into one and difficult to distinguish from one another.** Here, emotion is time, and time is emotion. It is only here that the emptiness (of life-meaning) that people feel in the face of death becomes "being" or "fullness" (*you* 有). **The sense of the impermanence of life became paramount in traditional Chinese literature precisely because all hopes, fears, worries, and anxieties—all surprise, despair, loneliness, and joy, and so on—all pale in the face of the sense of impermanence.** In contrast, the meaninglessness and valuelessness of practical time ("real" spatialized time) becomes abundantly clear; in other words, as it is said, the rivers and mountains are always there, while human affairs end in nothing 江山常在, 人事全非. As Li Bai's poem states, "Palace women, like flowers, filled the hall in spring, / Where today only partridges fly" 宮女如花春滿殿, 而今只有鷓鴣飛.[7]

Clearly, practical time in this sense is not time, or in other words, it is "non-being" (*wu* 無). Only in emotional experience does it become "being" (*you* 有), only then does time take on its foundational character. However, this "fundamentally true" time must be founded upon the cornerstone of "non-fundamentally true" practical time, otherwise it cannot exist. The reason for humankind's historical, biological existence can also only be deeply comprehended within this emotional time. "Bitterest sorrow is aimless grief" 閑愁最苦[8]—"aimless grief" (or the "anxieties of idleness") refers to the loss of practical time. For people to completely lose existentially purposeful action is equal to complete non-existence. Zhuangzi taught people to shed the dusty world and seek to be "free and easy" (*xiaoyao* 逍遙), and Buddhism used the notion of "emptiness" to teach people to break with the vulgar world and cut off affections 斷俗塵絕生念; yet people have to live, they have to eat food and wear clothes, and thus it is only in this emotional time that they can find refuge and a place to call home. When Schopenhauer used the contemplation of art as a way to dissipate the desires of life, this is what he was getting at. For only in art can time be countered or defied, and therefore using art to rehearse history causes the selfish desires of life to be dispelled while the human emotions flourish. The word "flourish" implies that because they touch on the maturing process of humanity's substance, rationality no longer controls or leads, but rather is deeply submerged in and permeates the emotions themselves.

The various relationships between time and the emotions, including their ratio within the emotio-rational structure, is a very large and complicated question that awaits greater attention. All of the schools of philosophy of the twentieth century were characterized by anti-historicism and anti-humanism, and thus if they did not reduce humans to the level of machines, they turned them into animals. How can we escape this misfortune? This is the reason I advocate an emotional ontology in this book [see 7.1]. The "emotions" belong to what is "aroused" or "expressed" (*yifa* 已發), therefore an emotional ontology denies the "unaroused" or "unexpressed" (*weifai* 未發), along with "stillness" and "quietude," believing that to leave aside "action," "expression," and "feeling" for quietude, the unexpressed and stillness would be to have "two roots" (*erben* 二本). "Feeling does not depart from stillness, nor stillness from feeling. To discard stillness and follow feeling is called the pursuit of things (*zhuwu* 逐物). To depart from feeling and hold fast to stillness is called being obstinate in emptiness (*nixu* 泥虛)" (Wang Ji 王畿 [1498–1583] "Zhizhi yibian" 致知議辯). The former, the "pursuit of things," is natural humanism that has lost any kind of consciousness of emotion-as-substance; the latter is the theory of Heavenly Principle and human desire, which also loses emotion-as-substance, and therefore is called "being obstinate in emptiness"; that is, it uses the "principle" of emptiness to destroy humanity. Both "Principle" and "nature" are emptiness and "non-being" (*wu* 無), and if there is no person present in the cycles of the natural world, they are also emptiness and non-being. Only in the emotional experience of the loss (or "non-being" *wu* 無) of practical time is there "being" (*you* 有). **The meaning of ruins and ancient objects is precisely here: because they lived in the emotions of people, they came to "being." "Humans all die" is an abstract proposition; every person is only concrete and real while they yet live, and it is only through the emotional experience of this living that there is "being." This is the real meaning of *Dasein* (*cizai* 此在).**

9.18. 子曰:「吾未見好德如好色者也。」

Confucius said, "I have never seen someone who can love morality as he loves female beauty."

Notes: *Qian Mu notes: Some say that the love of feminine beauty comes from sincerity, and people's love for virtue never equals the sincerity of their love of beauty. It is also said that, as the "Shiji" records: When Confucius was staying in Wei, he rode with the Duke of Ling and his wife in the same chariot, and they made Confucius get in last, swaggering ostentatiously through the streets, and that is what this statement refers to. [Qian Mu Comments:] What Confucius laments in this passage has been with us since ancient times and is still so today; how could it be limited to Duke Ling of Wei? In reading the "Analects," whether or not one honors his wife can be seen in the realities of life, and more often than in other texts, it advises against honoring one's wife.*

Comments: Qian Mu's comment is very good. "Beauty" in this passage may also be understood more broadly to refer not only to feminine beauty but to all kinds of excessively gorgeous ornamentation.

9.19. 子曰: 「譬如為山, 未成一簣, 止, 吾止也; 譬如平地, 雖覆一簣, 進, 吾往也。」

Confucius said, "Imagine that someone is erecting a mound, and lacks just one basketful of earth, but stops in the middle; this is what it would be like for me to stop. Imagine that someone is leveling ground, and has dumped only a single basketful of earth, but continues; this is what it is like for me to keep going."

Notes: *Zhu Xi notes: If a student applies himself unceasingly, then little by little he will accumulate much; if he stops in the middle, then his earlier efforts are completely wasted.*

Liu Baonan cites the "Urging study" ("Quanxue" 勸學) chapter of the "Da Dai Liji" 大戴禮記: If one builds up the earth into a hill, the wind and rain will come and awaken life in it; if one accumulates water into a pond, the flood dragon will be born in it . . . therefore, if one does not accumulate small steps, there will be no way to reach a thousand li; if there were not the accumulation of small streams, there would be no rivers. A swarthy thoroughbred in one jump cannot attain ten paces, while if you harness an inferior horse ten times, accomplishment will come through perseverance. If you start carving but leave off, not even a rotten tree will break; while if you engrave with perseverance, you will be able to shape gold and stone.

Comments: This is like the "Foolish Man who moved a mountain"—it emphasizes the fact that tenacity leads to achievement. Xunzi's "Urging Study" chapter is the same as the above-referenced chapter in *Da Dai Liji.* This fundamental spirit of the Chinese people is related to Confucianism, and not Daoism, Legalism, or yinyang thought. There can be no doubt that Confucianism is the pillar of Chinese culture.

9.20. 子曰: 「語之而不惰者, 其回也與!

Confucius said, "The one who, when you tell him [to do] something, will not slack off or be lazy, would probably be Yan Hui."

Comments: Reflecting the previous passage, "not slacking off or being lazy" means persevering.

9.21. 子謂顏淵, 曰: 「惜乎! 吾見其進也, 未見其止也。」

Confucius evaluated Yan Hui, saying, "It's really a pity! I only saw him making constant progress, and never saw him stop."

Notes: *Zhu Xi notes: Confucius pities Yan [Hui] because he died, saying that he was just making progress, and never stopped.*

Comments: The same as the previous passage.

9.22. 子曰: 「苗而不秀者有矣夫! 秀而不實者有矣夫! 」

Confucius said, "There are cases where the seedling comes up, but does not grow an ear of grain; there are cases when it grows an ear of grain, but is not able to fully ripen."

Comments: When one does not persevere tenaciously, it is often like this. We commonly see young people who, when they have achieved a little, become self-satisfied and even proud, then quickly cease to progress, and end by achieving nothing. A flowering plant that does not fruit will dazzle people with its splendor, but only for a time.

Using the metaphor of a ripening seedling (the growth of life) for human life and study is very apt. **Chinese theories of painting, literature, and poetry often describe theoretical concepts using bodily vocabulary such as bones, flesh, blood, and breath, all of which have to do with life. In China, we emphasize life and the senses, and this "this-worldly" view with its overflowing vitality is found almost everywhere.** Both large and small—the universe, medicine, calligraphy and painting, personality and courage, aesthetics and morality—all of these are reflections of life. This is why concepts like "spirit" (*shen* 神), breath (*qi* 氣), rhyme or sound (*yun* 韵), and bones (*gu* 骨) can be found all over, infusing literary, historical, philosophical, and medical studies, as well as the arts and mathematics. This is clearly a characteristic of Chinese culture.

9.23. 子曰: 「後生可畏, 焉知來者之不如今也? 四十、五十而無聞焉, 斯亦不足畏也已。」

Confucius said, "A youth is to be respected, for how can we know how the later person will compare with who he is today? When a person has reached forty or fifty years of age, and still does not understand the truth, then he is no longer worthy of respect."

Notes: *Cheng Shude collects Wang Yangming's comment on this passage from Lin Chunbo's* 林春溥 *"Sishu zhaiyi"* 四書拾遺: *The phrase* wu wen 無聞 *[literally, "has not heard"] means "has not understood the Dao," not that one has not heard of him.*

Comments: Clearly, looking down on youth seems to have a long history, and Confucius opposed it. But Mencius's "Three Great Respects" is still influential today. Many explain this to mean that "by forty or fifty he has not made a name for himself," but I do not follow that reading here. I prefer Wang Yangming's explanation, that this passage encourages us to advance in virtue and cultivate our work, for time and tide wait for no man.

9.24. 子曰: 「法語之言, 能無從乎? 改之為貴。巽與之言, 能無說乎? 繹之為貴。說而不繹, 從而不改, 吾末如之何也已矣。」

Confucius said, "How could one not assent to words that are in keeping with the regulations of the ritual system? It is correcting one's mistakes that is worthy of admiration. How could one not be happy with words that are in keeping with one's own heart's intent? It is the examination that is worthy of admiration. If a person is blindly happy, he will not engage in examination; on the surface he may receive them, but he does not make any real changes. About such a person I can do nothing."

Comments: The problem of being happy to hear good words while finding it difficult to correct one's mistakes is the same today as in ancient times. Confucius speaks of concrete problems, rather than engaging in empty discussions of nature and Principle; this is the way to actually shape human nature.

9.25. 子曰:「主忠信, 毋友不如己者, 過則勿憚改。」

Confucius said, "Make faithfulness and trustworthiness your rule, and do not have friends that are not your equal. If you make a mistake, do not be afraid to correct it."

Comments: This is a repetition of 1.8.

9.26. 子曰:「三軍可奪帥也, 匹夫不可奪志也。」

Confucius said, "The commander of the Three Armies can be deprived of his authority, but do not think to deprive an ordinary person of his will."

Comments: This is a famous saying that perfectly expresses the ideal of the moral personality. Liang Shuming, during the height of the movement to "Criticize Confucius," used this passage to withstand the insufferable arrogance of imperial authoritarianism and mass hysteria, and was not ashamed to be a practicing Confucian. In this respect he was worthy of admiration.

9.27. 子曰:「衣敝緼袍, 與衣狐貉者立, 而不恥者, 其由也與?『不忮不求, 何用不臧?』」子路終身誦之。子曰:「是道也, 何足以臧?」

Confucius said, "For a person wearing a shabby cotton gown to stand next to someone in high quality leather clothing without feeling embarrassed or ashamed, there is only Zilu! 'Not jealous, not envious, / In what way could he not be good?'[9] Zilu repeated these lines for the rest of his life, but Confucius said to him, 'Merely to be like this is still not good enough.' "

Comments: Confucius's educational method for Zilu was this: When people are satisfied with their learning or morals, deal them a blow, to make them continue to move forward. It is as it is said, "The movement of Heaven is full of power. / Thus the [noble person] makes himself strong and untiring" 天行健，君子以自強不息.[10] When the Chinese Communist Party emphasized, as part of their thought-reform program, "Live to old age, study to old age, improve to old age" 活到老，學到老，改造到老 (Zhou Enlai), the reason so many intellectuals gladly received it was likely due to the sedimentation of this traditional psychology within it.

9.28. 子曰：「歲寒，然後知松柏之後彫也。」

Confucius said, "It is only in the cold of winter that we know the pine and cypress do not wither."

Comments: In *Zhuangzi*'s "Resigning Kingship" chapter, as well as in the *Lüshi Chunqiu*, it is recorded that "when Confucius was hard-pressed between Chen and Cai, for seven days he had no cooked food." "He was pallid and drawn, yet sat in his room singing and playing the lute." When his disciples expressed concern, he said, "When the cold weather comes and snow and frost fall, this is how I understand the luxuriance of the pine and cypress." This has a similar meaning as the passage that says, "Do not think to deprive an ordinary person of his will" (9.26). It is only the harsh environment of severe cold, ice, and snow that can truly display the tenacious spirit of a noble will. In the original, the phrase "late to fade" 後凋 should be understood to mean "does not fade" 不凋. The ancients used "late" in place of "not" to make the diction more graceful and restrained. The use of objects in nature to suggest human affairs or moral character, employing emotion-laden poetic language (aesthetics), is one of the characteristics of Chinese culture and literature and the concrete outworking of the analogical association discussed above. In China, to this day the pine tree appears in numerous poems and paintings. Here, it is not the suffering (winter cold) itself but rather the ability to withstand and overcome suffering that produces this appreciative eulogy. This is precisely what differentiates China's culture of delight from the Russian idea that "suffering is salvation; it is where joy is found." Kant had what he called the "moral symbol"; but in China, the use of the pine and cypress to symbolize tenacity of spirit adopts a positive emotional attitude in order to inspire people, and in this way enters a deeper, supermoral aesthetic realm of reality, viz., the emotional assurance of a foundational reality: people participate in the unity of nature and the cosmos that the pine and cypress represent. Clearly, this ultimate reality can be perceived, understood, and intuited equally in everyday life as in art. "How to live," "why to live," and "in what manner to live," are here melded into one and difficult to distinguish.

Max Weber believed that the religious condition resided in the quality of the non-everyday, the uncommon. China uses aesthetics instead of religion to attain this highest reality and can do so in the midst of the everyday and the common, including the concern with suffering ("winter"). All the moral categories, whether humaneness, reverence, sincerity, or solemnity, have this aesthetic feeling, and therefore what [Chinese] put their faith in is not a severe god that is to be feared, but life itself, with its emotions ("Heaven, Earth, country, family, teacher"). In other words, they have faith in the ability of the human race to endure eternally like Heaven and Earth and to tend toward the Good (the Dao). What [I] call "storing up goodness in beauty" *yi mei chu shan* 以美儲善, is the meaning of "pine and cypress do not wither." Wen Tianxiang (1236–1283), in his lines "Only when duty is fulfilled / Is humaneness perfected" 惟其義盡, 所以仁至 and "In reading the works of the sages, / To what purpose is this study" 讀聖賢書, 所學何事,[11] very penetratingly captures the relationship between the sense of responsibility (*yi*, duty) and the sense of Heaven and Earth (*ren*, humaneness), between morality (duty) and emotion (humaneness). Wen Tianxiang completed this relationship through strenuous practice, attaining perfect beauty and sageliness through consummate greatness and strength. In this we see that he is a paragon of the ancient Chinese tradition.

9.29. 子曰:「知者不惑, 仁者不憂, 勇者不懼。」

Confucius said, "The intelligent person is not perplexed; the humane person does not worry; the courageous person is not afraid."

Comments: "The humane person does not worry" is the culture of delight [speaking]. The other two phrases are easy to understand, and actually are almost repetitive, though not quite. For what the last phrase ("is not afraid") describes is a psychological state. If we analogize from these two phrases, then "humane" should also [be taken to] describe a kind of state of spiritual delight. Clearly, to regard a "consciousness of suffering" as encapsulating Confucianism or Chinese culture would be to greatly miss the mark. Clearly, on the one hand there is "does not worry" (*bu you* 不憂), but on the other hand there are many things to "worry" (*you* 憂) about (as we see often in the *Analects*); this last should be taken to indicate "concern" and not "worry." The same can be said of "anxieties" (*huan* 患): one is not to worry about external profit or loss, glory or shame, but rather about one's own moral advancement and cultivation, one's private religious morality. What the *Shenjian* 申鑒 speaks of is especially appropriate to politicians: If a high official is not selfish, what does he have to fear?[12] Private religious morality should guide public social morality.

9.30. 子曰:「可與共學, 未可與適道; 可與適道, 未可與立; 可與立, 未可與權。

Confucius said, "There are those with whom one can study, but not necessarily walk the same path; there are those with whom one can walk the same path, but not necessarily uphold the same principles; there are those with whom one may uphold the same principles, but not necessarily be able to have the same degree of flexibility."

Comments: The words *jing* 經 and *quan* 權 present great difficulties in the field of Confucian studies. I believe they should best be translated as "principle" and "flexibility," as I have explained earlier [see 9.3]. How to handle these two concepts is what they call the "art of leadership," or the "art of being human," that is, grasping the "proper measure" appropriate to a particular concrete circumstance is what we really mean by the "Way" (or the Dao). The word *li* 立 (literally, "to stand") means to establish or set up. For example, "Be established in the rites" has to do with the realm of principle, or *jing*. Cheng Yi argued that "*Quan* is just the same as *jing*" 權只是經, thus denying the basic value or significance of *quan* ("flexibility"). Song-Ming Neo-Confucians loved vain arguments about nature and Principle (*li* 理), and did not know how to adapt to real life; they held rigidly to tenets, but did not know how to be flexible. Many of them were pedantic and inept, incompetent to accomplish anything. Meanwhile, schemers and politicians only emphasize adaptability and flexibility, considering only profit or loss, without regard for principles, to the point that there is nothing they will not do; yet these are often the ones who are sure to succeed, who accomplish their goals, and whose success is praised by later generations. This is yet another manifestation of the contradiction between ethicism and historicism. In the question of how to grasp the relationship between principle and flexibility, there is both principle and flexibility.

Flexibility (*quan*) has to do with individuality; it is an outworking and manifestation of individual freedom and autonomy. Because it means flexibility, it cannot be made into a universally applied tenet. As Zhao Qi 趙岐 commented in his commentary on the *Mencius*, "Flexibility (*quan*) is something that goes against principle (*jing*) and yet is good." Or as the *Hanshi waizhuan* has it, "The constant is called principle; what changes is called flexibility. Embrace the constant principle [of the Dao] and hold to its change and flexibility, and you will become a sage." It is very difficult to grasp—indeed, it is an art—just how this individual mastery of flexibility in use may "go against" or not "go against" (principle)—that is, the appropriate "proper measure." Confucians do not emphasize an absolute unchanging law or formal principles, but rather what is "constant" and what is "changing," the unity of "principle" and "flexibility." Furthermore, "flexibility" is closer to the Dao than "principle," for the Dao must rely on flexibility in order to be put into practice. The emphasis is still upon practice and pragmatics, for this is "pragmatic reason." Today, more than ever, we should pay attention to this individual, flexible initiative aspect of Confucianism, in contradistinction to the Song-Ming Neo-Confucians who emphasized principled ethical norms (*jing*) over flexibility (*quan*).

9.31. 「唐棣之華, 偏其反而。豈不爾思? 室是遠而。」子曰: 「未之思也, 夫何遠之有? 」

"Ah, the rose! / It sways forward and back again; / How could I not miss you? / It is that you live too far away!" Confucius said, "He does not really miss her, or what barrier would distance be?"

Comments: This passage has always been said to be difficult to understand, so it is best to translate it literally. The first four lines are lines of an ancient poem, and in the latter lines Confucius elaborates on the poem. If something sways forward and back again, one has never truly held onto it; otherwise, "if any person truly desires [humaneness], it will come" (*Analects* 7.30), so why should one fear distance?

Book 10

10.1. 孔子於鄉黨，恂恂如也，似不能言者。其在宗廟朝廷，便便言，唯謹爾。朝，與下大夫言，侃侃如也；與上大夫言，誾誾如也。君在，踧踖如也。與與如也。

When Confucius was in his home village, he was respectful and submissive, modest and unassuming, as if unable to speak. In the ancestral temple or at court, he spoke eloquently, but with circumspection.

At court, he spoke freely and frankly with his peers; with those above him in rank, he spoke gently and with respect; when he was with the ruler, he was reverent and alert, with a solemn bearing.

Notes: *Liu Baonan notes: The Master served Lu as vice minister of works and vice minister of justice, so he was a lower level official.*

Kang Youwei notes: What a contrast with what we see when people act proudly around their fellow villagers but are slow to speak when at court. This records the differences in how Confucius spoke and carried himself in the village, at the ancestral temple, and at court.

Comments: This chapter of the *Analects* has to do with various aspects of Confucius's public and private life, from his eating and drinking to his lodging. The only thing it leaves aside is his sex life. Ancient Greece had all kinds of sexual handbooks, and China also had its "Art of Peng Tzu and the Palace Woman" 彭祖御女術, but Confucians did not transmit such things, which would seem to be quite an omission. For if the Confucians had been able to transmit this aspect of things, due to the restraints of pragmatic reason, they would have avoided both the preposterous or fantastic and the asceticism of later Neo-Confucians. The reason they did not pass this down is that there were no rituals surrounding sexual arts. What this chapter records is Confucius's behavior and comportment, his attitude and expressions in the carrying out of ritual. The passages touch upon many aspects of the ceremonial system. Historical studies of these have proliferated over the years, but these have little meaning for us today and I will not discuss them here.

This passage records Confucius's words and attitudes when he was among various different kinds of people. On first examination, this passage seems almost comical. Why should one's speech and posture be different toward different classes of people? This is due to the fact that these are the rationalized traces of ritual, taboos, and so on, that evolved from various shamanistic ceremonies. Actually, even today we still speak differently toward our boss than toward our colleagues. Confucius was simply dutifully following the standardized ritual system that had evolved in ancient times from shamanism. Today we have the bureaucrats who fawn on those above and are rude to those below, just as Kang Youwei noted above. It is a shame.

10.2. 君召使擯, 色勃如也, 足躩如也。揖所與立, 左右手。衣前後, 襜如也。趨進, 翼如也。賓退, 必復命曰: 「賓不顧矣。」

When the ruler ordered him to receive an outside visitor, his expression immediately became serious, and he picked up his steps. He would bow and salute those standing opposite him, both to the left and to the right. His gown would float forward and back, all very proper. He would walk quickly, like a bird with its wings open. When the guest left, he would come back to report, saying, "The guest is no longer turning back his head."

Comments: This passage tells of Confucius's demeanor when put in charge of receiving outside guests. The last sentence says that he would not return himself until the guest had passed so far away that he no longer turned back his head to say goodbye. This shows his discretion and courtesy. How to treat guests was one of the important rituals of ancient times. This passage shows that Confucius conscientiously carried out the details of ritual prescriptions; its meaning is to show how ritual is the sacred ceremony of everyday life (here I am following Herbert Fingarette, who uses the example of shaking hands in the West in a very interesting manner).[1] It is because they are sacred that these ritual prescriptions are treated with such seriousness and strictness. Fingarette, however, does not explain that the reason the ritual system was so sacred comes from its origins in primitive shamanistic ritual.

10.3. 入公門, 鞠躬如也, 如不容。立不中門, 行不履閾。過位, 色勃如也, 足躩如也, 其言似不足者。攝齊升堂, 鞠躬如也, 屏氣似不息者。出, 降一等, 逞顏色, 怡怡如也。沒階趨進, 翼如也。復其位, 踧踖如也。

When Confucius entered the ruler's great hall, he would bow at the waist, as if feeling himself unworthy.

He would not stand in the center of the great hall, and would not allow his foot to touch the threshold.

When he walked up to the ruler's seat, his expression would grow serious, his steps would quicken, and he would appear to be speechless.

He would mount the steps to the dais holding the hem of his garment, bowing, and would breathe quietly, refraining from panting.

When he came out again, he would walk down one step, and relax his countenance, with a kind of comfortable, happy appearance.

When he had come all the way down the steps, he would walk quickly forward, like a bird stretching its wings.

He would return to his place, adopting a respectful and alert manner.

When carrying a ceremonial jade tablet, he would bend over, as if unable to rise due to his burden. Raising it higher, he would seem to be making obeisance; lowering it, he would seem to be offering to hand it over. His demeanor would be serious, with fear and trembling. He would take small, compact steps, as if [following] a straight line.

When presenting a gift, his face would be attentive and correct.

At a private audience, he would be relaxed and happy.

Comments: The line I have translated, "breathe quietly, refraining from panting," is usually translated as "hold his breath, as if not breathing," but I think this goes too far—it is not as if he were swimming underwater! Reading this passage, it is no wonder that young people would be contemptuous of Confucius. This cringing and servile posture is most unsightly to modern eyes. It is a bit like the later description of people "treating the ruler like a tiger," which does not seem right for the era of Confucius. In fact, this is the ritual system (that arose from the ceremonial reverence due to the clan leader or tribal ruler under the patriarchal system), which Confucius faithfully performed, and his disciples faithfully recorded.

Are these "small, compact steps" like those we still see among Japanese women today? In sum, this is a type of ceremonial bearing that displays respect and reverence. This passage shows how earnest and sincere, how full of grave reverence, was Confucius's unstintingly rigorous obedience to the movements, behavior, speech, and postures of the Zhou ritual system. This is because of the origins of ritual in shamanism—it is the product of the systematization and rationalization of primitive shamanistic ceremony—and it retained and sedimented these characteristics. Ritual is about performing or following (*lü* 履), following the footsteps of the shaman. Thus, any posture, language, or movement had a solemn sacredness. This is the kind of reverence and seriousness Confucius brought to his duties, so that when "carrying a ceremonial jade tablet, he would . . . [be] as if unable to rise due to his burden."

10.4. 君子不以紺緅飾。紅紫不以為褻服。當暑, 袗絺綌, 必表而出之。緇衣羔裘, 素衣麑裘, 黃衣狐裘。褻裘長。短右袂。必有寢衣, 長一身有半。狐貉之厚以居。去喪, 無所不佩。非帷裳, 必殺之。羔裘玄冠不以弔。吉月, 必朝服而朝。

The noble person does not use black in his collars or the trim of his sleeves, nor does he use red or purple in his everyday clothing.

In summer, he wears a simple undershirt and is sure to put on an outer garment before leaving the house.

He pairs black clothes with dark lambskin, white clothes with deerskin, and yellow clothes with fox fur.

The leather robe he wears at home is somewhat longer, but the right sleeve is somewhat shorter.

For his quilt he will be certain to have one that measures one and half times his height.

He sits upon a cushion of fox fur or a similar thick fur.

At the conclusion of a period of ritual mourning, he does not prohibit himself from any ornament or style of dress.

Apart from garments for attendance at court or the ceremonial offerings, his garments are cut and sewn.

He does not wear dark lambskin or wear a black hat to pay a condolence call.

On the first of every month, he puts on his ceremonial robes and offers his respects at court.

Comments: This passage treats the ritual aspects of Confucius's dress. In China, the color white is for mourning, and black is a positive color. Red and purple are precious colors used by the ruler, and could not be used freely. Ritual is characterized by "separation," the separation into various ranks and orders, in order to demonstrate who is higher, lower, on the left and on the right, who is respected or looked down upon, noble or base. Thus, even colors were differentiated in this way. From ancient times all the way down to the early twentieth century, every action or behavior, even including what one could wear, was closely controlled, leaving aside no realm of social life, whether public or private. This was excessively restricting. This is rare in other cultures and again can be traced to ancient shamanistic ceremony. Thus any "rebelliousness" in dress can be said to be a modern trend. Such movements appeared in both the late Ming and late Qing periods.

10.5. 齊, 必有明衣, 布。齊, 必變食, 居必遷坐。

When fasting, he is sure to wear a bathrobe made of cotton.

When fasting, he changes his food and drink, and changes where he sleeps.

Comments: When fasting, one had to bathe, and therefore one would have a bathrobe. It had to be of cotton, just as one ate vegetables and abstained from sexual relations, and so on, in order to restrict one's enjoyments and luxuries in a demonstration of one's sincerity, reverence, and awe. This is another remnant of ancient shamanistic rites. For Confucians, "respect" and "reverence" always retained this sort of ascetic religious character, which developed into the well-known Song-Ming Neo-Confucian theory, "extinguish human desire, uphold Heavenly Principle" 滅人欲, 存天理.

10.6. 食不厭精, 膾不厭細。食饐而餲, 魚餒而肉敗, 不食。色惡, 不食。臭惡, 不食。失飪, 不食。不時, 不食。割不正, 不食。不得其醬, 不食。肉雖多, 不使勝食氣。惟酒無量，不及亂。沽酒市脯不食。不撤薑食。不多食。祭於公，不宿肉。祭肉不出三日。出三日，不食之矣。食不語，寢不言。雖疏食菜羹，瓜祭，必齊如也。席不正，不坐。

He does not mind his rice being polished, or his fish or meat being cut fine.

He does not eat rice or vegetables that have gone sour, or meat or fish that has spoiled. If something has changed color or begun to stink, he does not eat it. If something is not completely cooked or is not yet in season, he does not eat it. If it is not butchered properly or not seasoned appropriately, he does not eat it.

Even if meat is plentiful, he does not overeat.

Although he does not limit his wine, he does not get drunk.

He will not drink wine that has been left overnight, or eat meat that is sold on the street.

He does not refrain from eating ginger, but does not eat very much of it.

When taking part in state sacrifices, the sacrificed meat should not be left until the next day. The sacrificial meat of one's own family should not be left to the third day; after the three days it should not be eaten.

When eating he does not converse; when someone is sleeping he does not talk.

Even if he is offering only coarse rice, vegetable soup, and melons, he is sure to abstain beforehand.

If the mat is not positioned correctly, he does not sit.

Notes: *Li Baonan notes: After three days, the meat is not edible. Wang Shiliu in the "Lunyi Zhengyi" quotes Ren Qiyun: While eating, one's mind is on the food, one does not have the ability to think about other things; this is everyday reality, therefore it is recorded. As for the ritual of eating together with others, is there not the language of acceptance, refusal, and deference? Confucius says when fasting one is to be serious and respectful in mien. Though these three [food items] are meager, in offering them one must be reverent. The "Quli" [section of the "Liji"] says: When the host kneels to adjust the mats (of a visitor), the other should kneel and keep hold of them, declining (the honor).*[2]

*Kang Youwei notes: Wine is for bringing people pleasure in company, and therefore it is not measured or limited. It is said, "One dipper and already drunk," or "One measure and already drunk," but this is speaking of a moderate drunkenness and not chaos. The lungs are the lord of the breath (*qi 氣*), and the throat has the windpipe through which sound passes. When sleeping and eating, the* qi *is obstructed and does not circulate, so speaking then may* *do someone harm. When the ancients ate or drank, each type of food would be brought out in small amounts. It would be arranged in a very small space. In the sacrifices, the previous generations would be served first, in order not to forget the root. The sacrifices in India today are the same.* Qi 齊 *means reverent in appearance. Even when Confucius had only paltry items he would still sacrifice, and his sacrifice was always reverent; this is the sage's sincerity.*

Comments: The previous passage addressed dress; this passage addresses food. These are Confucius's regulations for eating and drinking. Later Confucians read the first two lines in exactly the opposite way, so as to say that Confucius did not care about whether his food was polished or fine, reading *yan* 厭 as *yan* 饜 ("full" or "satisfied"), thus, "He would eat [fine food] but not to the point of being overfull." This is also a possible reading. For the *Analects* does have many passages such as "To eat coarse grain, and drink fresh water" (7.16); "A bowl of rice, a gourd of water" (6.11); or, "The intellectual . . . [who is] ashamed of coarse clothing or plain food is not worth seeking out for a discussion" (4.9). The passage as a whole records how particular Confucius was about food and drink and one's manner of living; this is a concrete expression of the weight Confucianism places upon life. Most of these statements would today be regarded as having to do with safety or health benefits. As for the idea of being "not butchered properly," there are many interpretations, none of which makes much sense. Here I have translated it ambiguously. The original may have referred to a sick animal—it is impossible to know. Wine that has been left overnight, or not eating meat from the marketplace, like the prohibition against eating sacrificial meat after three days, probably had to do with cleanliness and the avoidance of illness. The frequent consumption of ginger may possibly have been in order to avoid catching cold, or to kill bacteria? The most important line of the passage is "Although he does not limit his wine, he does not get drunk." This has seemingly become a characteristic of Chinese tradition. Those who drink alcohol are not a few, nor are those who get drunk, but there are very few drunken brawls or drunks on the street corners, because there is an emphasis on self-control that does not allow for a total lack of restraint but rather holds "tipsiness" in high regard. This is why I have called China's a "non-Dionysian" culture (see my book *The Chinese Aesthetic Tradition*).

The rest of these ritual prescriptions and descriptions of Confucius's behavior seem more universally recognized, like "When eating he does not converse; when someone is sleeping he does not talk," which avoids negatively influencing digestion or sleep, but is certainly not absolute, as the above Note indicates (can one urge a guest to eat without speaking?). As far as Confucius's speech and actions go, and the entire *Analects* for that matter, if a book is to be blindly obeyed, it would be better for there to be no book. The sacrificial meat served at state sacrifices will necessarily have sat longer than that served at home, therefore it should be consumed more quickly, and so on. As for not sitting if the "seat cushion is not positioned correctly," or needing to abstain before offering melons, these are all ritual prescriptions.

10.7. 鄉人飲酒, 杖者出, 斯出矣。鄉人儺, 朝服而立於阼階。

When eating and drinking with his fellow villagers, he waits for the older men to leave first, then leaves himself. If his fellow villagers are carrying out shamanistic ceremonies, he puts on his ritual clothing and stands on the eastern steps.

Comments: This passage again treats Confucius's manner and attitude when in his village. The *Liji* "Xiang yin jiu yi" chapter also records various detailed prescriptions for honoring the elders, and is worth consulting here.[3]

Exorcisms (*nuo* 儺) are still today practiced in remote regions of Hunan and Guizhou. These shamanistic ceremonies of expelling demons and welcoming the gods, preventing disasters and praying for blessing, are remnants in folk tradition of the ancient shamanistic-historical culture. Without claiming that Confucius believed in the efficacy of witchcraft, he did demonstrate an attitude of respect and reverence for the villagers, along the lines of his injunction to "respect the gods and spirits while keeping a distance from them" (6.22).

10.8. 問人於他邦, 再拜而送之。康子饋藥, 拜而受之。曰: 「丘未達, 不敢嘗。

When he was sending someone to ask after a friend in another state, he would send the person off by bowing twice at the waist and saluting. Kangzi once sent him a gift of medicine. He received it, bowing low, and said, "I don't understand the nature of medicines, so I dare not take them."

Comments: Bowing twice indicated he was relying upon the person, and thanking him. Some read the last phrase, 未敢嘗, as saying that he does not take medicine willy-nilly.

10.9. 廄焚。子退朝, 曰: 「傷人乎?」不問馬。

The horse stables burned down. When Confucius had returned from the court, he asked, "Was anyone injured?" He did not ask after the horses.

Comments: Some commentators read the last line as "'Was anyone injured?' 'No.' He then asked after the horses." In other words, after asking after the injured persons, if there were none, he asked after the horses. This is an intelligent reading. Some say this reading is influenced by Buddhism, but this is not necessarily the case. Confucians also can apply [the principle] "first people, then things" (*you ren ji wu* 由人及物).[4]

10.10. 君賜食, 必正席先嘗。君賜腥, 必熟而薦之。君賜生, 必畜之。侍食於君, 君祭, 先飯。疾, 君視之, 東首, 加朝服, 拖紳。君命召, 不俟駕行矣。

If the ruler sends him something to eat, he is sure to straighten his mat and taste it first. If the ruler sends raw meat, he will certainly cook it and then offer it to the ancestors. If he sends livestock, he will keep it to raise.

If he is waiting on the ruler at his meal, when the ruler is sacrificing, he will first set out the food.

If he is sick and the ruler comes to inquire after him, he will lie with his head facing east, and lay his ritual attire atop himself, with the great sash he wears for attending at court.

If the ruler summons him, he will not wait for the horse and carriage to arrive, but will immediately set out by walking.

Comments: This passage again records various "official rituals" that Confucius carried out in his behavior toward his ruler. For example, he "does not wait for the horse and carriage to arrive," but begins walking himself, so as to make the driver of the carriage catch up to him, in order to act immediately and thus demonstrate reverence and respect for the lord's order; this is a concrete expression of the so-called "fear of rulers and great men" 畏大人 (16.8). "Fear" is also a kind of "ritual." When sick, he would be unable to get dressed, but would still set out his court attire, laying on his sash of office in order to demonstrate his status. "Fear" should not be understood as simple terror or fright, but rather as the extreme respect for and seriousness toward any great responsibility, duty, or "great person" (of which the ruler is the objectified or personified representation) that one "fears" one's own inability to bear. It is, in other words, the expression of a proper regard for one's own limitations. These [descriptions] are far more concrete and real than empty remarks about "limitations" or some such.

10.11. 入大廟，每事問。

When Confucius entered the great temple, he would ask about everything.

Notes: *Cheng Shude notes: This is a repeated passage. [See 3.15.]*

10.12 朋友死，無所歸。曰：「於我殯。」朋友之饋，雖車馬，非祭肉，不拜。

If his friend died, and there was no one to do the laying out, he would say, "I will take responsibility for the funeral."

If a friend sent him a present, even if it were a horse and carriage, unless it was meat for a sacrificial offering, he would not do obeisance.

Comments: This demonstrates Confucius's manner of friendship: he emphasized the depth of emotion, and valued principle. In presents, he valued the meaning, not the expense or number of things. Because sacrificial meat had to do with the ancestors, it was ritually weighty, and therefore he would bow.

10.13 寢不尸，居不客。

When he slept, he would not lie on his back; when he sat, he would not cross his legs.

Comments: When he slept, he would lie on his side, not straight as a corpse. The second half of this passage has many interpretations. Here I have read it to mean that he did not feel the need to sit as if he were a guest, since in ancient times the proper way to sit on a mat on the floor was cross-legged. Perhaps when one was a guest one would adopt this posture, which was of course not very comfortable. Some have adopted the alternate reading, 居不容, "when at home he did not relax," which is more difficult to explain, and which I have not followed here.

10.14. 見齊衰者, 雖狎, 必變。見冕者與瞽者, 雖褻, 必以貌。凶服者式之。式負版者。有盛饌, 必變色而作。迅雷風烈, 必變。

When he saw someone in mourning for his or her parents, even if it was someone he normally was close to, he would be sure to change his expression. If he met someone wearing a formal cap or a blind person, even if it was someone he met often, he would be sure to act politely.

If he met someone dressed for a funeral, he would bow from his carriage and demonstrate reverence; he would greet someone carrying state documents in the same manner.

When seated at a sumptuous banquet, he would be sure to change his expression and give his compliments. If there was strong thunder or a great wind, he would be sure to change his countenance (as he stood or sat).

Comments: All these are ritual prescriptions. Among them, the statement that "when seated as a sumptuous banquet, he would be sure to change his expression and give his compliments" is very interesting. There are probably vestiges of this today. And it is very natural: in order to express one's thanks or for the sake of politeness, one will "change one's countenance."

10.15. 升車, 必正立執綏。車中, 不內顧, 不疾言, 不親指

When he entered a carriage: he would be sure to stand straight and hold onto the handrail.

Within the carriage: he would not turn his head to look inside, talk loudly, or point at things.

Comments: This would seem to have to do with safety, and yet it is a ritual prescription! At the time, entering a carriage would have been an important action, and therefore it had to be treated with seriousness. The point of this chapter is to show that in his everyday life, Confucius solemnly carried out the whole body of ritual prescriptions. This by itself has religious-moral educational implications, as it demonstrates a solemn, sincere, and reverent attitude toward everyday life and human life.

10.16 色斯舉矣, 翔而後集。曰: 「山梁雌雉, 時哉! 時哉! 」子路共之, 三嗅而作。

A bird was startled, flew around for a while and then alighted again. [Confucius?] said, "The wild pheasants here on this hillside—it is definitely their time! Definitely their time!" Zilu went to approach it, and after shying away many times, it flew away.

Comments: This passage has always been difficult or impossible to elucidate. Yang Bojun once remarked, "This passage is very difficult to interpret, and since ancient times no satisfactory explanation has been put forward. Many people suspect there may be mistakes or omissions." My translation here is a stretch. Yet the flight of pheasants and Confucius's sighing remark still make a remarkable tableau. Could the very lack of an explanation perhaps provide us an interesting interpretation to ponder?

Book 11

11.1. 子曰:「先進於禮樂, 野人也; 後進於禮樂, 君子也。如用之, 則吾從先進。」

Confucius said, "The first to carry out the rites and music tradition were the Yin people, who lived outside the cities. Those who adopted the tradition later were the noble people who today live within the cities. If I wanted to put it into practice, I would follow the former."

Comments: The meaning of this passage is difficult to understand, and there are many interpretations. One is that although the "rites and music" of the [literally] "wild people" *yeren* 野人 [here rendered "the Yin people"]) may have been coarse or vulgar, yet it was primary. The "noble people" (*junzi* 君子) may have been more elegant, but they were subsequent or secondary. Confucius venerated the ancients, and thus would choose to follow those who "came first." In the Spring and Autumn Period, there arose a distinction between states (cities) and the wild (the countryside). Those who did not belong to the Zhou aristocracy, including immigrants from the Yin, lived outside the cities, and thus were [considered] "wild people." Confucius always "followed the Zhou," and praised the rites of the Zhou, so why in this passage would he say he follows those [wild people] who came before? There is no explanation. Perhaps the rites carried out by the noble people of his day had already changed?

Perhaps, in order to connect this passage with our modern situation, we should take all the sources and traditions of various cultures and temporarily cast them aside, to seek a "reasonable" common denominator to form society's systems of government and morality. It must be that this lowest common denominator can be found in the "wild people," who were the "first to carry out" [the rites]. This interpretation, of course, does not accord with the "original intent" of the text, yet today it seems quite important.

There are also those who interpret "first" and "later" as referring to "earlier and later disciples," which has the advantage of connecting up with the next passage (11.2). In this case, the end of the passage would read "if I were to recommend [for office]," meaning that Confucius would recommend the older disciples like Zilu. This reading seems more straightforward and easier to understand.

11.2. 子曰:「從我於陳、蔡者, 皆不及門也。德行: 顏淵, 閔子騫, 冉伯牛, 仲弓。言語: 宰我, 子貢。政事: 冉有, 季路。文學: 子游, 子夏。」

Confucius said, "Of those disciples who followed me in Chen and Cai, today there are none left here. Excelling in virtuous conduct were Yan Hui, Min Ziqian, Ran Boniu, and Zhonggong. Able in diplomacy were Zai Wo and Zigong. Able in government were Ran You and Zilu. Fluent in ritual ceremony and offerings were Ziyou and Zixia."

Notes: *Zhu Xi notes: Confucius experienced difficulties in Chen and Cai, and of the many disciples who followed him, none are there any longer. Therefore, in thinking of them Confucius is not likely to forget those who followed him into difficulty.*

Comments: When Confucius was "short of provisions" in Chen, or "in difficulties" in Cai, these were very difficult and dangerous moments. Confucius was inclined to recollect and was oriented toward the past; he could not help himself. Zai Wo was strongly scolded by Confucius repeatedly, but here Confucius fondly remembers and praises him. This passage also has other possible interpretations, most dividing it into two sections; here I follow Zhu Xi, who united it into a single passage, in order to emphasize the emotion behind the relation of these well-known names, "not forgetting those who followed him into difficulty." The term *wenxue* 文學 does not refer, as it does later, to literature, but largely to learning about the ritual and ceremonial systems.

Looking backward in time can unite the past, present, and future into one, and interweave ancient times with modern, [arousing] many feelings, and from this one can find continual sources of encouragement in one's efforts to improve oneself. As Lu Xun's poem for his son demonstrates, even revolutionaries valued the emotions of feudal relationships:

> 無情未必真豪傑,
> 怜子如何不丈夫?
> 知否興風狂嘯者,
> 回眸時看小於菟。

> The ruthless are not necessarily the true heroes,
> Are not those that cherish their sons also great men?
> Don't you know that the one that growls so fiercely as to
> rouse the wind
> Turns back now and then to look at his cubs?

11.3. 子曰:「回也非助我者也, 於吾言無所不說。」

Confucius said, "Yan Hui is not someone who helps or benefits me; he happily assents to everything I say."

Notes: *Zhu Xi notes: "One who is of help to me," as Zixia advocates, is one who learns and grows by means of asking questions [see 19.6]. Yan Hui eagerly accepts all the Sage's words without question, therefore the Master speaks thus. Though his words seem to treat this as a matter for regret, yet he actually appreciates [Yan Hui] deeply.*

Comments: It is just as Zhu Xi comments. Confucius expresses regret yet seems to deeply appreciate him. Wang Yangming said something similar. Learning (*xuewen* 學問) [involves] study (*xue* 學) and questioning (*wen* 問); it is in asking many questions that learning is extended, to the benefit of both teacher and disciple.

11.4. 子曰:「孝哉閔子騫! 人不間於其父母昆弟之言。」

Confucius said, "Min Ziqian truly is filial! Others cannot but agree with what his parents and brothers have to say of him."

Notes: *Liu Baonan relates a story from the "Yiwen leiju" chapter on "Filiality," quoting from the "Shuo Yuan"* 說苑*:*[1] *Min Ziqian was one of two brothers. His mother had died, and his father had remarried, then had another two sons. Ziqian was driving a chariot for his father when he lost his hold of the reins. His father, holding his hand, [discovered that] his clothing was very thin. His father returned and called his second wife's sons, and taking them by the hand, saw that their clothing was very thick and warm. He said to his wife, "I married you for the sake of my son, but today you have cheated me," and wanted to throw her out. Ziqian said, "If mother stays, one son's clothing is thin, but if she leaves four sons will suffer the cold." His father fell silent. This is why Confucius says, "Min Ziqian truly is filial!" . . . The "Hanshi waizhuan" version of the story says: The mother subsequently repented, and became exceedingly fair, and thus a loving mother.*

Comments: The story quoted above is both concrete and accurate.

11.5. 南容三復白圭, 孔子以其兄之子妻之。

Nan Rong frequently recited the poem [from the *Book of Songs*] on the white jade scepter. Confucius gave him his niece in marriage.

Notes: *Zhu Xi notes: The poem "Yi" from the Greater Odes section of the "Book of Songs" says, "A scratch on a sceptre of white jade / Can be polished away; / A slip of the tongue / Cannot ever be repaired"* 白圭之玷、尚可磨也。斯言之玷、不可為也。[2] *Nan Rong recited this three times a day, as mentioned in the "Family Sayings" [of Confucius]* 家語. *Clearly, he must have been deeply concerned about the integrity of his speech. . . . If Nan Rong was this concerned about the integrity of his speech, he must also have had integrity in his actions.*

Comments: The word "three" in the original means many times. The poem on the white jade scepter, as the Note explains above, warns of being careful in one's speech. In popular parlance we have sayings like "Disaster proceeds from the mouth" 禍從口出, "When once the command has been uttered, a team of four horses is difficult to call back" 一言既出, 駟馬難追, and so on. See also 5.2, where it is clear how very prudent

Nan Rong is in speech and action; he is extremely steady, and not likely to meet with mishap.

11.6. 季康子問:「弟子孰為好學?」孔子對曰:「有顏回者好學, 不幸短命死矣! 今也則亡。」

Ji Kangzi asked, "Who among your disciples loves study?" Confucius answered, "There is one called Yan Hui who loved study, but unfortunately his life was cut short, and today there is no one."

Notes: *Liu Baonan quotes Huang Kan's "Lunyu yishu": This is similar to the answer to Duke Ai [in 6.3]. Commentators have explained the differences in the answers in two ways. The first is to suggest that because Duke Ai would "become angry with others" and "repeat the same mistakes," Confucius used his answer to admonish him. Since Kangzi did not have these faults, he did not bother to mention them.*

Comments: The translation follows the original almost word for word, there is no need for explanation. That Chinese written language can be understandable after the passage of two thousand years is indeed a miracle.

11.7. 顏淵死, 顏路請子之車以為之椁。子曰:「才不才, 亦各言其子也。鯉也死, 有棺而無椁。吾不徒行以為之椁。以吾從大夫之後, 不可徒行也。」

When Yan Hui died, his father Yan Lu asked that Confucius's chariot be sold in order to buy the outer coffin. Confucius said, "Whether or not he was talented, he was still your son. Even when my son Li died, he had only an inner coffin, and no outer coffin. I cannot sell my chariot and get around by walking in order to buy him an outer coffin, because I have held high office, and cannot go about by walking."

Comments: Probably according to the ritual system, one who has served in office could not "go about by walking" any longer, just as we see today, unfortunately. Confucius's defense of aristocratic position, ritual systems, and status was actually quite different from what we see in Mozi and Zhuangzi. Even though this passage has to do with his favorite disciple, he is not willing to sacrifice his "principledness." This "principledness" should be seen as belonging to the public regulations of the day, that is, to (public) social morality, while one's personal feelings belong to private morality.

11.8. 顏淵死。子曰:「噫!天喪予!天喪予!」

Yan Hui died. Confucius said, "Ah! Old Man Heaven is destroying me! Old Man Heaven is destroying me!"

Comments: The previous passage emphasizes rational principles (of the ritual system), while this passage expresses deep individual emotion. The two are not at all contradictory; one should not lose sight of principle in the name of emotion, nor should one overcome emotion with principle.

The humane person is long-lived (6.23). Yet Yan Hui, whom Confucius so often praised for his humaneness, dies young. Confucius is not only mourning for Yan Hui; he is expressing sadness for the "humane." Is this not the meaning of "Old Man Heaven is destroying me"?

11.9. 顏淵死,子哭之慟。從者曰:「子慟矣。」曰:「有慟乎?非夫人之為慟而誰為!」

Yan Hui died, and Confucius wept for him with excessive grief. Those following said, "You are grieving excessively." Confucius said, "Grieving excessively? If I do not grieve excessively for a man like this, then for whom would I?"

Comments: As above. Even if excessive grief might damage his health, Master Confucius would not care, for this matter has to do with his personal heart and not with the societal ritual system.

11.10. 顏淵死,門人欲厚葬之,子曰:「不可。」門人厚葬之。子曰:「回也視予猶父也,予不得視猶子也。非我也,夫二三子也。」

Yan Hui died, and the students wanted to bury him with rich ceremony. Confucius said, "That is not allowable." But the students still gave him a grand and solemn burial. Confucius said, "Ah Yan Hui, he treated me as a father, but I was unable to treat him as a son! This was not me, it was the students!"

Comments: Confucius very clearly distinguished between the expression of individual emotion (as in the previous passage) and the keeping of societal rites (as in this passage and 11.7). The individual cannot in the end equal society, **nor can emotion be completely submitted to reason, otherwise a person would be nothing but a machine. This is why on the one hand he permits himself to be given over to sorrowful weeping, to the point of being overly grieved, while on the other hand he opposes an overly ostentatious funeral, and staunchly upholds the ritual system. In social behavior, he upholds principle, while in matters of individual emotion, he practices flexibility.** This is why I have always advocated for the study of literature and the arts in tandem with science and politics. Any emotion—whether excessive or not, whether it is correct or "reactionary," harmonious or decadent, active or passive—can be expressed in literature and the arts, or in one's private life, with no need for reason to exercise oversight, control, or suppression. But in scholarly work, social interaction, or political activity and such, this is not necessarily the case. This is why literature and the arts give scope to the utmost freedom. For the emotions, after all, are something that rational principles cannot completely grasp or fully control. One such as Qu Yuan, who ardently pursued Confucian principles, was unable to overcome his emotion, and wept on the banks of the river, blaming Heaven and man, and died by drowning himself, yet was still the subject of unending praise among scholar-officials of later generations. Clearly, the Confucian balance between reason and emotion, or melding of desire and principle, is also a kind of ideal concept, while in reality there were many less than well-balanced or properly blended situations. And this is precisely what gives human nature or human life its blend of emotion and reason; otherwise it would be overly mechanistic and dull. Later Neo-Confucianism did not develop to this point but followed prescribed patterns, and as such turned human life into something withered and dry in the extreme.

11.11. 季路問事鬼神。子曰:「未能事人, 焉能事鬼?」敢問死。曰:「未知生, 焉知死?」

Zilu asked about how to serve the gods and spirits. Confucius said, "If you cannot serve men, how can you serve the spirits?"

"What is death?" [he asked.] Confucius answered, "If you don't understand life, how can you understand death?"

Comments: This passage is very famous and has a plethora of interpretations. In short, it demonstrates that Chinese pragmatic reason does not engage in unprofitable argument or useless discussion. Here I mean "unprofitable" or "useless" in regard to human affairs. It emphasizes the present life, this present generation, or in other words, what I have called its "this-worldly" orientation. As in other passages like "Confucius did not speak of the strange, of violence, of rebellion, or of ghosts and spirits" (7.21); "When sacrificing to the ancestors, it seems as if the ancestors are present" (3.12); "Respect the gods and spirits while keeping a distance from them" (6.22); and so on, when it comes to questions or things that transcend this world or this life, Confucius adopts the attitude that "they exist but need not be spoken of." In other words, he neither affirms nor denies them.

11.12. 閔子侍側, 誾誾如也; 子路, 行行如也; 冉有、子貢, 侃侃如也。子樂。

Min Ziqian was standing by Confucius, gentle and submissive; Zilu was resolute and upright; Ran You and Zigong were eloquent and loquacious. Confucius was very happy.

Comments: This is probably what Mencius was speaking of when he said, "He has the good fortune of having the most talented pupils in the Empire. This is the third delight" 得天下英才而教育之, 三樂也.[3] In the *Analects*, these well-known disciples, as well as the discussions and interactions between the students and their teacher, afford very vivid descriptions of their various experiences, personalities, and characteristics. Other famous classics and documents are either dominated by reasoning (including Mencius and Xunzi), imagination (as in Zhuangzi), or again stories (as in Hanfeizi), and thus lack this more accessible realistic atmosphere.

11.13. 。「若由也, 不得其死然。」

[Confucius said,] "One like Zilu I'm afraid will not meet a happy end!"

Comments: In Huang Kan's *Lunyu yishu* and other texts this appears as a separate passage. Zilu did later meet a violent death, and Confucius mourned for him profoundly.

11.14. 魯人為長府。閔子騫曰:「仍舊貫, 如之何? 何必改作?」子曰:「夫人不言, 言必有中。」

The people of Lu were rebuilding the Treasury. Min Ziqian said, "What was wrong with the way it was? Why must it be rebuilt differently?" Confucius said, "This person does not speak, but when he does, he hits the mark."

Comments: This is an opinion expressed regarding a concrete question. Later commentators have taken it to express a general principle of frugality, but this is not necessarily correct.

11.15. 子曰:「由之瑟奚為於丘之門?」門人不敬子路。子曰:「由也升堂矣, 未入於室也。」

Confucius said, "Why does Zilu bring his zither here to play?" The students therefore did not respect Zilu. Confucius said, "Zilu has already entered the hall; it is just that he has not yet entered the chamber."

Notes: *Zhu Xi quotes the "Family Sayings"* 家語*: Zilu in playing the zither had a kind of northern martial sound, which was aggressive in character and perhaps not adequately harmonious, thus this criticism.*

Cheng Shude quotes Huang Kan's "Lunyu yishu": Zilu's nature was hard, and his zither playing also bore this quality of strength. Confucius, knowing he would not enjoy a long life, would always try to restrain him.

Comments: The phrase "Ascend the hall and enter the chamber" 升堂入室 has already become an idiom. This passage shows that Confucius, after criticizing, went on to offer encouragement; in other words, Zilu had attained quite a high level, but needed to advance yet further.

11.16. 子貢問:「師與商也孰賢?」子曰:「師也過, 商也不及。」曰:「然則師愈與?」子曰:「過猶不及。」

Zigong asked, "Of Zizhang and Zixia, which is the better?" Confucius answered, "Zizhang has gone past the mark, while Zixia has not reached it." "Then Zizhang is somewhat better?" Confucius said, "Going too far is the same as not going far enough."

Comments: "Going too far is as bad as not going far enough" 過猶不及 has also become an idiomatic expression that remains in wide use today. It serves to warn against excessiveness or overdoing things, instead encouraging the grasp of "proper measure" (*du* 度).

11.17. 季氏富於周公, 而求也為之聚斂而附益之。子曰: 「非吾徒也。小子鳴鼓而攻之, 可也。」

The head of the Ji clan was even richer than the Duke of Zhou, and Ran You practiced extortion on his behalf, thus adding to his wealth. Confucius said, "He is not my student! You all may oppose him with as much fanfare as you like."

Notes: *Yang Bojun notes: The history behind this passage can be found in the "Zuozhuan," eleventh and twelfth year of the Duke of Ai. The ruler of the Ji clan wished to employ a land tax to add to his revenues, and he sent Ran Qiu [Ran You] to seek the opinion of Confucius. Confucius advocated "In giving, practice generosity; in affairs, practice moderation; in collections follow meagerness." The result was that Ran Qiu persisted in obedience to the Ji clan leader, and put the land tax system into practice. On amassing wealth through heavy taxation, the "Daxue" chapter of the "Book of Rites" says, "A clan with a hundred chariots does not employ an official who exacts heavy taxes; rather than employ such a one, they might as well employ an official who steals"* 百乘之家不畜聚斂之臣, 與其有聚斂之臣, 寧有盜臣。

Comments: This passage has to do with the shift at that time to a land tax system, on which see the account in the *Zuozhuan*, eleventh and twelfth year of the Duke of Ai. Confucius opposed new fiscal systems that were advantageous to aristocrats and disadvantageous to the common people; this is why he is in such a bad temper here.

The opposition to forced levies and cruel taxation in favor of amassing stores for the people ("make them numerous and enrich them" 庶之富之 [see 13.9]) has always been part of the Confucian tradition of thought regarding government. This has at times had a buffering or moderating effect on the government's excessive financial expropriations, severe levies and heavy taxation. A typical expression of the important function of the mutual alternation of Confucianism and Legalism in the history of Chinese political thought is the heated debate at the Han Dynasty court conference on the salt and iron monopolies (see the "Debate on Salt and Iron" 鹽鐵論), where literati of virtue and ability (Confucians) represented the "people," and the Imperial Secretary (a Legalist) represented the government. The Confucian notion of "humane government" always occupied an (apparently secondary but actually dominant) important controlling position. Even in (what Mao Zedong called) the "Qin government system followed by a hundred generations,"[4] the governing system and policies basically consisted of a centralized, authoritarian, autocratic system of imperial authority characterized by forcible oppression and exploitation. Yet the warm-hearted affection of Confucianism—with its origins in clan society, and its emphasis on "loving the people like children" 愛民如子 and "going light on taxation and corvee labor" 寬徭薄賦 and so on—always formed a necessary supplement, counterweight, and antidote to this system, serving a sort of balancing function, which manifested itself particularly in culture and thought, concepts and ideals. This constructed a tension between the ideals of Confucianism ("returning to the height of the Three Dynasties") and the regulations of the Legalists in actual government.

11.18. 柴也愚, 參也魯, 師也辟, 由也喭。子曰: 「回也其庶乎, 屢空。賜不受命, 而貨殖焉, 億則屢中。」

Gao Chai is stupid, Zengzi is dull, Zizhang is boastful, and Zilu is crude and rash.

Confucius said, "Only Yan Hui is more or less alright, and yet he is often penniless. As for Zigong, he does not accept the arrangements of 'fate' but works hard at business, and many times has actually made the mark."

Comments: Throughout the whole book of the *Analects*, Zigong and Zilu are the figures one most appreciates and likes (at least this is true for myself). In general, one is appreciated for his wisdom, and the other for his courage, while both are ordinary, real-life human beings.

If we compare them, Zigong is somewhat superior, in that wisdom is superior to courage. Others, like Ran You, Zai Wo, and so on, are also very likable, and quite unlike the dry and stiff characters of Yan Hui, Zengzi, Minzi Qian, and so on, who were so strongly commended by Confucius and the Song-Ming Neo-Confucians. If the Neo-Confucians were to rise again, they would most likely greatly deride this type of impression or evaluation. But actually, the quintessence of Confucianism is in emotion, not in nature or principle—in real-life people, not in symbols.

The phrase "does not accept the arrangements of fate" can also be understood as "does not accept the fate of Heaven" or "does not accept the commands of his teacher (Confucius)," and so on. What Confucius says here of Zigong is not at all negative, but actually seems intended to commend. For Yan Hui to refuse to accept an official position and be content with poverty and rejoice in the Way is certainly good; for Zigong to refuse official position and rely on his own talent and wits to achieve wealth is also not bad. Clearly, Confucius is not opposed to obtaining wealth through commerce, although he never advocates it directly. Actually, fate is chance, as I have already discussed. Thus, when the passage speaks of [Zigong] not accepting "the arrangements of fate," what it means is that he does not believe that chance is inevitability, but rather struggles against it; it means that he does not believe in evil, or fear spirits, but rather believes in human effort.

In this reading, I have over and over alluded to the individuality of Confucius's disciples in order to point out, on the one hand, that people's behavior is shaped by culture and thus bears a certain sedimented universality; and on the other hand, that a person's behavior has to do with his (or her) individual existence and thus bears a certain sedimented particularity. This is why within the same culture and same tradition one still finds a great variation among people. Clearly, as individuals, **people differ not only in their bodies and their physiology but also in their psychology and their emotio-rational structures. This is precisely where the creativity and vitality of the individual resides, for the notions I have spoken of as "apprehending truth through beauty" (*yi mei qi zhen* 以美啟真) and "storing up goodness in beauty" (*yi mei chu shan* 以美儲善) both emphasize the freedom of the individual spirit. Unfortunately, this aspect of the theory of sedimentation is often ignored or overlooked.**

11.19. 子張問善人之道。子曰:「不踐跡, 亦不入於室。」
Zizhang asked how a person could be made good. Confucius said, "If you do not follow in the footsteps, you will not be able to enter the room."

Notes: *Zhu Xi notes: The good person is one whose nature is beautiful and not one who has learned [goodness]. Chengzi says, To follow in the footsteps means to stay on the path and follow the ruts.*

Comments: This can also be translated so as to suggest that the "way" (*dao*) administered by the "good person" will teach people to follow in the footsteps of the sages. If we simply take "goodness" (*shan* 善) here as a verb, does that not make it more concise and to the point? I do not agree with Zhu Xi; where does he get this "good person" who "has not learned"? Nowhere in the *Analects* is the term "good person" used in this sense. Zhai Hao's *Sishu kao yi* says, "The good person's inborn nature may be beautiful, but if he does not put it into practice, he will not reach the profound mysteries." This emphasis on "practice" also accords with Confucius's meaning.

11.20. 子曰:「論篤是與, 君子者乎? 色莊者乎?」

Confucius said, "If someone is praised as honest and sincere, the question is whether he is a true noble person (*junzi*) or is only pretending."

Comments: There are too many who pretend, and today they do not even pretend. To be honest and sincere is practically to be a laughingstock, alas!

11.21. 子路問:「聞斯行諸?」子曰:「有父兄在, 如之何其聞斯行之?」冉有問:「聞斯行諸?」子曰:「聞斯行之。」公西華曰:「由也問聞斯行諸, 子曰『有父兄在』; 求也問聞斯行諸, 子曰『聞斯行之』。赤也惑, 敢問。」子曰:「求也退, 故進之; 由也兼人, 故退之。」

Zilu asked, "If one has learned something, should he go and do it?" Confucius said, "While your father and your older brothers are still alive, how could you learn something and go do it?"

Ran You asked, "If one has learned something, should he go and do it?" Confucius said, "If you have learned something, go and do it."

Gongxi Hua asked, "When Zilu asked you if someone has learned something, should he go do it, you said that his father and brothers were alive. When Ran You asked the same question, you said if he has learned something, he should go do it. I am confused. Can you explain?" Confucius said, "Ran You shrinks back from action, that is why I encouraged him to move forward. Zilu is more active than others, that is why I wanted to restrain him."

Comments: When read together with the repeated instances in which Zilu is described as courageous, rash, frank, and unyielding, this passage is very easy to understand. [Confucius] is educating according to the person: he desires Zilu not to be overly bold to the point of endangering his life, but rather to think of the existence of his aged father and brothers. All very concrete and reasonable. In fact, this is precisely Confucius's approach to education—not simply to spout platitudes about mind and nature, but to fit education to the concrete nature of a person. The meaning of "fitting education to the materials" is to develop and manifest the variety of individual psychological characteristics of different people. **This attention to individual distinctives should be regarded as one of the major characteristics of Confucius's thought,** and is why questions about humaneness, ritual, government, or filiality all meet with different answers. This is also what distinguishes Confucius's pragmatic and specific "how-to" approach from the logical and universal "what is" approach of Socrates and Plato. Confucius believed that the question of how to was superior to the question of what is. Actually, this is also what makes aesthetic knowledge superior to moral knowledge and the reason I disagree with modern-day neo-Confucian moral metaphysics, preferring to substitute aesthetics instead. Individualistic creative philosophy (i.e., anthropo-historical ontology) acts upon the subjectivity[5] of the individual; this is also where the significance of sedimentation lies (see my *Questions and Answers on Philosophy*, no. 2). In order for every variety of individual spirit to exercise the freedom of creativity, one can rely neither upon a "sacred" moral command (whether Principle [*li* 理], the Dao, the "solemn and remote will of Heaven" [*wumu tianming* 於穆天命],[6] or [Hegelian] absolute spirit) nor upon rational authority to govern or control the sensuous existence of a truly vital human being. This is also what penetrates throughout my foundational concepts of "one-world," the "culture of delight," and "pragmatic reason." To emphasize individuality is to emphasize chance, distinctiveness, and unique creation, that is, what I have called "apprehending truth through beauty" (*yi mei qi zhen* 以美啟真) and "storing up goodness in beauty" (*yi mei chu shan* 以美儲善). My philosophy ultimately takes aesthetics as its compass, so that an anthropo-historical ontology undergoes sedimentation to become a philosophy of individual creative action.

11.22. 子畏於匡, 顏淵後。子曰: 「吾以女為死矣。」曰: 「子在, 回何敢死?」

Confucius was hemmed in in the land of Kuang,[7] and Yan Hui arrived afterward. Confucius said, "I thought you had died." Yan Hui said, "While you, my teacher, yet live, how could I die?"

Comments: It is important that this is not spoken in flattery, but in an attitude of honest sincerity.

11.23. 季子然問: 「仲由、冉求可謂大臣與?」子曰: 「吾以子為異之問, 曾由與求之問。所謂大臣者: 以道事君, 不可則止。今由與求也, 可謂具臣矣。」曰: 「然則從之者與?」子曰: 「弒父與君, 亦不從也。」

Ji Ziran asked, "Can Zilu and Ran You be called 'high officials'?" Confucius said, "I thought you would ask me about something else, but you asked about Zilu and Ran You. So-called 'high officials' are those who serve their ruler according to the meaning of the Dao, or if they are unable to do so, will resign. As for Zilu and Ran You, we can only say that they are preparing to serve as officials."

"Then are they people who will follow orders?" Confucius said, "If they were required to kill their fathers or their rulers, even they would not follow such orders."

Comments: Confucius's answer is probably referring to some concrete circumstance that is difficult for us to discover. In the line "or if they are unable to do so, will resign" (不可則止), the word *zhi* 止 ("to stop") is glossed [by Liu Baonan] in *Lunyu zhengyi* as "resigning or refusing one's post." The term *juchen* 具臣 ("ready officials") means "preparing for the circumstance of serving as officials." Part of virtuous behavior is the loyal service to one's ruler; this is the reason for the final question.

11.24. 子路使子羔為費宰。子曰:「賊夫人之子。」子路曰:「有民人焉,有社稷焉。何必讀書,然後為學?」子曰:「是故惡夫佞者。」

Zilu wanted Zigao to serve as magistrate of Bi. Confucius said, "[This amounts to] harming someone else's child."

Zilu said, "There are people there, and land and crops. Why should one have to study books to be considered learned?"

Confucius said, "This is why I despise people who engage in sophistry."

Notes: *Zhu Xi notes: In governing people or in serving spirits, it is imperative that those who have studied should serve; therefore one must first study until one is ready, and only then can one take on the duties for which one has studied. . . . Zilu's words . . . twist the sense and wring the meaning from the words, using the arguments of his mouth to oppose people. This is why the Master does not say he is wrong, yet despises his sycophancy.*

Comments: Because Confucius always stresses practice and emphasizes effort, book learning is of secondary importance. Zilu is using this statement to shut Confucius up, to trap him in a contradiction. Confucius seems to have nothing to say in response, but can only make this answer, and we can imagine his expression. This is why I disagree with Zhu Xi's comments here.

Is there actually a difference between the two words *min* 民 and *ren* 人 (together translated here as "people")? And if so, what is the difference? Even today, this is not terribly clear. Zhao Jibin 趙紀彬 (1905–1982) in his *Lunyu xinjie* regards the difference as one of class, while Roger Ames believes the terms differ in number. The latter explanation is closer to the truth; *min* includes the many, while *ren* is usually used of an individual. This is why the former refers to the large mass of people, while the latter is used to speak of the cultivation of the noble person. This is the source of error in Zhao's explanation.

11.25. 子路、曾皙、冉有、公西華侍坐。子曰:「以吾一日長乎爾,毋吾以也。居則曰:『不吾知也!』如或知爾,則何以哉?」子路率爾而對曰:「千乘之國,攝乎大國之間,加之以師旅,因之以饑饉;由也為之,比及三年,可使有勇,且知方也。」夫子哂之。「求!爾何如?」對曰:「方六七十,如五六十,求也為之,比及三年,可使足民。如其禮樂,以俟君子。」「赤!爾何如?」對曰:「非曰能之, 願學焉。宗廟之事, 如會同, 端章甫, 願為小相焉。」「點! 爾何如?」鼓瑟希, 鏗爾, 舍瑟而作。對曰:「異乎三子者之撰。」子曰:「何傷乎? 亦各言其志也。」曰:「莫春者, 春服既成。冠者五六人, 童子六七人, 浴乎沂, 風乎舞雩, 詠而歸。」夫子喟然歎曰:「吾與點也!」三子者出, 曾皙後。曾皙曰:「夫三子者之言何如?」子曰:「亦各言其志也已矣。」曰:「夫子何哂由也?」曰:「為國以禮, 其言不讓, 是故哂之。」「唯求則非邦也與? 」「安見方六七十如五六十而非邦也者?」「唯赤則非邦也與?」「宗廟會同, 非諸侯而何? 赤也為之小, 孰能為之大?」

Zilu, Zengzi, Ran You, and Zihua [Gongxi Chi] were sitting with Confucius.

Confucius said, "I am just a few years older than you, but do not worry [for the moment] that I am your teacher. You often say, 'No one understands me'—if there were someone who understood or appreciated you, what would you want to do?"

Zilu immediately answered, "If there were a land of a thousand chariots pressed between two large states, and outside its borders there were the threat of enemy armies, and inside a great famine—if I were to be employed, within three years I could cause the people to find their courage and understand the Dao."

Confucius gave a little smile.

"Ran You, what about you?"

[Ran You] answered, "Give me an area of sixty or seventy square *li* or fifty to sixty square *li*, and if I were to be employed [in governing it], within three years I would make the people prosper. As for promoting the rites and music, for that I would need to wait for a noble person (*junzi*)."

"Zihua, what about you?"

[Zihua] answered, "I would not say I had the ability, but that I would be willing to learn to do this: If I could carry out sacrifices, or receive foreign visitors, wearing the ritual robes and hat, I would be willing to be the lowliest master of ceremonies."

"And Zengzi, what about you?"

[Zengzi] was just then lightly playing upon the zither; he let one more note ring out, then stopped playing, set aside his zither and answered, "My answer is different from those of these three others."

Confucius said, "What does it matter? We are just each speaking of our own aspirations, that's all."

Zengzi said, "In the season of late spring, when the spring clothes have been finished, I would like to go with five or six young men and six or seven boys to bathe and swim in the Yi River, then catch the breezes below the altar for the Rain Dance and return home singing."

Confucius sighed and said, "I would go with Zengzi!"

The three of them left, and Zengzi remained behind them. He asked, "What about what the three of them said?"

Confucius said, "They were each just speaking of their aspirations, that's all."

Zengzi said, "Master, why did you smile at Zilu?"

Confucius said, "In governing a state, one should be careful of ritual and deference; his speech was not at all modest, therefore I smiled."

"Then was Ran You not speaking of governing a state?"

"Where would there be an area of sixty or seventy *li* square, or fifty or sixty *li* square, that would not be a state?"

"Then was what Zihua spoke of not also about governing a state?"

"If making sacrifices at the ancestral temple and receiving foreign guests don't have to do with governing a state, what does? If Zihua thinks he can only be a minor master of ceremonies, who would be able to be a major one?"

Notes: *Zhu Xi notes: Zengzi's learning probably grasped the locus of humanity's greatest desire, which flows with the Heavenly Principle, filling all things, without the slightest deficiency. Therefore when it is set in motion, it is carefree like this. When he speaks his aspiration, it is nothing more than the place he currently finds himself, enjoying the ordinariness of every day, and includes no sense whatever of self-sacrifice. His heart reaches a great distance, extending to Heaven and Earth and flowing with all things above and below, so that each achieves its particular wonder, and what is subtly hidden appears beyond the words.*

Cheng Shude in "Lunyu jishi," and He Yan in "Lunyu jijie" record Zheng Xuan's 鄭玄 *(127–200) comments: The affairs of the ancestral temple were the sacrifices. During the times of the feudal lords, the reception of visitors was called* hui 會. *Yin Fei says the same. . . . Black robes and ritual headwear at the time of the lords would have been seen as court attire. A "minor master of ceremonies" would have been one who manages ritual for a ruler. During this period of upheaval when Confucius for his entire life had not been employed by a ruler, let alone these three disciples hold office, their aspirations were to govern; only Zengzi knew the times well enough to set his aspirations on bathing himself and swimming in virtue, expressing his heart and rejoicing in the Way. This is why the Master was "with him." The*

*"Jingdian shiwen" 經典釋文 says: For 撰 [*zhuan*, meaning to have] Zheng Xuan has 僎 [*zhuan*, meaning good]. The "Lunyu guxun" 論語古訓 says:* Zhuan 僎 *should be read as* quan 詮, *and not as a variant. Zang Zaidong 臧在東 [臧庸1767–1811] says: "Different from these three others" means to be unequal to them in goodness [*shan 善*]. Zhang Lüxiang 張履祥 [1611–1674] in his "Beiwanglu" 备忘錄 notes: The four disciples are sitting in attendance, and thus each states his aspiration; however, their approaches to governing [follow] a certain order: when chaos has been suppressed, then one can put policies and education into effect. In early times, teachers were traveling about amid famine; thus Zilu's [wish to] "cause the people to find their courage and understand the Dao" is the means to suppress the chaos. Once chaos is quelled, then it becomes easy to improve the customs, and Ran You's wish to prosper the people is the means to improve the customs. Once customs have been improved, then it becomes easy to follow upon that with education, so Zihua's wish to carry out sacrifices and receive foreign visitors is the means to transform the people and perfect their customs. When transformation has been effected and the customs are beautiful, the people's lives are harmonious, and they happily wander in the ways of Tang, Yu, and the Three Dynasties, somewhat similarly to Zengzi's "catching the spring breezes and swimming in the Yi." Since Confucius's own aspiration was in line with that of the Three Dynasties, how could he not sigh in admiration?!*

Comments: This passage is very famous and also extremely important. Both its wording and its content have given rise to various explanations over the years. In some places my reading emphasizes certain meanings in the translation; otherwise it would have been a disservice to this excellent passage. In terms of content, Buddhist- and Daoist-influenced Song-Ming Neo-Confucians made much of Zengzi's "atmosphere of Heaven and Earth" 天地氣象. This is then made the basis of a Confucian quasi-religious spiritual attitude, as Zhu Xi remarks in the Notes above: "[His] heart reaches a great distance, extending to Heaven and Earth and flowing with all things above and below, so that each achieves its particular wonder, and what is subtly hidden appears beyond the words." However, Zhu Xi himself in his later years came to be conscious of this with some regret, saying, "As I near my end I regret not revising my notes on the passage on bathing in the Yi; this will have to remain for later scholars to correct" (quoted in Cheng Shude, *Lunyu jishi*). Originally Confucius simply sighs in admiration; it is wrong to assign this level of significance to his remarks. This is precisely the function of hermeneutics:

the Song-Ming Neo-Confucians certainly explored and developed the depths of the religious character of Confucianism, and gave people a different and deeper appreciation of the classics. However, unlike many Neo-Confucian scholars, Confucius did not look down on or despise the previous three disciples' aspirations or undertakings due to their [limitation within the] "realm of Heaven and Earth." On this point, the original text is quite clear (in Confucius's answer to Zengzi's question). As for the relationship among the four responses, Zhang Lüxiang's Qing dynasty annotation is strained but interesting (in that he takes pains to tease out an order); I have included this in the Notes above. As for the phrase "swimming in the Yi River," and "catching the breezes below the altar for the Rain Dance," there are a variety of ways to understand this. If we read 浴 (*yu*) as a variant for 沿 (*yan*), and 風 (*feng*) as a variant for 放 (*fang*); and if we take 放 (*fang*) to mean "arrive" (see Yu Yue 俞樾, *Qunjing pingyi* 群經評議), then we should read the phrase as "To stroll along the banks of the Yi River, until we arrive at the altar for the Rain Dance (in order to take part in the sacrifices)."

Book 12

12.1. 顏淵問仁。子曰:「克己復禮為仁。一日克己復禮, 天下歸仁焉。為仁由己, 而由人乎哉?」顏淵曰:「請問其目。」子曰:「非禮勿視, 非禮勿聽, 非禮勿言, 非禮勿動。」顏淵曰:「回雖不敏, 請事斯語矣。」

Yan Hui inquired what humaneness was like. Confucius said, "To control oneself in order to conform to the ritual system is humaneness. If one day everyone would do this, then all of China would return to 'humaneness.' To do this depends entirely on oneself; how could it depend on others?"

Yan Hui said, "May I ask about the concrete path [to humaneness]?" Confucius said, "Don't look at things that don't conform to ritual; don't listen to things that don't conform to ritual; don't say things that don't conform to ritual; don't do things that don't conform to ritual."

Yan Hui said, "Although I am not diligent, I will certainly do according to these things you have said."

Comments: This passage is another of the most important passages in the *Analects*. When people want to emphasize the centrality of ritual to Confucius's thought they do so based upon this passage. But what does it mean to "control oneself in order to conform to the ritual system"? What is "self-control"? There are many different opinions. Furthermore, could the phrase "To control oneself in order to conform to the ritual system is humaneness" be a case in which "the ancients passed it down, Confucius did not invent it"? (See Wang Yinglin, *Kun xue ji wen*.) Or is this Confucius's [own] explanation of humaneness? On this, there are also various opinions. For the most part, the former view ("words of the ancients passed down") is more correct, and accords with the non-Dionysian, restrained character of the "Chinese ritual system" (see my *The Chinese Aesthetic Tradition*). The Song-Ming Neo-Confucians created a whole philosophical explanation of mind and nature based on "eliminating desire" 滅人欲 ("self-control") and "maintaining Heavenly Principle" 存天理 ("conforming to the ritual system"). Zhu Xi's commentary reads, "Now, the virtue of the mind-and-heart in its wholeness is nothing but Heavenly Principle and thus can only be harmed by human desire. . . . If each day one subdues it [the self] and finds no difficulty in doing so, the selfish desires will be cleansed entirely and Heavenly Principle will prevail and one's true goodness will thereby be more than sufficient."[1] Here "ritual" becomes equal to "Principle," and "self" can be read as "human desire." This explanation has been thoroughly castigated by later scholars. Actually, the crux of the whole problem lies in the question of why "controlling oneself and conforming to ritual" (which has to do with behavior) should be considered "humaneness" (which has to do with psychology). By directly equating "controlling oneself in order to conform to ritual" with the problem of the mind and nature and the subordination of selfish desire to morality, Neo-Confucianism did take things to a deeper level, but a bit too narrowly. What one sees, listens to, says, and does clearly does have to do with behavior and demeanor—in other words, with the practice of ritual "ceremony." It is precisely by way of these various types of ritual practice and action that ritual attains to principle (rationality), and not through analysis, language, or seeking the mind or nature (this is true both individually and collectively).

Secondly, this also demonstrates the concrete process by which Confucius transforms the external ritual system into inner desire, and reason and desire are melded into one to become emotion (human nature, i.e., humaneness). "Humaneness" is not natural human desire, nor is it "Heavenly Principle" that controls or destroys "human desires"; rather it involves restraining oneself (self-control), so that all one sees, hears, says, or does conforms to the ritual system, in such a way as to produce the emotions that belong to human nature (humaneness). **The concrete form of this "restraint" may change, grow or contract according to the time period and the social environment, but the need for human nature (humaneness) to be cultivated through human culture (ritual) is universal and inevitable.** As I have mentioned in my *Critique of Critical Philosophy* and other works, in childhood we begin to restrict and regulate natural human desires (e.g., the desire for food) by way of saying "you may not do" certain things—this is actually the beginning of education in what it means to be human. For adults, therefore, one must "begin with the self in practicing humaneness"—one must proceed from the self in deciding on, governing, and producing these "four don'ts" that restrain the self (i.e., moral self-regulation) and in this way set a course for and ultimately attain the kind of supermoral realm of life (speaking of the individual) or social realm (speaking of the collective) characterized as a "return to humaneness." Older commentators read "return to humaneness" as "being recognized as being humane" ("All will recognize you as a humane person"), but this is too shallow. For "all under Heaven" to "return to humaneness" means for society to return to the goodness of the ancient period. The idea that in ancient times "men's hearts were simple and honest, and manners and morals were pure" 人心淳樸, 世道清明 constitutes Confucius's social-political ideal in a nutshell.

Clifford Geertz says,

> In attempting to launch such an integration from the anthropological side and to reach, thereby, a more exact image of man, I want to propose two ideas. The first of these is that culture is best seen not as complexes of concrete behavior patterns—customs, usages, traditions, habit clusters—as has, by and large, been the case up to now, but as a set of control mechanisms—plans, recipes, rules, instructions (what computer engineers call "programs")—for the governing of behavior. The second idea is that man is precisely the animal most desperately dependent upon such extra-genetic, outside-the-skin control mechanisms, such cultural programs, for ordering his behavior.[2]

He continues in the same essay, "Becoming human is becoming individual, and we become individual under the guidance of cultural patterns, historically created systems of meaning in terms of which we give form, order, point, and direction to our lives."[3] This seems to very effectively explain the two aspects of "ritual" as a cultural-psychological formation: first, it is a historically constructed "control mechanism" that governs and rules people's behavior. Secondly, it is practiced in the various individual minds and bodies of different personalities to make them into true individuals. As I have discussed before, one aspect comprises the three forms of cultural-psychological formation: the internalization of reason (the knowledge of form), its solidification (moral will), and its sedimentation (aesthetic experience). The other aspect reflects the respective individual "freedoms" of these three forms of the formation: free perception, free will, and free experience (see my "An Outline of the Various Theories of Subjectality" 諸主體性論綱 and *Four Essays on Aesthetics*). And as I say in the question and answer session below (on modern ways to interpret "controlling the self and conforming to ritual" and "[humaneness] depends entirely on oneself"), it is both a result of human history and an individual psychological formation; both a cultural "control mechanism" (human culture) and reflective of individual psychological liberty (personality):

> Q (Gao Jianping 高健平): In your discussion of the "cultural-psychological formation," your emphasis is on the psychological. However, since you also say that this formation is "cultural" and involves the vehicle of "education in the broad sense"—rather than being passed along through heredity or genetics from one generation to another—then from the point of view of each individual, it involves the passage from culture to the psyche. Thus, culture is more foundational than psychology. Rather than saying it is a kind of psychological formation, it would be better to say it is a kind of cultural formation. This formation exists within culture, and continually creates a response within the human psyche. Therefore, couldn't your "cultural-psychological formation" be said to be a "psychological-cultural formation"?
>
> A (Li Zehou): [The term] cannot be reversed; if it is reversed it becomes something dead. When I say it is a psychological formation (and this term should be translated "formation," not "structure"), this emphasizes human individuality. Culture creates an effect on the psyche, yes, but **humans are not a sum of all their social relationships. Humans are emotional individuals, and in their reception of the effects of the culture that surrounds them, they have initiative. The individual is creating his own psychology in interaction with the culture that surrounds him, and this process also has non-rational elements and aspects. In other words, although the psyche bears aspects of cultural form and social regulation, it also**

> **bears aspects of unique individual experience and sensory impulse. Therefore, this "formation" is not stable, but is precisely in a dynamic state. Therefore I say it is "forming."[4]**

I would also like to point out here that during the time of Confucius, due to the legacy of clan society, the construction of the individual psyche and the molding of human nature (humaneness) were connected and intermingled with the social order and the system of government (ritual); this is also clearly expressed in this passage. Therefore, it is of no use today, except to be taken apart and deconstructed. The external "ritual" of the social governmental system can only regulate and govern people's behavior; as such, what it requires is a sort of commonly pursued social morality, like fairness. In the modern era, this can become the baseline and standard of so-called law-abiding [behavior]. The internal "humaneness" of inner cultivation and the realm of human nature, on the other hand, has to do with the cultivation and molding of human emotions and [thus] constitutes a religious morality sought by the individual. The former ("ritual," social morality) has the power of coercion, while the latter ("humaneness," religious morality) is a purely personal, voluntary choice. If a general is defeated or surrounded, he can surrender, and today this would not be considered immoral; it accords with the modern "ritual system." But if he chooses to commit suicide, this would arouse great admiration, and this would be purely a decision of his personal religious morality, what we would call "dying to achieve humaneness." The relationship between these two (social morality and religious morality) is of course complicated, with many connections between them, but in today's China, it seems that the first priority should be to be able to distinguish between them, to differentiate between and separate the public regulations and collective demands of social morality ("ritual," which differs according to time period, society, nation, class, and group) and the religious morality of the human realm of personal aspiration ("humaneness," which seems to be more absolute, yet cannot be reduced to universal requirements). Only in this way can we get past the unity of church and state and the confusion of the concepts of law and ethics.

The call of Song-Ming Neo-Confucians for "high standards and strict requirements" in their theory of the mind-nature and Principle instead spawned a mass of hypocrites and "fake noble people (*wei junzi*)," as well as the tendency to "kill people with Principle." The distinction between "ritual" and "humaneness" seems to be the only answer to both the conflation of ritual and humaneness, and their opposition. The difficulty is that these "four don'ts" can apply either to the self-cultivation of religious morality or to the collective regulation of social morality. The fact that the two are often the same is precisely where the traditional Chinese brand of the "unity of church and state" is found. Because of this, as I have said above, the crucial issue for us today is how to separate the two and allow each to have its place and its full sphere of development. That is to say, religious morality (religion, private virtue) should usually be spread and adopted by means of an emphasis on education, while social morality (government, public virtue) will usually be clearly regulated by the law. To enable both people's interior (psyche) and their exterior (behavior) to truly mature and be restrained by reason—this is what I call the separation of "ritual" (social morality, law, behavior) from "humaneness" (religious morality, psychology, emotion). But both the internal shaping of human nature (humaneness) and the external regulation and ordering of behavior (ritual) require a certain amount of self-control as a necessary condition. In this book I often speak of the separation of humaneness and ritual, and of the need for religious morality to exercise a guiding function over social morality; but here I must emphasize that the accumulation of social morality onto religious morality creates and transforms the above-mentioned important function. For even though from the point of view of its origins humaneness (human nature) grew out of ritual (culture), only subsequently was it able to govern ritual.

12.2. 仲弓問仁。子曰:「出門如見大賓, 使民如承大祭。己所不欲, 勿施於人。在邦無怨, 在家無怨。」仲弓曰:「雍雖不敏, 請事斯語矣。」

Zhong Gong asked what humaneness was like. Confucius said, "When going out to work, it should be as if you were receiving an important guest; in governing the people, it should be as if carrying out grand sacrificial rites. What you do not want yourself, do not force upon others. Have no resentment in the way you carry out affairs of state, and have no resentment in your own family life."

Zhong Gong said, "Although I am not diligent enough, I will certainly go and do according to what you have said."

Notes: *Liu Baonan quotes Jiuji* 臼季 *of the Jin in the "Zuozhuan" (thirty-third year of the Duke of Xi): "I have heard it said, 'When you go out, treat others as guests; in carrying out business, do so as if carrying out the sacrifices'; these are the principles of humaneness." Clearly this saying is of ancient origin.*

Comments: This is yet another concrete answer regarding "humaneness," and all of the statements have to do with concrete practice or behavior. In the *Analects*, questions from the disciples about humaneness are very numerous, from which we can clearly see how great an emphasis Confucius placed upon it, and what a new teaching it was. The answers are all different from one another, and mostly have to do with real life. The saying "What you do not want yourself, do not force upon others" remains a commonly used aphorism still today, and corresponds to and inverts the Bible's "Do unto others as you would have them do unto you." The Bible teaches a religion of love, involving zealous initiative to give oneself up for the salvation of others, and in this sense its golden rule is more difficult to put into practice. The *Analects* teach a humanistic pragmatic reason that is more measured and sober, and thus relatively easy to obey. Unfortunately, in the past this teaching has been limited to individual self-cultivation, when in actuality it could serve as a traditional basis for a public morality for modern society. For all individuals live in an equal and independent communal environment based on the principle of contractual relationships, in which even without the cultivation of the individual, respecting others as one respects oneself can actually be put into practice simply as a social agreement. This is where social morality comes from.

Why "in carrying out business, do so as if carrying out the sacrifices"? The circumspection and reverence one shows in serving the people is similar to that one shows in serving the gods. As religious morality shifts toward society in the process of rationalization, religion and government are united into one, and the government takes on a sacred and solemn religious significance.

12.3. 司馬牛問仁。子曰:「仁者其言也訒。」曰:「其言也訒, 斯謂之仁已乎?」子曰:「為之難, 言之得無訒乎?」

Sima Niu asked what humaneness was like. Confucius said, "A person with the virtue of humaneness will be slow and circumspect in his speech."

"Do you really mean that speaking slowly and with circumspection is humaneness?" Confucius said, "If it is very difficult to do, how can one but be slow to speak of it?"

Notes: *Yang Bojun quotes Sima Qian's "Records of the Lives of the Disciples of Confucius" in the "Shiji": Sima Geng, style name Niu. Niu was talkative and rash; he asked Confucius about humaneness. Confucius answered, "A person with the virtue of humaneness will be slow and circumspect in his speech." According to Sima Qian's explanation, Confucius's answer is intended to address the questioner's fault of being "talkative and rash."*

Comments: The Note above suggests that because of Sima Niu's "talkative and rash" character, Confucius is addressing this particularly to that weakness. But Confucius always advocates for the noble person to "speak less" (*Analects* 4.24) and says that "the strong, the resolute, the simple, and the slow to speak all are close to humaneness" (*Analects* 13.27).

In Confucianism, speech is itself action, and therefore the whole of the *Analects* emphasizes the importance of being careful and slow to speak. **Speech is considered action because it directly gives rise to serious consequences, and it is invested with such a solemn and even sacred quality due to its origins in shamanism.** The same is true of the word-magic of shamanism. Apart from this it would be rather difficult to explain the great importance placed upon language. This is quite different from the Western view of language as describing or instigating action, rather than being itself action, as has been thoroughly discussed by such as A. C. Graham, Chad Hansen, and Roger Ames (see David Hall and Rogers Ames, *Thinking Through Confucius*, and *Anticipating China*, etc.).

12.4. 司馬牛問君子。子曰: 「君子不憂不懼。」曰: 「不憂不懼, 斯謂之君子已乎? 」子曰: 「內省不疚, 夫何憂何懼? 」

Sima Niu asked what it took to be a noble person. Confucius said, "The noble person has no worry or fear."

"So having no worry and no fear makes one a noble person?" Confucius said, "If in examining one's heart one has nothing to be ashamed of, then what cause would one have to worry or fear?"

Comments: If we leave aside Sima Niu's concrete situation, then the word "fear" should probably be understood as Heidegger's Angst (*wei* 畏).

What it refers to is not the terror of some concrete thing, but "angst" about human life—the terror of the individual's actual death, in all its inevitability and uncertainty. If when one examines oneself one has nothing to be ashamed of, no inner remorse, that demonstrates that this life and one's immediate existence ("immediate" denotes something of which one has a historical, experiential assurance) is one's own, that one does not owe anything to "Heavenly Principle" (morality) or to other people, but that one is emotionally detached and independent, deeply conscious of the richness of one's life, and thus has "no worry or fear." Bao Xian (6 BCE–65 CE) notes, "*Jiu* 疚 is a sickness (*bing* 病). If in examining oneself one finds no fault, then of course one will have no need to worry or fear." The ancients in China also surprisingly used the phrase *wuzui* [meaning without sin or without fault]; if one examines oneself and finds no fault or sin, then of course there will be no cause for worry or fear; this is the religious pursuit of human nature and realm of human life and is quite distinct from the demands of social morality we saw in the previous passage. It is just that this religiosity—this realm of religious pursuit—lacks the concept of original sin.

12.5. 司馬牛憂曰:「人皆有兄弟, 我獨亡。」子夏曰:「商聞之矣: 死生有命, 富貴在天。君子敬而無失, 與人恭而有禮。四海之內, 皆兄弟也。君子何患乎無兄弟也?」

Sima Niu worriedly said, "Other people all have brothers, only I have none." Zixia said, "I have heard it said, 'Life and death are governed by fate, wealth and nobility by Heaven.' To be a noble person, be rigorous, never indulge yourself, and treat others respectfully and according to ritual, then wherever you go all will be your brothers. Why should the noble person fret over having no brothers?"

Notes: *Zhu Xi notes: Fate is given at the beginning of life; it is not something that can be changed today. Heaven does what is done by no one;*[5] *I cannot force it to do anything but rather must simply accede to it.*

Comments: Most commentators have interpreted "I have heard it said" to mean [Zixia] has heard the teacher Confucius say. The character 失 (*shi*, meaning "fault" or "slip") should be 佚 (*yi*, meaning "leisure"). The phrase 四海之內 (literally, "within the four seas") refers to the ancient Chinese belief that China was surrounded by nothing but uninhabited seas. The phrase "life and death are governed by fate, wealth and nobility by Heaven" 死生有命，富貴在天 is a commonly used saying among Chinese still today. The term "fate," however, is usually understood to mean "determined by fate," or fatalism. In this book, I emphasize that "fate" refers to chance. As I have discussed above, it is only because it is difficult to understand or grasp that it is considered to be given or determined by Providence, or what we refer to as "Heaven" or "God's will." In this way, "fate" or "Heaven's will" evolves from simple chance that is difficult to understand or grasp, to become an inevitability, regularity, and so on, that dictates, controls, or even governs the self. In the face of it, humans, because they are helpless to change it, obey, submit to, accept, or even happily put their faith in it (as in Zhu Xi's Note above). Nietzsche's strong man or *übermensch* was anti-God; in today's China, a strong person or *übermensch* should be anti-Heaven's will (天命 *tianming*). This would seem to be the complete opposite of Confucius's "creed." Therefore, Xu Fuguan distinguished between "fate" and "Heaven's will," regarding "fate" as equaling "fatalism," while "Heaven's will" does not. Xu emphasizes opposition to fatalism and emphasizes the fact that the fundamental spirit of Confucius and the Confucians was unrelenting self-improvement, not at all allowing oneself to be ordered about by fate (see Xu Fuguan, *Zhongguo renxinglun shi* [*A history of Chinese humanism*], referred to above).

The ancients' "fear of Heaven's will 畏天命" (see *Analects* 16.8) was due to the contemporaneous low level of production and technology, with which it was difficult to withstand natural disasters or human disasters (like war) without total destruction; therefore, people were warned to "fear the will of Heaven," or "Respect virtue, cultivate industry" 敬德修業 while "awaiting the will of Heaven" 俟天命, or in other words, do one's utmost to obtain the "help of Heaven," the "blessing of Heaven," or a good fate. It was said that the state of Zhou was like this. Although it was a small state, and was oppressed by its neighboring kingdom of Yin, in the end through human effort it was able to receive the mandate of Heaven and rule China. This is what Confucius meant by "fearing Heaven's will." Yet Confucius seldom discussed fate, because fate is difficult to explain; he preferred to discuss humaneness (*ren* 仁). To speak of humaneness is to speak of human effort. I have already discussed this above.

Beginning with the line in the *Zhongyong* (the *Mean*), "The will of heaven is called nature" 天命之謂性, fate (命 *ming*), and nature (性 *xing*, "human nature") have been linked together. "Fate" has become the a priori (universally inevitable) standard; this is precisely the "transcendent yet inner" moral metaphysics of which modern New Confucians (in particular Mou Zongsan) love to speak. In other words, the moral order is the order of the universe, and the order of the universe is the moral order. "Fate" (or "Heaven") and "nature" (*xing* 性) ("humanity") are connected and mutually continuous. Therefore, moral laws are "fate" for Heaven, and "nature" for humans. Although I believe that "human nature is good" 人性善 follows from "the movement of Heaven is full of power" 天行健,[6] I believe, first, that this is a supposition of Confucianism's suffusion with emotionality, and not a statement of the nature of the universe or morality themselves; otherwise we would have a "moral theology." I do not advocate "moral theology," which is deeply rooted in a Western Christian other-worldly worldview, and not the Chinese proposition of "one world, one life." Secondly, "the movement of Heaven is full of power" does not actually refer to fate, and fate and "the will of Heaven" should not be regarded as completely interchangeable. **For the individual as for society, there is no "fate" determined by "Heaven" (also known as "historical inevitability"), but only chance, which is difficult to predict. It can be truly terrifying but is not a matter of submission or yielding to the "will of Heaven" or "inevitability." Furthermore, it is up to humans to make effort to struggle with their "fate"; even if they are defeated, there is honor there.** Sayings such as "It is up to men to try, but success is from Heaven" 謀事在人, 成事在天, "Make great human efforts while listening for Heaven's command" 盡人事以聽天命, or "Knowing it cannot be done but doing it anyway" 知其不可而為之 **all emphasize people's initiative and effort and at the same time respect the existence of chance.** I believe this is the true spirit of Confucianism and the true meaning of Confucius's "fear of Heaven's will."

The phrase "Within the four seas, all are brothers" 四海之內, 皆兄弟也, originally intended as words of comfort, was extended by later Confucians to mean the sentimental love of "the people are my siblings" 民吾同胞[7]—this is also hermeneutics.

12.6. 子張問明。子曰: 「浸潤之譖, 膚受之愬, 不行焉。可謂明也已矣。浸潤之譖膚受之愬不行焉, 可謂遠也已矣。」

Zizhang asked what "understanding" is like. Confucius said, "Someone who remains unperturbed by an accumulation of insidious slanders, who is unaffected by cutting vilification—this is what can be called 'understanding.' A person who remains unperturbed by an accumulation of insidious slanders, who is unaffected by cutting vilification—this can be called having foresight."

Comments: This passage is largely directed toward those in power or rulers, but it also has a more universal quality. Many are the rulers over the years who have listened to insidious slanders, refused to hear straight talk, killed their loyal advisors, and made huge mistakes [as a result]. It is difficult to maintain absolute authority without listening to slander and becoming corrupt.

12.7. 子貢問政。子曰:「足食。足兵。民信之矣。」子貢曰:「必不得已而去,於斯三者何先?」曰:「去兵。」子貢曰:「必不得已而去,於斯二者何先?」曰:「去食。自古皆有死,民無信不立。」

Zigong asked about how one should govern. Confucius said, "Provide a sufficiency of food, a fully equipped military, and retain the confidence of the people."

Zigong asked, "If there were no other way than to forego one of these, which would that be?" [He responded,] "Forego the military equipment."

Zigong asked again, "If there were no other way than to forego yet another, which would that be?" [He responded,] "Forego the food. From of old, people have always had to die. But without the trust of the people, a government cannot be sustained."

Comments: Many commentators read this passage as addressing individual self-cultivation, but the original is clearly answering the question of how to govern. However, the passage should not be taken to mean that food for the people is not important to a government; rather, it emphasizes the fact that if the government does not retain the confidence of the people, it cannot be sustained and has lost the foundation of its existence. Actually, trust is the foundational principle and necessary condition for a human collective that lacks clear hierarchy to organize, standardize, and eventually establish a state. This also accords with contemporary contractual theory. The *Fanshen lu* 反身錄[8] is a good reference in this regard. From anarchy to postmodernism, [there are views that] put an undue emphasis on individual freedom and deny all order, rules, or trust—but this kind of society or state cannot exist, and [in it] individual existence would also have very little security, or in actuality would be unable to subsist. These lofty words are certainly attractive, but very hard to put into practice.

12.8. 棘子成曰:「君子質而已矣, 何以文為?」子貢曰:「惜乎! 夫子之說, 君子也。駟不及舌。文猶質也, 質猶文也。虎豹之鞟, 猶犬羊之鞟。」

Ji Zicheng said, "For a noble person, the important thing is to have simplicity of character; what would he want with ritual and refinement?" Zigong said, "It's a pity that you describe the noble person in this way. 'A team of horses cannot take back what has been said' 一言既出, 駟馬難追. If refinement meant simplicity of character, and simplicity of character refinement, then the hide of a tiger or leopard would be the same as that of a dog or goat."

Comments: This is another passage that is difficult to interpret. Here the phrase "Master" (*fuzi* 夫子) refers to the questioner [Ji Zicheng], rather than referring to the Master Confucius. The last line says that if one paid no attention whatsoever to ritual comportment and refinement, that would be akin to regarding the skins of tigers, leopards, dogs, and goats as all the same—since they are all skins. Hides (*kuo* 鞟) are skins from which the fur has been removed. That is to say, in order to uphold the existence of society, there must be external forms such as ritual ceremonies and [degrees of] refinement to distinguish and express the varying status, position, rank, standing, and order of the high and low, older and younger, and so on. This is also the ritual system, which is why "ritual" (*li* 禮) and "refinement" (*yi* 儀) cannot be separated. Although "ritual" does not equal "refinement," without "refinement" "ritual" would have no way of being expressed or embodied.

12.9. 哀公問於有若曰:「年饑, 用不足, 如之何?」有若對曰:「盍徹乎?」曰:「二, 吾猶不足, 如之何其徹也?」對曰:「百姓足, 君孰與不足? 百姓不足, 君孰與足?」

The Duke of Ai asked You Ruo, "This year of famine, the harvests have been bad, and revenues are not adequate. What should I do?" You Ruo answered, "How about implementing a 'tithe' tax?" [He responded,]

"Even twenty percent would not be adequate—how could ten percent suffice?" [You Ruo] answered, "If the common people do not have enough, how can you have enough? If the common people have enough, how could you not have enough?"

Comments: About how to understand the term "tithe" (*che* 徹), there are a great number of references, all of which are vague. What You Ruo is advocating is the old clan society concept of "storing wealth in the people"; this is an example of the concrete content of primitive Confucian humanism. In the past, these ideas were never actually put into practice, but in later generations they served to criticize actual ills, and were often cited in opposition to autocratic government, oppressive taxation, excessive levies, or unbridled extortion at the hands of officials. I have already discussed this many times above. This is one of the important functions of government in Confucianism; the so-called alternation of Confucianism and Legalism (*rufa huyong* 儒法互用) and the idea of "containing the Legalists" (*qianzhi fajia* 牽制法家) both carry the same import.

12.10. 子張問崇德、辨惑。子曰: 「主忠信, 徙義, 崇德也。愛之欲其生, 惡之欲其死。既欲其生, 又欲其死, 是惑也。『誠不以富, 亦祇以異。』」

Zizhang asked how one can have great esteem for virtue, and find one's way through confusion. Confucius said, "Take sincerity and trust for your pillar, and let your behavior accord with ritual; this is how to esteem virtue. When you love, wish for him to live; when you hate, wish for him to die. Wishing for someone to both live and die, this is confusion."

Comments: This passage was also probably directed toward some specific circumstance. There is wisdom (reason, knowledge) in humaneness; it must not be regarded as the equivalent of irrational, blind love. Love and hate are not constant; both are unstable and tend toward extremes. Both are irrational and based on nature—they are not the emotio-rational construction of "humaneness" that melds reason and desire. This is why they are said to be a kind of "confusion." Most commentators consider the last two lines of the original passage to have been inserted here by mistake. I have not translated them nor will I comment on them here.

12.11. 齊景公問政於孔子。孔子對曰:「君君, 臣臣, 父父, 子子。」公曰:「善哉! 信如君不君, 臣不臣, 父不父, 子不子, 雖有粟, 吾得而食諸?」

Duke Jing of Qi asked Confucius about how to govern. Confucius answered him, saying, "The ruler is the ruler, the minister is the minister; the father is the father, the son is the son." Duke Jing said, "What you say is excellent. If the ruler doesn't follow the ruler's rules, or the minister the minister's rules, if the father doesn't follow the father's rules or the son the son's rules, even if there were grain to eat, would I be able to eat any of it?"

Notes: *Zhu Xi notes: Duke Jing liked Confucius's answer but was unable to put it into practice; the result was the disaster that ensued because of his failure to clarify his successor: Chen Heng assassinated the ruler and roiled the state.*

Comments: This passage is regarded as one of the most famous in the classics. In the past, it was frequently invoked to uphold traditional ethical relations. Today, its significance lies in its abstraction, namely, its emphasis on the social collective's need for a structure and an order. People live in a collective, after all, and any individual must abide by the order of the collective as a prerequisite and condition for his or her existence. The "absolute freedom" of an atomized individual will always be a fantasy. Therefore, apart from spiritual freedom—and aside from those who are not entirely fettered within the narrow confines of family relations, state government, national duty, and administration (through the course of history, these fetters will gradually decrease)—a certain ordered structure of norms, distinctions, and discriminations will always be a given for both humanity as a whole and for individuals. Only in this way can everyone eat without being consumed in a tangle of warfare. As Xunzi said long ago:

> [Humans] are not as strong as oxen or as fast as horses, but oxen and horses are used by them. How is this so? I say it is because humans are able to form communities while the animals cannot. Why are humans able to form communities? I say it is because of social divisions. How can social divisions be put into practice? I say it is because of *yi* [義 "justice, obligation"]. And so if they use *yi* in order to make social divisions, then they will be harmonized. If they are harmonized, then they will be unified. If they are unified, then they will have more

> force. If they have more force, then they will be strong. If they are strong, then they will be able to overcome the animals.[9]
>
> 力不若牛, 走不若馬, 而牛馬為用, 何也? 曰: 人能群, 彼不能群也。人何以能群? 曰: 分。分何以能行? 曰: 義。故義以分則和, 和則一, 一則多力, 多力則彊, 彊則勝物。(王制)

Humans, based on the use and production of tools, have a structure and organization of society that entails a certain division of labor. This is the reason that humans (both as a race and as individuals) have been able to hold on to existence and continue. This is the origin of Confucian "ritual propriety" (*liyi* 禮義): it transforms social history into ethical consciousness. The *Analects*, along with all of Confucianism, greatly emphasizes "fathers being fathers, sons being sons"—that is, the love that a father has for his children and the filial reverence of children for their parents—in other words, the order of human societies, which also entails the "rectification of names" (*zheng ming* 正名). "Names" are of such great importance because they are the actual carriers of the ritual system. A "name" here is a norm, a duty, a behavior, an activity. See Chad Hansen, "Language in the Heart-Mind," in *Understanding the Chinese Mind.*[10] Confucius's rectification of names is just this "the ruler being a ruler, the minister a minister, the father a father, the son a son."

12.12. 子曰: 「片言可以折獄者, 其由也與? 」子路無宿諾。

Confucius said, "If there is anyone who can decide a case based on one or two sentences, it is Zilu." When Zilu agreed to do something, he never put it off overnight.

Notes: *Kang Youwei notes: All lawsuits have great potential to be falsified, and even the most sagely [judge] must listen to both sides; although Zilu was sagely, he did not understand this.*

Cheng Shude quotes the "Virtue of the Five Emperors" chapter of the "Da Dai Liji": Saying that Zai Wo would not wait overnight to ask means he was never sluggish.

Comments: Many commentators have explained the phrase *pian yan* 片言 as "one-sided argument," as in Kang's Note above. Only Zhu Xi explains, "*pian yan* is *ban yan* 半言 [half a word/sentence]; *zhe* 折 is *duan*

斷 ["pass judgment"]. Zilu was trustworthy and decisive, so that as soon as he spoke people would accept what he said and carry it out, without waiting for his words to be finished." This is a sensible reading. This passage once again uses concrete behavioral qualities to demonstrate Zilu's rash, frank, and decisive character. The second part should be a separate passage, as it has no real connection with this one, but it also expresses Zilu's personal characteristics. Unfortunately, no records have survived of Zai Wo's propensity for asking questions [referred to in the Note above].

12.13. 子曰: 「聽訟, 吾猶人也, 必也使無訟乎! 」

Confucius said, "In handling a lawsuit, I am about like other people. What is important is how to avoid having lawsuits."

Comments: This of course is a kind of ideal or fantasy. However, still today Chinese people do not like to sue, go to court, or confront someone with an accusation. They prefer harmony, negotiation, mediation, or settling out of court. In modern life in which the number of cases that go to court is increasing daily, and lawsuits are proliferating, this is a tradition that would be worth thinking about how to preserve. Having the court resolve one's case should be a basic principle or standard, but one need not go to court over everything. The present Citizen's Committees, if stripped of their political quality, could play a very positive social role and have the potential to greatly develop the public space and "negotiation ethics." The spirit of "avoiding lawsuits" that Confucius voices here seemingly connects several thousand years of Chinese traditional society to produce (i.e., to be sedimented into) this type of cultural-psychological formation. This is also what I call the "alternation of Confucianism and Legalism, with Confucianism being primary." Ever since the establishment of the Qin-Han authoritarian empire, the style and implementation of Legalism has always been shot through with the basic Confucian spirit and doctrine that emphasizes morality, filial love, and human feeling (what we call "according with feeling and with reason"), in the ritual-legal tradition of "let ritual instruct the law, and the law be melded into custom" 授禮入法, 融法於俗. From here on, the law in China must modernize, so as to link up and tally with the social morality that is built upon the foundation of economics (major industry, contemporary property relations, etc.) and politics (the social contract, democratic freedoms, etc.). On the other hand, the question of whether or not this type of traditional religious morality can still play a normalizing role in the transformational creation of the above-referenced Chinese style of "negotiation ethics" or "harmonization of people" remains a crucial topic that is worth serious attention.

12.14. 子張問政。子曰:「居之無倦, 行之以忠。」

Zizhang asked about how government should be carried out. Confucius said, "Be unwearying in your position, and honestly carry out your duties."

Notes: *Zhu Xi notes: The character* ju 居 *[to stay, or to occupy] means to hold it in one's heart.* Wujuan 無倦 *[unflagging] means steadily from beginning to end.* Xing 行 *[to walk or to implement] means to put into practice. Honesty means the appearance and the reality are one. Master Cheng says, Zizhang lacks humaneness. Without a sincere love for the people, one will certainly grow weary and be unable to exert one's whole heart; this is why he tells him this.*

Liu Baonan says: This is saying that when implementing the way of government, one should hold onto it oneself, without slacking off or becoming weary; in implementing it with the people, one must do so with honesty.

Comments: Here again, the argument is based on individual character, behavior, and self-cultivation. For the reading of the character *ju* 居, I have not followed the above Note.

12.15. 子曰:「君子博學於文, 約之以禮, 亦可以弗畔矣夫! 」

Confucius said, "If one broadly studies the documents and classics, and uses ritual to restrain and control oneself—this is the way to avoid violating (the truth)."

Comments: Later readers often took "breadth" and "restrain" to refer to the way of studying. Hu Shi famously said, "Scholarship should be like a golden pagoda of words—it should be both broad and tall." But how easy is this to say? To study broadly but be short on the essentials, so that one rambles afar but has no place to settle down—this is a common phenomenon. The beautiful [cases of this] are called "a basket of a hundred treasures," or "a living dictionary"; the ugly are "a pile of trash" or "an old warehouse." Though they may sometimes be useful, in the era of computers this [kind of scholarly achievement] is nothing to boast of. "Specialists" who only study one point and do not pay attention to or know about anything else, knowing nothing of current affairs (those we today love to call "experts")—although they may sometimes be useful, actually they are alienated individuals not worthy of a place in the twenty-first century. "Breadth but short on essentials, labor with little achievement" was Sima Tan's criticism of Confucianism in his *Liu jia yao zhi* 六家要指 [*A basic guide to the Six Schools*]. **Yan Fu's criticism of China's "Old Learning" (which largely referred to Confucianism) was that "China brags of much learning, while Western people respect new knowledge."**[11] Clearly, the key is not in whether "breadth" or "restraint" is superior or inferior, but in the various ways these two things can be ordered or can relate to one another. Today it is impossible and indeed unnecessary for a person to be encyclopedic in their knowledge, yet neither can we blindly praise "experts" who know only one thing.

12.16. 子曰:「君子成人之美, 不成人之惡。小人反是。」

Confucius said, "The noble person perfects people's good qualities, and does not help others do bad things. The petty person does the opposite."

Comments: This aphorism is still in use today.

12.17. 季康子問政於孔子。孔子對曰:「政者, 正也。子帥以正, 孰敢不正?」

Ji Kangzi asked Confucius about how to govern. Confucius said, "Government is uprightness. If you would lead, first make yourself upright, then who will dare not be upright?"

Notes: *Cheng Shude notes: This is also probably an ancient aphorism. This chapter contains especially many passages that quote aphorisms.*

Comments: Here again is repeated the equation of ethics and government, that is, the clan government based on "the first thing is to make self-cultivation the root" 壹是以修身為本. Clan leaders used their own behavior as a model, and only thus were able to obtain the confidence of the people and administer or rule. This is quite without parallel in later government, yet it remained something Confucians upheld and emphasized, to the extent that its influence is felt still today. Philology has demonstrated that the word *zheng* 政 ["government"] originated in the word *zheng* 正 ["upright or correct"], which in turn originated in the word *zheng* 征 ["to levy," as taxes], which meant to impose punishments on people. This is actually close to Xunzi's notion of "rites and music, punishment and government," and different from what we see in this passage.

12.18. 季康子患盜, 問於孔子。孔子對曰: 「苟子之不欲, 雖賞之不竊。」

Ji Kangzi was struggling with thieves, and asked Confucius what he should do about them. Confucius answered, "If you were not greedy for wealth, even if you encouraged them to steal, no one would do it!"

Comments: The sense of this is similar to the above passage. Today this is not necessarily so. An individual who maintains integrity in an official position cannot ensure the disappearance of economic crimes.

12.19. 康子問政於孔子曰: 「如殺無道, 以就有道, 何如?」孔子對曰: 「子為政, 焉用殺? 子欲善, 而民善矣。君子之德風, 小人之德草。草上之風, 必偃。」

Ji Kangzi was asking about how to govern, and said to Confucius, "If I kill the bad people, and draw near to the good, how would that work?" Confucius said, "If you are governing, why should you kill people? If you are a good person, the common people will follow you and become good. The noble person's morality is like the wind, and the common people's morality is like the grass; the grass bends with the wind."

Comments: As above. Government in clan society always involved being "full of tender feeling" toward one's own clan, because government was built upon the social order of blood relations. This is the fundamental historical reason why Confucian notions of government can never depart from "humaneness" and "virtue." This did exercise a certain restraint on later authoritarian governments; the so-called "Confucian yang to Legalist yin" or "alternation of Confucianism and Legalism" meant that at least on the surface the appearance of "virtuous government" was upheld. Actually, it was not only on the surface, for through the centuries remonstrating officials, the Qingliu ("purification") [clique], scholar-officials and so on, all took as their standard an ethical government based on this kind of Confucian notion of humane love, with which they opposed killing, wars, or similar governmental actions on the part of the emperor or the government. So, in a sense this truly did serve a kind of suppressing or restraining function.

12.20. 子張問:「士何如斯可謂之達矣?」子曰:「何哉, 爾所謂達者?」子張對曰:「在邦必聞, 在家必聞。」子曰:「是聞也, 非達也。夫達也者, 質直而好義, 察言而觀色, 慮以下人。在邦必達, 在家必達。夫聞也者, 色取仁而行違, 居之不疑。在邦必聞, 在家必聞。」

Zizhang asked how intellectuals could achieve "eminence." Confucius said, "What do you mean by what you call 'eminence'?" Zizhang answered, "To have a reputation in the state, and a reputation in the clan." Confucius said, "That is 'reputation,' not 'eminence.' To have 'eminence' is to be upright and true to one's word, to pay attention to the words and countenance of others, and always to consider how to defer [to others]. This will certainly win you universal respect in the state and in the clan. A person of good reputation may be humane on the surface but engage in behavior that does not accord with it, and may think himself very successful. This is having a reputation in the state and a reputation in the clan."

Notes: *Zhu Xi quotes Master Cheng: A scholar should be motivated by duty, and not by attaining reputation. To purposely seek repute is to lose the main root. Then why study? To study for the sake of repute is hypocrisy. Most scholars today are in it for repute.*

Comments: Some say that the line "to pay attention to the words and countenance of others, and always to consider how to defer [to others]" refers to a petty person, not a noble person, and that there must be an omission or error in the text. This is an erroneous tradition of later generations, for actually the original meaning lies in paying attention to or respecting others, putting others before oneself. The word *da* 達 ("eminence") means universal respect or honor, based on how it appears in the "Three Eminences" 三達尊 (*Mencius*),[12] and the "Five Eminent Ways" 五達道 and "Three Eminent Virtues" 三達德 (*Doctrine of the Mean*).[13] Zhu Xi's Note is interesting: studying for the sake of reputation has been around since ancient times, and today is even more prevalent.

12.21. 樊遲從遊於舞雩之下, 曰: 「敢問崇德、脩慝、辨惑。」子曰: 「善哉問! 先事後得, 非崇德與? 攻其惡, 無攻人之惡, 非脩慝與? 一朝之忿, 忘其身, 以及其親, 非惑與? 」

Fan Chi was following Confucius on an excursion to the Rain Altars, and asked Confucius, "How can I honor morality, get rid of evil thoughts, and tell right from wrong?" Confucius said, "Good question! First work hard, then receive your reward—is this not honoring morality? To correct one's own faults and mistakes and not go attacking those of others, is this not getting rid of evil thoughts? In a moment of anger to forget oneself and even forget one's parents, is this not confusion?"

Comments: "Virtue (*de* 德) is gain (*de* 得)," but one must first put forth the "gain" of hard work before one can attain "virtue." To obtain reward without hard work—to take shortcuts, be overly calculating, or be excessively concerned for personal gain or loss—none of these amounts to "honoring morality." "Fan Chi was courageous and determined to study, simple in character yet narrow-minded, meaning that he tended to calculate and plot for gain, be easy on himself yet hard on others, excitable and unafraid of difficulty" (*Lunyu ji* 論語稽);[14] this is why Confucius gave him this answer. Each thing he says is targeted. Here "right and wrong" and "confusion" are not meant epistemologically but ethically and psychologically.

12.22. 樊遲問仁。子曰: 「愛人。」問知。子曰: 「知人。」樊遲未達。子曰: 「舉直錯諸枉, 能使枉者直。」樊遲退, 見子夏。曰: 「鄉也吾見於夫子而問知, 子曰, 『舉直錯諸枉, 能使枉者直』, 何謂也? 」子夏曰: 「富哉言乎! 舜有天下, 選於眾, 舉皋陶, 不仁者遠矣。湯有天下, 選於眾, 舉伊尹, 不仁者遠矣。」

Fan Chi asked what humaneness was like. Confucius said, "Love people." Fan Chi asked about knowledge. Confucius said, "Understand others."

Fan Chi did not understand. Confucius said, "By promoting people of integrity over the crooked, you can make the crooked straight as well."

Fan Chi came out and saw Zixia, and said, "Just now I saw the teacher and asked him what 'knowledge' was, and the teacher said, 'By promoting people of integrity over the crooked, you can make the crooked straight as well.' What does this mean?"

Zixia said, "How rich this saying is! When Shun ruled China, from among many people he chose to promote Gao Yao, and bad people fled afar. When Tang ruled China, from among many people he chose to promote Yi Yin, and bad people fled afar."

Comments: As to whether what Fan Chi "did not understand" referred to both humaneness and knowledge or only knowledge, there have been numerous opinions among later commentators. I tend toward the view that Fan Chi did not understand why "knowledge" should be understood as "knowing people." "Wisdom," after all, is much more than "knowing the right man for the job" 知人善任! Taken together with Confucius's criticism of Fan Chi when he asks about learning farming or growing vegetables [in *Analects* 13.4], and Zixia's thoroughly historical explanation, apparently this Mr. Fan was unlike Confucius's other disciples who tended to focus their interests on politics; perhaps he had "non-political tendencies," or perhaps he tended toward an agrarian utopian type of government, in which everyone tended their own crops and did not need to be ordered or divided into ranks of governing and governed, and so on. This may be why Confucius was always correcting him.

12.23. 子貢問友。子曰: 「忠告而善道之, 不可則止, 無自辱焉。」

Zigong asked about how to make friends. Confucius said, "Admonish him faithfully, and lead him with good intentions; if he does not listen to you, then leave it be. Do not go looking for insults."

Comments: The way of friendship is one of equality and independence and is not easy to force on someone. Even with sincerely offered admonition, one should know when to stop. If it is not received, then forget it, otherwise you will be asking for a snub. This type of "social advice" is still useful today. But what makes this more than just "social advice" is that it manifests as its substance a kind of concrete emotio-rational boundary of human relationships. If it crosses this boundary, the relationship can no longer be maintained. In Confucian studies, the way of friendship is easiest to fit into modern social morality, because it is based upon relationships of independence, autonomy, and equality among individuals. No wonder Tan Sitong believed that "Four Relationships"[15] could all be cast aside, as long as the relationship between friends was retained; this was a modern trend.

12.24. 曾子曰: 「君子以文會友, 以友輔仁。」

Zengzi said, "The noble person makes friends by way of scholarship and writing, and by way of friendship helps his humaneness and virtue to grow."

Comments: Why should one make friends over "scholarship and writing?" Here again commentators have had many different discussions, including " 'Writing' means writing about the rites and music, the legal system, and administrative records"; and "Writing that is a daily necessity (like food and clothing) is not the writing of ancient prose, contemporary writing, or the embellishment of triflers; one makes friends for the purpose of collecting one's mind and conserving one's body—this is the first duty of a scholar" (*Fanshen lu*). In other words, "the first thing is to make self-cultivation the root." Today, people use scholarly "writing" (how many scholarly conferences and articles there are!) to meet friends, in order to learn from each other, to refine and polish, to speak and discuss, but what this results in is not "humaneness" but "knowledge."

Book 13

13.1. 子路問政。子曰：「先之, 勞之。」請益。曰：「無倦。」

Zilu asked how to govern. Confucius said, "Starting with yourself, everyone works hard." Zilu wanted him to say a little more; Confucius said, "Do not slack off."

Comments: Does "work hard" refer to oneself or to the people? There are different interpretations, but in this translation I have adopted the view that both must work hard. This again melds ethics and government into one, as in the "Government is uprightness" 政者正也 (12.17) train of thought.

13.2. 仲弓為季氏宰, 問政。子曰：「先有司, 赦小過, 舉賢才。」曰：「焉知賢才而舉之？」曰：「舉爾所知。爾所不知, 人其舍諸？」

Zhonggong [Ranyong] was serving as manager of the Ji clan, and asked Confucius how to govern. Confucius said, "First pay attention to your high-ranking officials, don't worry about small offences, and promote the capable and talented."

Zhonggong said, "How shall I know who is capable and talented, so that I can promote them?" Confucius said, "Promote those you know. As for those you do not know, will others neglect them or fail to put them forward?"

Notes: *Cheng Shude quotes Lu Zhi* 陸贄 *(754–805) in his "Lu Jingyu Zouyi": The difficulty of knowing [the true nature of] people was something over which the wise and sagely worried themselves sick. One may listen to* *someone's words but not know his deeds, or inquire into his deeds but then have questions about his talent. If one must rely upon reports of someone's accomplishments, deceit and falsehoods abound, and an upright and faithful person is difficult to find. Those that worship at the altars of reputation and glory use their networks and curry favor, while the more retiring and deeply learned are not promoted. For this reason, extended relationship and interaction is required in order to understand the ins and outs of a person, study his intent and actions, and thoroughly explore his talents and abilities; only in this way can we recognize those that keep the Way and are useful to government, and not be taken in by those who dress themselves up to buy fame. This is why earlier dynasties developed the method of recommendation by village elders, and the system of recruitment to office by local senior officials, with which to test and investigate a candidate's experience, extend the search beyond established channels, and encourage people to put their talents to use, while ending the practice of currying favor and chasing after fame.*

Comments: "A talented person is hard to find" is an age-old dictum but is not actually true. As long as a good system is in place, there is no need to worry that talent will go unnoticed. What Lu Zhi points out [in the Notes above] refers to ancient systems, but in our modern economic and political system there is even more room for people to "develop their talent." If a good system is not in place, and one must depend solely upon the proverbial "Bo Le" to recognize a "thousand-*li* horse" (or upon the method Confucius suggests here), then the situation will be critical. It has always been the case that those who hold the reins of the government do not understand this point, and this is still so today. As for "overlooking small faults," no one is perfect—who can avoid mistakes? In the time of battle, talent easily shows itself, and minor virtues are not emphasized. In peaceful times, the opposite is the case, and therefore sages and great talents can often be strangled or imprisoned by the demand for "both virtue and talent," while in actuality many spend their whole lives in resentful service to the punctilious perfection-seeking of "principle."

13.3. 子路曰:「衛君待子而為政, 子將奚先? 」子曰:「必也正名乎! 」子路曰:「有是哉, 子之迂也! 奚其正? 」子曰:「野哉由也! 君子於其所不知, 蓋闕如也。名不正, 則言不順; 言不順, 則事不成; 事不成, 則禮樂不興; 禮樂不興，則刑罰不中；刑罰不中，則民無所措手足。故君子名之必可言也，言之必可行也。君子於其言，無所苟而已矣。」

Zilu said, "The ruler of the state of Wei is waiting for you to go there to run the government; what is the first thing you will do?"

Confucius said, "That will definitely be to rectify the terms for the various statuses."[1]

Zilu said, "Really! You are so pedantic. Why would you go rectifying status terms?"

Confucius said, "What a boor you are, Zilu! The noble person should maintain silence about things he knows nothing about. If the term or name is not correct, speech will not be smooth; if speech is not smooth, nothing can be accomplished; if nothing can be accomplished, the rites and music will not be revived; if the rites and music are not revived, punishments will not be appropriate; if punishments are not appropriate, the people will never know how they should behave or act. Therefore, if the ruler has rectified status terms, he will certainly be able to speak and what he says will certainly be able to be carried out. The noble person in his speech must not have an iota of carelessness or mediocrity."

Comments: As I have pointed out before, this is Confucian linguistics more or less—the extreme emphasis on the practical meaning and value of language, and the demonstration of its importance in developing people's behavior and action. The reason this is so is that "names" (*ming* 名) (the signifier, or written language) come from symbols (*zhishi* 指事 simple ideographs) that demonstrate a type of order, norm, principle—which is also "reality" (the signified). Even today, people will criticize a person's action or behavior using the phrase, *bu xiang hua* 不像話 [meaning "outrageous" or "shocking," but literally "it does not resemble the word"]. Clearly, words (language) have always had a solemn sacredness in China. Language is not just sounds uttered into the air—it does not simply represent, but rather it itself *is* human behavior and action, as in the saying "a team of horses cannot take back what has been said." The awesome primitive function of language and writing is retained in the high view of language in Confucius and later thinkers. For this reason, the study of names [or terms] in ancient China was not Logic, for the heart of what was discussed was the practical use of language or words and the possible instances of actual paradox. Those thinkers that have a bit more independence and a more logical way of thinking, like Gongsun Long, Hui Shi, or the Mohist Dialectics (*mobian* 墨辯), have been rejected by

Confucians (like Xunzi), and forgotten by later generations. Through the present time, it was only after the West proved the efficacy and practicality of this kind of logical argument with their science and technology that Chinese people were eager to receive it. When Yan Fu first spoke of the field of Logic, he received an enthusiastic welcome among Chinese intellectuals and scholars who were hearing of it for the first time. It is not that the Chinese do not have the capability but that they have never had the interest to develop this aspect. Jin Yuelin's (金嶽霖, 1895–1984) *Lun Dao* 論道 and *Renshi lun* 認識論 and Feng Youlan's *Zhenyuan liu shu* 貞元六書 were published around the same time and are quite similar in their thinking, yet Feng's book enjoyed a great influence, and Jin's very little, probably due to this reason. Han Fei's theories also had a strong logical character, but they were unable to develop into an abstract study of Logic. Han Fei precisely emphasized the uselessness of pure argument or the notion of "truth," as in his chapter "Shuo nan" (說難, "Difficulties of persuasion"). The *Hanfeizi* can be seen as a book that "benefits people with its deep wisdom" because of its cold rationality in telling people many cruel realities about life, and not because of the logical character of the argument itself. Reading the *Hanfeizi* is useful to understanding the role of "logic" in China. **Since Confucianism takes "emotion" as substance, it naturally has some antipathy for logic. Many of the arguments in *Mencius* are directly opposed to formal logic.**

This emphasis on "rectification of names" foreshadowed later Legalist methods of political control characterized by "using the name to criticize the reality; following the name to find the reality" 以名責實，循名求實. In a certain sense, the Legalists developed out of Confucianism, for did not Confucius say, "The ruler is the ruler, the minister the minister; the father the father, the son the son"? This is the problem of naming reality, or the rectification of names. **A "name" is a concrete principle of the social order, its norms and ritual system; if it is carefully maintained without fail, then it is possible to govern by "inaction" (*wuwei* 無為). The Confucians, Daoists, and Legalists all spoke of "governing through inaction," and all discussed "names." This "name" is not [a matter of] linguistics or logic, but of pragmatic government.** H. Creel has recognized, with good grounds, that the "inaction" of Shen Buhai 申不害 (420–337 BCE) is derived from the *Analects* (see his *What is Taoism*). Chad Hansen believes that "names" refer to "ritual," that is, "making distinctions," which makes sense. Tan Sitong fiercely opposes the "teaching of names" (the teaching of ritual), or "making names into a teaching," because these "names" confirm the existence of the order of social ranks and distinctions, which is related to the maintenance of traditional ethics and government. When **Confucius demanded the "rectification of names," "the ruler is the ruler, the minister the minister, the father the father, the son the son," it was because this was the only way to lead people to properly act (practice); this is Confucian epistemology. In Chinese [thought], there is no distinction between fact and value, theory (knowledge) and practice, name and reality, and this has linguistic roots:** (a) Chinese characters (written language) are not the record of spoken language, but the record of historical experience ("simple ideographs"); (b) therefore, characters exercise the important function of directly effecting people's behavior; this in turn has a connection to the origins in shamanism, for the recording of "historical experience" is fundamentally entangled with shamanistic ceremony. Because Chinese characters originate in ideographs and the recording of historical experience, and because Chinese emphasizes single characters and nouns, having no need for plurals, articles, gender, and so on, its function lies in using historical experience to lead people to act and live, and not in representing, describing, or duplicating concrete things, nor in recording spoken language. These are all important aspects and elements in the construction of "pragmatic reason," in great contrast to the Western tradition based on the Greeks and Hebrews.

13.4. 樊遲請學稼, 子曰: 「吾不如老農。」請學為圃。曰: 「吾不如老圃。」樊遲出。子曰: 「小人哉, 樊須也! 上好禮, 則民莫敢不敬; 上好義, 則民莫敢不服; 上好信, 則民莫敢不用情。夫如是, 則四方之民襁負其子而至矣, 焉用稼?」

Fan Chi asked about learning to plant crops. Confucius answered, "I am not as good as an old farmer." Fan Chi asked about planting vegetables, and Confucius answered, "I am not as good as an old vegetable grower."

Fan Chi left. Confucius said, "What a petty person Fan Chi is. A leader is particular about ritual, and the people do not fail to be respectful and reverent; a leader is particular about being reasonable and appropriate, and the people will not fail to follow; a leader is particular about trustworthiness, and the people will not fail to tell the truth about a situation. If this is so, people from all over will come to him to seek shelter, bearing their children on their backs. What does he want to go planting crops for?"

Comments: Clearly, a "petty person" refers to an ordinary person, rather than being a derogatory moral term. Beginning with the Spring and Autumn and Warring States period, the class of *shi* 士 ("intellectuals"[2]) arose in China. "Study and excel, and you will take office" 學而優則仕 is the life's path of an intellectual (*shi*). The Han dynasty had its commandery quota system of examination and elevation of officials (*chaju* 察舉), and from the Sui and Tang on, the examination was the system the government used [to identify talent]. The duty of "intellectuals" was to "be devoted to the ruler and benefit the people," to "bring peace to the state and stability to the country," handling the affairs of government, and as such they became a mainstay and backbone within the structure of society. Before the appearance of democratic government and modern bureaucracy, China's system of literate officials was the most complete and effective system, and its foundational concept can be said to originate here. We see clear expression of this in Mencius's words, "The one who labors with his mind rules others; the one who labors with his strength is ruled by others" 勞心者治人, 勞力者治於人 (*Mencius* III.A.4). Opposite to this there has always been the stream in Chinese thought, from the agrarians and Mohists down to Mao Zedong, that opposed the distinction between those who labor with their minds and those who labor with their strength or muscles, following the utopian concepts of the producers directly managing the work of government. Fan Chi can probably be numbered among them. Does not the Master always speak of "returning to the ancients" (*fu gu* 復古)? Then would it not be even better to simply return to the time of "Great Peace" (*taiping* 太平) when the emperor or the king did the plowing or sowing himself? This is behind [Fan Chi's] question about learning to plant crops or grow vegetables. But Confucius does not agree.

The word *qing* 情 (here translated "the truth about a situation") does not mean [as it does in modern Chinese] "feelings," but truth, reality or the situation (*qingkuang* 情況). A. C. Graham has written about this in great detail, arguing that in the pre-Han period *qing* referred to reality or substance, and not to feelings (see his *Studies in Chinese Philosophy and Philosophical Literature*); this probably has merit. Yet there is an even greater significance to the fact that the word *qing* 情 meaning "feeling," "emotion," or "affect" evolved from the word *qing* 情 meaning "substance," "essence," "truth," or "situation." The two share some kind of important connection. The *Xunzi*, in the chapter on the rectification of names, says, "The love and hate, delight and anger, happiness and sorrow of nature are called feelings (*qing*)." In the "Liyun" chapter of the *Liji* it says, "What are human feelings (*qing*)? They are like and hate, sorrow and fear, love, hate, and desire." In these passages the word *qing* constitutes a kind of meeting or exchange of both "reality" and "emotion": emotion is the substance, reality, or truth of humanity; it is where we find so-called human nature. Therefore, Confucians **emphasize the shaping of emotion and the cultivation of one's nature in order to have a successful life.**

13.5. 子曰: 「誦詩三百, 授之以政, 不達; 使於四方, 不能專對; 雖多, 亦奚以為? 」

Confucius said, "If someone has thoroughly studied the 300 poems of the *Shijing*, but when entrusted with government proves inept, or when he leaves the country to practice diplomacy cannot come up with a response unaided—though he may have studied a lot, of what use is it?"

Comments: At the time, the *Shijing* was far from just an aesthetic work of art; it had a very important practical use. The *Shijing* was often employed in diplomatic speech, in order to demonstrate the authority and norms on which it rested. See the Zuo Commentary (*Zuozhuan*).

13.6. 子曰: 「其身正, 不令而行; 其身不正, 雖令不從。」

Confucius said, "If your own conduct is correct, you will be able to accomplish things without giving any orders; if your conduct is not correct, you may give orders but no one will obey them."

Comments: This is, again, the [notion of] ethical government that we have spoken of many times above, that is, the theoretical vestiges of the "art of leadership" of clan heads. Later this would become a traditional aphorism.

13.7. 子曰: 「魯衛之政, 兄弟也。」

Confucius said, "The government of the state of Lu and that of the state of Wei are like brothers."

Notes: *Zhu Xi notes: Lu refers to [the state of Lu] after the time of the Duke of Zhou; Wei refers to [the state of Wei] after the time of Kang Shu. They were originally the states of brothers that had now declined and become chaotic, and their governments likewise; for this reason Confucius lamented over it.*

Comments: What does this mean? Does it mean that these two states in the past were more or less alike? Or that they are presently equally messed up? Or that the two governments should cooperate harmoniously like two brothers? There are many explanations, including that of Zhu Xi in the note above.

13.8. 子謂衛公子荊,「善居室。始有, 曰: 『苟合矣。』少有, 曰: 『苟完矣。』富有, 曰: 『苟美矣。』」

Confucius said, "The Duke of Wei's son Jing knows how to handle his household affairs. When he had just a little wealth, he said 'Truly, it is enough.' When it had increased a bit, he said, 'All is truly provided for'" When it had increased even more, he said 'This is really absolutely perfect.'"

Notes: *Liu Baonan notes: On "knowing how to handle his household affairs"* 善居室*: Huang Kan notes: In living in his home he is able to govern it and not be wasteful, therefore he is said to be "good" at it. "When he has it"* 有*, means when he has wealth;* gou 苟 *means sincere, trustworthy.*

Cheng Shude quotes the "Fanshen lu": In his living situation he does not seek flashy resplendence, but his intentions are plain and transparent; he is truly a fine prince, hovering over this corrupt world. It happens in the world that someone has just entered upon his official duties and built a new house when he is sent away or recalled to another position, and the construction is still not finished. . . . People do not have a body that lasts a hundred years without rotting, and nor is there a dwelling that lasts a hundred years without rotting. What would be the purpose in seeking after the perfect house? How many are the painted halls, towers, and terraces of the past that have today become barren mounds and ruins of broken stone? Before his splendid gold and glorious jade, there is none who doesn't look around rejoicing, yet today where are they? From of old it has been thus; it is best to let good enough alone. . . . In recent times, there was a distinguished official who retired and returned to his home, then initiated a great construction project, doing his utmost, supervising the workmen, hammering the foundations and laying the walls, working hard to make it solid. One carpenter was not working hard, and he severely reprimanded him. The carpenter answered him as he hammered, "In the city, a certain official built a certain house, and employed me for all of it. At the time, he was only concerned that it would not be solid[ly built], but today although it [remains] perfectly solid, the house has already had three masters. Although it is solid yet it was all in vain." When the official heard this, he was filled with gloom and disheartened.

Comments: The Chinese people's attitude toward life is apparent in both the original text and the notes. The phrase I have rendered "handling household affairs" could also be translated as "building houses." This touches on an interesting question: **Many ancient primitive civilizations have left behind the ruins of large-scale stone edifices; only China has not (the Great Wall is primarily a packed-earth construction).** Why? To this day we do not have an answer. I believe the reason may lie in the fact that China's ancient clans and tribes, with their primitive humanism and primitive democracy, did not have adequate authoritarian power to enslave the common people in the service of erecting huge stone edifices. By the time Qin Shihuang attained this type of power, packed-earth and wooden buildings had long become a tradition that would not have been easy to change. In addition, this advice against seeking perfection in building dwellings expresses traditional Chinese thought: people easily age, while human affairs are difficult to make last 人生易老, 世事難長; one should seek other things in life, rather than just splendid residences or the enjoyment of material possessions.

13.9. 子適衛, 冉有僕。子曰: 「庶矣哉! 」冉有曰: 「既庶矣。又何加焉? 」曰: 「富之。」曰: 「既富矣, 又何加焉? 」曰: 「教之。」

Confucius went to the land of Wei, and Ran You was driving. Confucius said, "The population is very large!"

Ran You asked, "If the population is large, what should be the next step?" [Confucius said,] "Enrich them."

"They are already enriched, then what should be done?" "Educate them."

Comments: Confucius advocated "enriching them," and "educating them," and the order is first to enrich, then to educate. Mencius said, "[A clear-sighted ruler ensures] that the people always have sufficient food in good years and escape starvation in bad; only then does he drive them towards goodness; in this way the people find it easy to follow him" 樂歲終身苦, 凶年不免於死亡。此惟救死而恐不贍, 奚暇治禮義哉 (*Mencius* I.A.7).[3] Guanzi said, "Any method of governing a country must first enrich the people" 凡治國之道, 必先富民 (*Guanzi* "Zhi guo" 治國); and "Let the storehouses be full, and they will understand their ritual obligations; let food and clothing be adequate, and they will understand glory and shame" 仓廪实而知礼节, 衣食足而知荣辱 (*Shiji*, "Biography of Guan Zhong and Yan Ying"). This seemingly common sense political concept has often been neglected or overlooked by later true or false moralisms that have done completely the opposite and bewildered the people. Beginning from the precedent set by the Song-Ming Neo-Confucian emphasis on "The Way of the Great Learning lies in illuminating luminous virtue, treating the people with affection, and resting in perfect goodness" ("Daxue"), while forgetting to "enrich them, educate them"; all the way down to [Mao's] "People should have a little spirit" 人是要有一點精神的, and [the post–Cultural Revolution slogan] "rather take the grass of socialism than the sprouts of capitalism" 寧要社會主義的草, 不要資本主義的苗—are these not all the same? **Economic development that takes the means of production (technology) as its core, and educational development that takes the cultivation of human nature (psychology) as its core, should always be the two hands, hard and soft, [enabling] the existence and development of the human race.** This is still the case today and will continue to be so in the future. For the past hundred years, China has paid little attention to either of these two hands, concentrating its spirit, strength, talent, and knowledge on the military and on government; there are of course many complicated objective and subjective reasons for this. Today, a reversal is beginning to take shape, in which economics is taking the lead, but the neglect of education remains unchanged. Perhaps this will change.

"Enlarging the population" and "enriching them" still occupy the first and second position. The strong interest of Song-Ming Neo-Confucians in [such formulations as] "In its capacity to produce and reproduce, we call it 'change'" 生生之謂易,[4] "The great virtue of Heaven and Earth is called 'generation'" 天地之大德曰生,[5] and Zhou Dunyi's leaving the grass to grow outside his window to preserve the intention of Heaven, and so on—all remain on the level of the spirit and morality, ignoring the fact that **"production and reproduction" 生生 is first and foremost a**

question of "people living." This "philosophy of eating" of mine has on the one hand been criticized by leftist Marxists that revere class struggle as the standard, and on the other hand been opposed by New Confucians who revere moral metaphysics as the standard, each blaming me for "vulgarizing" Marx and Confucius. In actuality, both Marx and Confucius emphasize the simple fact that people must first eat in order to exist (or live), so how can this be said to be "vulgarizing"?

13.10. 子曰: 「苟有用我者。期月而已可也, 三年有成。」

Confucius said, "If someone were to make use of me, within one year I would be able to do an okay job, and within three years I would have achieved quite a success."

Comments: It seems that old Master Confucius is not a modest gentleman or one who pretends to modesty or deference. At times he even advertises or recommends himself (perhaps not unlike today's candidates for political office?). Some doubt that this passage records the words of Confucius himself. Actually, among the five hundred passages of the *Analects*, there are many that express great differences in both thought and style. Surely there are not a few that did not come from Confucius, but as I discussed in the introduction, since they have already been ascribed to Confucius for over two thousand years, to set out to distinguish between them one by one is neither necessary nor very possible.

13.11. 子曰: 「『善人為邦百年, 亦可以勝殘去殺矣。』誠哉是言也! 」

Confucius said, "'If good people were to govern the affairs of the country for a hundred years, it would be possible to eliminate all acts of violence and abolish the death penalty.' This saying is quite right."

Comments: Clearly, everything has to happen gradually; violence cannot be eliminated immediately, and even less can the death penalty be abolished all of a sudden. Even if a "good person" or "sage-king" is attempting to do so, these things need time. There must be a long process of improvement.

13.12. 子曰:「如有王者, 必世而後仁。」

Confucius said, "Should a sage-king arise, it would still take thirty years to make the people's hearts humane."

Comments: Should "humaneness" here refer to "humaneness of heart-mind" or "humane government"? It seems the former is what is meant. But neither can be accomplished in one fell swoop. In particular, causing the people to all have humane heart-minds must depend entirely upon education, and thus even a "sage-king" would need at least thirty years [to accomplish it].

13.13. 子曰:「苟正其身矣, 於從政乎何有? 不能正其身, 如正人何?」

Confucius said, "If you have corrected yourself, what difficulty will you have in practicing government? If you cannot correct yourself, how can you correct others?"

Comments: Here again we see the same notion of ethical government. This type of oft-repeated statement is an early sign of what enabled the moralism of later generations. Cheng Yi admonished the Song emperor Zhezong not to "hurt Heaven's intention" by breaking off a willow branch, and Liu Zongzhou answered the Ming emperor Sizong's questions about national salvation saying, "If Your Majesty has a calm heart, then all under heaven will be calm"—all of these became laughingstocks over the centuries, but none did not originate here [in this passage]. A great emperor, at base, is not the leader of a small clan, and ethics and government had long parted ways—how could "correcting oneself" cause the people of the world to all be "correct"? This is the fundamental reason why the Way of Confucius and Mencius was never practicable in their own time, let alone in later generations. In the past, however, very few people have tried to draw attention to this in light of the historical or societal background. Of course, this is not to say that "correcting oneself" is of no importance for those who hold the reins of government. One may have "governing methods," but one must still "govern people." This is even more true of the individual pursuit of personal religious morality.

13.14. 冉子退朝。子曰:「何晏也?」對曰:「有政。」子曰:「其事也。如有政, 雖不吾以, 吾其與聞之。」

Ran You returned from the court. Confucius said, "Why are you so late?" He answered, "I had governmental duties." Confucius said, "Those were just ordinary duties. If there had been any major governmental duty, even it had nothing to do with me, I would have known about it and participated in it."

Comments: Here, Confucius seems to distinguish between work affairs and work that is truly governmental in nature!? There was probably a contemporary situation here that we do not know about.

13.15. 定公問:「一言而可以興邦, 有諸?」孔子對曰:「言不可以若是其幾也。人之言曰:『為君難, 為臣不易。』如知為君之難也, 不幾乎一言而興邦乎?」曰:「一言而喪邦, 有諸?」孔子對曰:「言不可以若是其幾也。人之言曰:『予無樂乎為君, 唯其言而莫予違也。』如其善而莫之違也, 不亦善乎? 如不善而莫之違也, 不幾乎一言而喪邦乎?」

Duke Ding asked, "For someone to be able with one sentence to vitalize the country, is there such a thing as this?"

Confucius answered, "One must not expect that of language. People say, 'To be a ruler is difficult; to be a minister is also not easy.' If people know the difficulty of being a ruler, should not this one sentence be almost enough to vitalize the country?"

He asked again, "For someone to be able to lose the country with one sentence, is there such a thing?"

Confucius answered, saying, "One must not expect that of language. People say, 'I am not at all happy to be a ruler, it is just that no one dares to contradict me.' If you speak so well that no one dares to contradict you, is that not a good thing? If you speak badly and no one dares to contradict you, then isn't that precisely 'being able to lose the country with one sentence'?"

Notes: *Zhu Xi notes: The character* ji 幾 *is* qi 期 *[meaning "to expect" or "await"]. Fan [Zuyu* 范祖禹 *(1041–1098)] notes: If one's speech is not good and there is no one to contradict it, then loyal speech will not reach [the rul-*

er's] ear. The ruler will daily grow more proud, and the ministers daily more fawning; none would not lose the country in this situation. Xie [Liangzuo 謝良佐 *(1050–1103)] notes: If there are only his words and none to contradict, then people who slander, fawn, and flatter to the [ruler's] face will multiply. The state may not necessarily be suddenly vitalized or lost, but the root of its being so lies here.*

Comments: In authoritarian governments, a single person holds power, and the masses stand mutely in line; the emperor has "a golden mouth and jade teeth," and no one contradicts him. Therefore, as to the sentence about "losing the country," there are many examples to point to. "One sentence is equal to ten thousand sentences," and can kill many people. Duke Ding originally wants to take a shortcut, and thus hopes that a single sentence will be able to solve a problem. But Confucius tells him that if one knows how difficult it is to be a ruler or a minister, this answer is also a single sentence—this reply is marvelous. The answer to the question about losing a country with a single sentence is similar; it is much stronger than what Zhu Xi's note suggests.

13.16. 葉公問政。子曰:「近者說, 遠者來。」

The Duke of She asked how to govern. Confucius said, "Keep those of the people who are close by happy, and those who are far off will come near."

Notes: *Kang Youwei notes: The "Mozi" has "[They] draw near those who are far away, and renew the old."*[6] *The original should be corrected in this way. . . . For this reason, those who are not good at governing remain in the great Hall at a distance of ten thousand* li, *while for those who are good at governing, a distance of ten thousand* li *shrinks to be as though it were near at hand. What with today's railroads, electrical lines, and steamboats, distances have shrunk to be within a hand's breadth and can be crossed with a breath; transportation has progressed and improved, so that "they draw near those that are far away." For even if utensils are better when old, policies had better be new. For it is [often] the case that while the old are clogged and stagnant, the new flow freely; the old are spoiled, the new are fresh; the old are declining and decadent, the new are strong and in good order; the old are undisciplined and sloppy, the new are unified; the old are corrupt and* *left behind, the new are being developed and carried forward; the old remain only in form, so that people do not appreciate them, while the new display vigor and spirit, so that people's feelings are spurred onward along with them. Yi Yin said, Utilize the new, get rid of the stale, and if it is defective do not keep it. Thus getting rid of the defective lies entirely with getting rid of the old and renewing [things].*

Comments: Kang Youwei's note uses the ancient to explain the modern, the old in service of the new, beating the drum of modernization; this also characterizes contemporary Chinese interpretations, in another example of the traditional spirit of "renovating day by day, and again renovating"[7] 日日新, 又日新.

13.17. 子夏為莒父宰, 問政。子曰: 「無欲速, 無見小利。欲速, 則不達; 見小利, 則大事不成。」

Zixia was the magistrate of the area of Jufu. He asked about how to govern. Confucius said, "Do not seek speed, nor look for petty gain. If you seek speed, you will not reach your goal; if you look for petty gain, you will be unable to get major things done."

Comments: It is not only government that is like this—this is also the lesson and wisdom of life experience. In contemporary China, the experience of seeking speed and not attaining has been particularly painful. An apt example is the saying, "Ten thousand years is too long; / We struggle for just a day and a night" 一萬年太久, 只爭朝夕.[8] Although the things sought by the radical youth of today are different, and their doctrine is also different, they actually do not depart from these old ruts, sad to say.

13.18. 葉公語孔子曰: 「吾黨有直躬者, 其父攘羊, 而子證之。」孔子曰: 「吾黨之直者異於是。父為子隱, 子為父隱, 直在其中矣。」

The Duke of She said to Confucius, "We have in our place an upright man; his father steals sheep, and the son comes to expose him." Confucius said, "In our place upright men are not like this—the father covers for his son, and the son covers for his father; uprightness lies in this."

Comments: This is a larger question that is worthy of study. In the clan government advocated by Confucius and Mencius, the family is most important, and "filiality and [parental] love" are paramount. Mencius tells how if a father kills someone, his son (Shun) can carry him away on his back to protect him (*Mencius* VII.A.35). In later generations this would change, and Confucians would also say "Great righteousness may harm one's relations" 大義滅親, and "Loyalty and filiality cannot both be perfect" 忠孝不能兩全, and the like. In modern society, this is of course against the law, and constitutes the crime of falsifying evidence; but it is also a human emotion that can still be seen in real life. This issue touches on many problems in sociology and psychology. Chinese traditional law allowed family members to cover for each other within certain limits. Sociologically speaking, this practice demonstrates respect for the family as the solid foundation of society. Psychologically speaking, it demonstrates the importance of the training of emotions above all else. For this reason, so-called uprightness or correctness here does not refer to legal right or wrong; the social righteousness it implies highlights the difference between and contradiction between public social morality and private religious morality. In the *Analects*, to be upright ("straight" *zhi* 直)—righteous, just—is related to sincerity of emotion, and in every passage that pertains to "straightness" it is the same, whether "A person should live with integrity" 人之生也直 (6.19), or "Who says this Weisheng Gao is forthright?" 孰謂衛生高直 (5.24), and so on.

13.19. 樊遲問仁。子曰:「居處恭, 執事敬, 與人忠。雖之夷狄, 不可棄也。」

Fan Chi asked what humaneness is. Confucius said, "In one's manner of living, to be serious and circumspect; in handling one's affairs, solemn and diligent; in one's relations with people, honest and trustworthy; and not to lose or change in this respect, even if one goes to an uncivilized region."

Comments: Beginning with Confucius, the distinction between "China" and the "Yi and Di" 夷狄 [or "barbarians"] is a cultural concept, and not a racial one. Although it might have been said, "If they are not of my kind, they must differ in mind and heart," as long as someone accepted the culture of the Central Plains they would be considered to be of the "same kind." Confucian civilization not only "educates" the ordinary people, it also "educates" all the "Yi and Di." Neither the Han nor the Tang hesitated to give "foreigners" high official positions or to allow them to handle great authority; they never asked about their race or "nationality." The Chinese people were confidently established on the foundation of faith in their own culture, with the result that they used their culture to assimilate and even occupy a position of dominance over various races. From the Five Barbarians and Sixteen Kingdoms to the Manchu Qing dynasty, has this not always been the case? Only when they lost faith in their own culture were they afraid of "foreign imports." Was this not the case from the late Qing bureaucrats through the old "Leftists"?

13.20. 子貢問曰:「何如斯可謂之士矣?」子曰:「行己有恥, 使於四方, 不辱君命, 可謂士矣。」曰:「敢問其次。」曰:「宗族稱孝焉, 鄉黨稱弟焉。」曰:「敢問其次。」曰:「言必信, 行必果, 硜硜然, 小人哉! 抑亦可以為次矣。」曰:「今之從政者何如?」子曰:「噫! 斗筲之人, 何足算也。」

Zigong asked, "What sort of person should one be to be called an intellectual (*shi* 士)?" Confucius said, "One who in his behavior and actions maintains a sense of shame, and who when sent abroad does not prove unworthy of his lord's mission—this sort of person may be called an intellectual."

Zigong said, "May I ask about the next lower rank?" Confucius said, "All in the clan praise him for his filiality towards his parents, and all in the village praise him for his respect for his elders."

Zigong said, "May I ask about yet the next lower rank?" Confucius said, "In his speech he keeps to his word, in his behavior he is dependable. Such people are like little pebbles thumping around, or like the most ordinary of people, yet this can still be considered the next lower rank."

Zigong said, "What about those who seek to govern today?" Confucius said, "Ai! Such narrow-minded, short-sighted people—how can they amount to anything?"

Comments: In the "Duke Ai" chapter of the *Xunzi*, it says, "Confucius said, 'That which my lord asks about is a question worthy of a sage ruler. I am a nobody. How would I be capable of knowing it?' "[9] 孔子曰:「君之所問, 聖君之問也, 丘、小人也, 何足以知之?」Here, the term *xiaoren* 小人 ("a nobody") means an "ordinary person." Clearly, it does not refer to a morally bad person, but rather just to an everyday, normal person. Furthermore, for such a person to be described as, "In his speech he keeps to his word, in his behavior he is dependable" is no easy feat. Of course, in comparison with a learned ruler, he will rank lower, but compared to "those who govern today" he is far above them. As for the "shame" referred to in the line "conscious of shame," this is much broader than "shame" as we use it today, and includes the idea that the person always feels he is lacking in some respect. An intellectual not only has knowledge, but must express that knowledge in his behavior and action; the same should be true today. For someone to pretend to have knowledge and yet have little historical responsibility for the people of his country, or if though he is learned he is depraved in his behavior, can he be considered an intellectual? The reason that Confucianism is considered more than a philosophy, more than high-sounding words, lies precisely here. This is exactly what we would call the "critical point." The order of ranking here is according to one's favor or reputation at the level of the country, family (clan) and the individual. "Those who govern today" do not even have the character of an ordinary person, and therefore are not worth speaking of.

13.21. 子曰:「不得中行而與之,必也狂狷乎!狂者進取,狷者有所不為也。」

Confucius said, "If it is not possible to be with someone who accords with the Mean, then I'd rather be with a wild knight and a puritan. The wild knight actively forges ahead, while the puritan has things he will not do."

Notes: *Zhu Xi notes:* Xing 行 *means* Dao 道 *(the Way)*. Kuang 狂 *means someone whose intent extends high and his action does not measure up to it. The one who is* juan 狷 *["puritan"] has too little knowledge and an excess of conservativism.*

Comments: The "middle," "moderation," "the middle way," and "the Mean" all mean the same thing: to be measured in advancing or retreating. **To be "wild" is to actively forge ahead, while to be "puritan" is to passively resist.** "Forging ahead" and "having things one will not do" are both easy to understand in the original Chinese and do not need to be translated into modern Chinese. **Both the "wild" and the**

"puritan" share the characteristics of going against the flow and being unrestrained by common norms. Clearly, Confucius would not have liked the "hypocritically modest gentlemen" 謙謙君子 of later generations. The accumulation of merit and demerit through "thrice daily self-examination" of Zengzi's school of thought (see 1.4) would seem quite incompatible with either the "wild" or the "puritan," would it not? Or perhaps it could be counted as a different type of "puritanism"? Confucius's explanation of *juan* ("puritan") as one who "has things he will not do" is much stronger than Zhu Xi's annotation would suggest. I always say that in the actual circumstances of the past decades in China, "forging ahead" or "having things one *will* do" has been very difficult or even impossible, while "having things one will not do" (or refusing to go along with evil deeds or go with the flow) has actually been possible to do to various degrees. Chen Yinke 陳寅恪 (1890–1969) was an example of such a one.

13.22. 子曰:「南人有言曰:『人而無恆, 不可以作巫醫。』善夫!」「不恆其德, 或承之羞。」子曰:「不占而已矣。」

Confucius said, "The people of the south have a saying: 'If a person does not have a constant heart-mind, he cannot be a prognosticator or practice medicine.' This saying is very good." "If he cannot persevere, he will call disgrace upon himself." Confucius said, "Then it's better he not do it."

Comments: This passage is difficult to explain, and there are many old interpretations; I have to offer a tentative translation and let that suffice. The core meaning, however—emphasizing the importance of a constant heart-mind, and a spirit of tenacious perseverance—is quite clear. In ancient times, medicine men also practiced prognostication. In early primeval history, prognostication was a very complex and tedious job that may have been a hereditary position and required tremendous patience and will. "If he cannot persevere, he will call disgrace upon himself" is an ancient prognostic saying.[10] It roughly means that if one does not persevere, one will fail and thus summon disgrace. I believe that Chinese culture originated with the shaman-historian (the rationalization of shamanism), on which, see elsewhere. "Constancy" (*heng* 恆) in ancient shamanistic prognostication meant "mysterious and eternal."

13.23. 子曰:「君子和而不同, 小人同而不和。」

Confucius said, "The noble person is harmonious but does not conform; the petty person conforms but is not harmonious."

Notes: *Cheng Shude quotes the "Zhengyu"* 鄭語 *chapter of the Guoyu* 國語: *Now harmony produces the living things, while uniformity does not lead to development. . . . The former kings took earth and mixed it with metal, wood, water, and fire, to make the myriad things. For this reason, one harmonizes the five flavors in order to suit people's taste; one strengthens the four limbs in order to keep the body healthy; one harmonizes the six tones in order to make sounds that delight the ear. . . . [The former kings] took their consorts from other clans, and sought out riches from every quarter; they chose ministers who were willing to directly remonstrate with them, and managed a multitude of matters, seeking harmony but not uniformity. If the notes are one, there is nothing to listen to; if there is only one type of thing there is no pattern; if there is only one flavor, there is no resulting [mix of flavors]; if there is only one type of thing, there is nothing to explain [or compare]. To this [Yanzi] answers [in the "Yanzi Chunqiu"]: Harmony is like a soup. . . . The former kings ordered the five flavors and harmonized the five sounds, in order to calm their minds and perfect their government. Sound is like flavor—the one* qi, *the two forms, the three categories, the four instruments, the five sounds, the six tones, the seven notes, the eight winds, the nine songs—this is how they mutually complete each other. Clear or cloudy, small or great, lacking or overflowing, grieving or rejoicing, hard or soft, slow or fast, high or low, entering or exiting, dense or sparse—this is how they order each other. The noble person listens to it to calm his mind, and when his mind is calm, his virtues are harmonized.*

Yang Bojun notes: "Harmony" and "uniformity" are two common terms from the Warring States period. The "Zuozhuan" (twentieth year of Zhaogong) records Yanzi's discussion with Duke Jing of Qi criticizing Liang Qiuju, which together with the record of Shibo's speech in the "Zhengyu" chapter of the Guoyu are both very detailed. "Harmony" is like the balancing of the five flavors, and the harmonizing of the eight tones—one absolutely must have all kinds of different ingredients—water, fire, soy sauce, vinegar—in order to balance the flavors; one absolutely must have all kinds of different notes—high and low, long and short, fast and slow—in order to make a piece of music harmonious. Yanzi said, "The ruler and his ministers are like this also: what the ruler says is permissible has what is not permissible in it; the minister offers his denial in order to complete his permission. What the ruler says is not permissible has what is permissible in it; the minister offers his permission in order to get rid of his denial." This is why Shibo also said, "To use one to calm the other is called harmony" 以他平他謂之和. *Uniformity is not like this; as Yanzi said, "If the ruler says it is permissible and you in turn say it is permissible, or if the ruler says it is not permissible you in turn say it is not permissible, [this is like] using water to control water: who then will be able to eat? If the zither or lute is the only instrument, who will be able to listen to it? The same is true of the impermissibility of "uniformity."*

Comments: As in the passages "The noble person . . . gets on well with others while avoiding partiality" (15.22) and "The noble person is broadly magnanimous toward people, and is not partial or pandering" (2.14), this demonstrates that **only by maintaining individual distinctiveness and independence can social and interpersonal harmony be achieved.** Even in government this is the case. Terms like "uniformity," "partiality," or "pandering" suggest that it is easy to lose or destroy this type of independence or distinctiveness. This passage is still very much of interest to us today, for insisting upon "unanimity," "uniformity," or "being of one mind" never leads to a good result, and only with "multipolarity," "pluralism," and "diversity" can there be development. From the Notes it is evident that **the precondition for "harmony" is the recognition, affirmation, and admission of one another's differences, distinctions, and divergent views.** Only in this way can these differences and distinctions be ordered and deployed into positions, circumstances, and structures that reflect some sort of appropriacy, so that each is in its place and the whole achieves "harmony"—harmoniousness or development. Chinese philosophy has always **emphasized "harmony," which is the same as emphasizing "appropriate measure"** (appropriacy in handling all kinds of difference and plurality). Along with its emphasis on "not going too far" and "the Mean," the rationale for this is the same; as Confucius said, "My thought and behavior are strung together into a unity" (4.15). This is Chinese dialectics (the Mean, harmony, appropriacy, not going too far).

13.24. 子貢問曰:「鄉人皆好之, 何如?」子曰:「未可也。」「鄉人皆惡之, 何如?」子曰:「未可也。不如鄉人之善者好之, 其不善者惡之。」

Zigong asked, "If all the people in a village like someone, what then?" Confucius said, "No, that's no good." Zigong asked again, "If all the people in a village detest the person, what then?" Confucius said, "No, that's no good. It is better that the good people in a village like him, and the bad detest him."

Comments: This passage is similar in meaning to 15.28, which says, "If everyone hates someone, you should definitely investigate; if everyone likes someone, you should definitely investigate." Confucius does not at all like "people pleasers" or "hypocrites," but "people pleasers" are always the successful ones in life; they are fortune's favorites and people of wealth, whether those with high position and handsome salaries or those who have always had a smooth ride through life. From ancient times to now this has everywhere been the case, unfortunately.

13.25. 子曰: 「君子易事而難說也: 說之不以道, 不說也; 及其使人也, 器之。小人難事而易說也: 說之雖不以道, 說也; 及其使人也, 求備焉。」

Confucius said, "It is easy to serve under a noble person, but it is difficult to please him. If one tries to please him using unjust means, he will not be pleased. When he hands out duties, he uses people according to their strengths. It is difficult to serve under a petty person, but easy to please him. If one tries to please him using unjust means, he will still be pleased. But when handing out duties, he demands perfection."

Comments: This life wisdom from two thousand years ago seems true to life still today.

13.26. 子曰: 「君子泰而不驕, 小人驕而不泰。」

Confucius said, "The noble person is dignified but not proud; the petty person is proud but not dignified."

Comments: There are other interpretations and translations of this passage. In this reading, I adopt the $A \neq A \pm$ explanation, emphasizing the appropriacy of neither too far nor not far enough. This is a unifying thread throughout Confucianism.

13.27. 子曰:「剛毅、木訥, 近仁。」

Confucius said, "The strong, the resolute, the simple, and the slow to speak all are close to humaneness."

Comments: Here again the importance of being slow to speak is brought out. This is quite the opposite of modern society, when language is permitted exaggeration and cleverness, and dominates everything.

13.28. 子路問曰:「何如斯可謂之士矣?」子曰:「切切、偲偲、怡怡如也, 可謂士矣。朋友切切、偲偲, 兄弟怡怡。」

Zilu asked, "What kind of person can be called an intellectual?" Confucius said, "Someone who urges others on and helps them, getting along with others harmoniously and happily, can be called an intellectual. Among friends he should urge them on; among his brothers, he emphasizes harmoniousness."

Comments: How is a "*shi* 士" [scholar-official, here "intellectual"] manifest in everyday relationships? Why does Confucius here only speak of relationships among brothers and friends? Perhaps because the other three types of relationships (between ruler and minister, father and son, and husband and wife) must be upheld by all people, while in relationships among brothers and friends there is relatively more individual independence and autonomy, and perhaps this better demonstrates the ways that "intellectuals" are different from ordinary people. The reason why in friendship, criticism and encouragement to do better are more emphasized is that friends are usually made on the basis of taste, and therefore it is easy to either refrain from speaking about anything serious, or to be pandering and partial, or again to have a relationship based simply on eating and drinking together. The reason why harmoniousness is more emphasized among brothers is that because of the natural blood ties, the relationship is close, and one may speak frankly, and thus it is easy to let small things turn into disputes and make people into enemies. All of this is based upon experience. Clearly, Confucian discussions of order in human relationships does not only emphasize external social relationships or roles, but places more emphasis on the formation of the inner emotions and psyche that are related to a sense of responsibility.

Friendship and brotherhood each has a different, mutually irreplaceable emotional relationship or emotio-rational construction.

13.29. 子曰:「善人教民七年, 亦可以即戎矣。」

Confucius said, "If a good man teaches the ordinary people for seven years, they will be ready to face a war."

13.30. 子曰:「以不教民戰, 是謂棄之。」

Confucius said, "If one does not undertake military training of the people, this can be called throwing them away."

Comments: Some explain this as "using untrained people to go to war"; I disagree. Together, these two passages teach the necessity of military training and preparation. Confucius is no bookworm, only interested in self-cultivation, culture, and so on, quite unlike the pedants of later generations.

Book 14

14.1. 憲問恥。子曰: 「邦有道, 穀; 邦無道, 穀, 恥也。」「克、伐、怨、欲不行焉, 可以為仁矣?」子曰: 「可以為難矣, 仁則吾不知也。」

Yuanxian asked what shame was. Confucius said, "When the government is clean, draw a salary; to draw a salary when the government is not clean, this is shameful."

"To have neither competitiveness, boasting, resentment, nor covetousness, can this be called 'humaneness'?" Confucius said, "It can be said to be precious and hard to achieve. As to whether or not it can be called 'humaneness,' I don't know."

Comments: This passage should be divided into two sections. The first section seems to be written to reflect the "roly-polies"[1] or "political whores" that still exist today: they gain advantage from all sides, trimming their sails, always managing to stay in high office with a fat salary—these really can be said to have no sense of shame, and how numerous they are! The second segment again distinguishes humaneness from any other sort of virtue or good deeds, demonstrating the active, initiating, emotional aspect of humaneness, rather than simply the passive aspect of restraint or conciliation.

14.2. 子曰: 「士而懷居, 不足以為士矣。」

Confucius said, "An intellectual who yearns for an easy life is not worthy to be an intellectual."

Comments: I have already spoken above about "regarding all under heaven as one's duty," and "when the Xiongnu have not been defeated, why would one return home" (although this was spoken by a military person), and so on, as well as Sartre's statement that "intellectual" does not mean merely having knowledge. This is Confucian religious morality, which at the time was actual social morality.

14.3. 子曰: 「邦有道, 危言危行; 邦無道, 危行言孫。」

Confucius said, "When government is clean, language is honest and action is upright. When government is in darkness, action may be honest and upright, but language must be prudent and circumspect."

Comments: This passage means, "In a chaotic generation, protect yourself and keep yourself alive," just as the Daoists did. **Clearly, although Confucius advocates "knowing something is not possible yet going and doing it" 知其不可而為之 (14.38), he does not believe that in every time or place one must throw oneself half-naked into battle or be foolhardy.** Most young people do not understand this, thinking that this [kind of self-preservation] is weakness or timidity, not realizing that "tall and straight is easy to break," and that the type of "strength" that acts on a temporary burst of will does not often survive long. Therefore, **the key lies in ruthless struggle. Lu Xun often spoke of this, regretting that youth do not pay attention and make this mistake time and again.** So-called upright action means having things one will not do, refusing to go along with evil deeds or take part in mass criticisms.

14.4. 子曰: 「有德者, 必有言。有言者, 不必有德。仁者, 必有勇。勇者, 不必有仁。」

Confucius said, "A moral person must speak well, but a person who speaks well is not necessarily moral. A kindhearted person must be courageous, but a courageous person will not necessarily be kindhearted."

Comments: This passage again concerns the relationship between the inner (humaneness, virtue) and the outer (courage and speech). If one has the inner without thought of the outer, one will necessarily also have the outer.

14.5. 南宮适問於孔子曰:「羿善射, 奡盪舟, 俱不得其死然; 禹稷躬稼, 而有天下。」夫子不答, 南宮适出。子曰:「君子哉若人! 尚德哉若人!」

Nangong Kuo asked Confucius, "Yi was good at shooting arrows, and Ao's strength was so great he could turn over a boat, but neither of these met a good end. Yu of the Xia and Houji personally tended their plots, and they obtained all under heaven." Confucius made no answer.

After Nangong Kuo left, Confucius said, "This man is truly a noble person. This man truly reverences virtuous action."

Comments: Both Yi and Ao are famous clan leaders and heroes in the Chinese tradition. This passage again emphasizes the leader's "virtuous action"; those who depend upon their strength or wantonly engage in military aggression usually reap as they sow. Nangong's words naturally were greatly to Confucius's liking.

14.6. 子曰:「君子而不仁者有矣夫, 未有小人而仁者也。」

Confucius said, "A noble person will have times that he does not practice the virtue of humaneness, but there is no petty person who practices the virtue of humaneness."

Comments: If by "noble person" and "petty person" here Confucius is referring to the objective social status of people, that is, scholar-officials vs. ordinary people, then this would be in contradiction to some other sayings, such as that a "petty person" can also be a "scholar" (shi 士) or that all people have the capability to "practice humaneness," and so on. If he is referring to the level of virtue or morality, then this is a repetition of those same sayings. But his reason for saying that a "noble person" also has times that he does not practice "humaneness" is to show how difficult humaneness is; was not even Yan Hui said to be able to go only "three months without violating it"? (6.7). Thus, whether we understand "humaneness" as perfect virtue or as peak experience, here we must understand it to refer to some sort of mystical experience. As I have repeatedly noted above, there are many contradictions among the passages of the *Analects*. Whether these contradictions originate with Confucius himself or with those who transmitted his teachings, it is very difficult to find out for certain, and we do not need to try to force a resolution.

14.7. 子曰: 「愛之, 能勿勞乎? 忠焉, 能勿誨乎? 」

Confucius said, "If you love them, can you refrain from encouraging them? If you are loyal to them, can you refrain from teaching or guiding them?"

Notes: *Liu Baonan quotes Wang Yinzhi's* 王引之 *(1766–1834) "Jingyi shuwen"* 經義述聞 *on this passage: The "Lüshi Chunqiu" has an annotation by Gao You* 高誘 *(168–212):* Lao 勞 *means* mian 勉 *["encourage"]. The meaning of "encourage" is close to "instruct," therefore* lao *here is in parallel with* hui 誨 *("instruct"). Gao You notes:* Lao *means* you 憂 *("worry"). And according to the "Liren pian"* 里仁篇, lao er bu yuan 勞而不怨 *is equivalent to* you er bu yuan 憂而不怨. *To worry* (you 憂) *is to think of someone with care.*

Comments: This passage can have a political or an educational interpretation and can be understood either as regarding governmental policy toward the common people or as a guiding principle for the head of the family or a teacher toward children or students. In antiquity, these two were one and the same. The leader treated his clan's members as the head of a large family would treat his children, and therefore a leader was the same as a father or a teacher. The reading of *lao* according to Gao Yao's second note to mean *you* ("worry"), meaning to both love and worry about someone, is not as persuasive as Wang's reading. Many read *lao* as "work hard," "labor," or "be diligent." *Hui* ("instruct") can also be read to mean *mou* 謀 (meaning to "strategize" or "plan"), in which case this would have the same meaning as 1.4: "In trying to find solutions for others, have I done my utmost?"

14.8. 子曰: 「為命: 裨諶草創之, 世叔討論之, 行人子羽脩飾之, 東里子產潤色之。」

Confucius said, "In issuing commands, Pi Chen drew up the draft, Shi Shu would deliberate and comment upon it, special-duty official Ziyu[2] would add to and revise it, and Zichan of Dongli would polish and embellish the writing."

Comments: When duties are divided in a collaborative manner, people can fully employ their talents.

14.9. 或問子產。子曰:「惠人也。」問子西。曰:「彼哉! 彼哉!」問管仲。曰:「人也。奪伯氏駢邑三百, 飯疏食, 沒齒, 無怨言。」

Someone asked what kind of man Zichan was. Confucius said, "One who practices kindness."

They asked about Zixi. Confucius said, "Oh him! Him!"

They asked about Guanzhong. Confucius said, "He is a character! He stripped the head of the Bo clan of three hundred households' land. The head of the Bo clan [was reduced to] eating coarse grains, but to the end of his life, never said a resentful word [against Guanzhong]."

Comments: The line "Oh him! Him!" is not worth discussing, as today we still have this way of speaking. The line "to the end of his life, never said a resentful word" probably means that even though he was treated with this degree of severity, because this treatment was just, he had nothing to say about it. It is said that Zhuge Liang's impartiality in action had the same result. This is what is referred to as the Legalist spirit. From this it is apparent that **from its start, Confucianism could accommodate Legalism.** (Guan Zhong and Zhuge Liang have always been thought to have been Legalists.) The fact that Confucius many times praised Guan Zhong is the template for the later alternation of Confucianism and Legalism with Confucianism as the yang to Legalism's yin. Clearly, Confucianism and Legalism are connected from the beginning, just like Confucianism and Daoism. **Both the "alternation of Confucianism and Legalism" and "Confucian-Daoist mutual complementarity" can be traced back to Confucius and the Analects.**

14.10. 子曰:「貧而無怨難, 富而無驕易。」

Confucius said, "To be poor and without resentment is difficult; to be rich and without pride is relatively easy."

Comments: It is appropriate that this passage is constantly recited by the many types of "nouveau riche" we have today because it is really not so easy to put into practice. The pride of the wealthy makes the poor more resentful, and this is the origin of the philosophy of struggle.

14.11. 子曰:「孟公綽, 為趙魏老則優, 不可以為滕薛大夫。」

Confucius said, "Meng Gongchuo is more than qualified to be a senior official of a great state, but he could never be the steward of a small state."

Comments: This has to do with the particularity of human talent. Someone who can serve as a high official (Zhao and Wei were large states) cannot necessarily accomplish concrete tasks. Furthermore, there are various types of high officials. Some, due to their high "virtue" or depth of experience, may be employed especially to serve as ornaments, and not be expected (or indeed able) to accomplish anything real. Meng Gongchuo may have been one of these.

14.12. 子路問成人。子曰:「若臧武仲之知, 公綽之不欲, 卞莊子之勇, 冉求之藝, 文之以禮樂, 亦可以為成人矣。」曰:「今之成人者何必然? 見利思義, 見危授命, 久要不忘平生之言, 亦可以為成人矣。」

Zilu asked what a perfect person was. Confucius said, "In intelligence, to be like Zang Wuzhong, to have few desires like Meng Gongchuo, to be courageous like Bian Zhuangzi, and skilled and talented like Ran You. On top of this, to express oneself with the refinement of the rites and music—then one can be said to be a perfect person." He added, "Why should a perfect person be like this today? People who can see profit and consider whether it is ethical or not, who can meet danger and be willing to risk their life, or face long-term poverty and yet not forget the promises they have made—such can also be called perfect persons."

Comments: The highest standard is "the ultimate in cultural and moral refinement" (*wenzhi binbin* 文質彬彬)—there is not much room for error; we can do no better than to look for second-best, and even there one must be just ("see profit and consider whether it is ethical or not"), courageous ("meet danger and be willing to risk their life"), and true to one's word ("face long-term poverty and yet not forget the promises they have made"). Although this also is not easy, it is realistic, practicable, and attainable.

Some commentators believe that the second half of the passage (after "he added") is Zilu's words, that is, Zilu's standard of a "perfect person." This argument is plausible and consistent with Zilu's speech, conduct, and personality.

14.13. 子問公叔文子於公明賈曰:「信乎夫子不言、不笑、不取乎?」公明賈對曰:「以告者過也。夫子時然後言, 人不厭其言; 樂然後笑, 人不厭其笑; 義然後取, 人不厭其取。」子曰:「其然, 豈其然乎?」

Confucius asked Gong Mingjia about Gongshu Wenzi, "Is it really so? That the old master does not speak, or laugh, or demand payment?"

Gong Mingjia answered, "Those who report such things exaggerate. The master speaks only when it is the right time to do so, and so people do not detest his speech; he laughs only when he is truly joyful, so people do not detest his laugh; he demands payment only when it is right, so people do not detest his demands."

Confucius said, "Is it so? Is it really so?"

Comments: This seems to suggest that Confucius doubts it is so. This passage has no particular significance. There are many passages in the *Analects* that are similarly insignificant, and it is not necessary to give the same careful attention to explaining each one.

14.14. 子曰:「臧武仲以防求為後於魯, 雖曰不要君, 吾不信也。」

Confucius said, "Zang Wuzhong, on the basis of the town of Fang, demanded that his sons and grandsons be given positions in the state of Lu. Although he said he did not want to coerce the ruler, I do not believe it."

Comments: Historical records of this are difficult to find, and explications abound; it is not necessary to force an interpretation.

14.15. 子曰:「晉文公譎而不正, 齊桓公正而不譎。」

Confucius said, "Duke Wen of Jin was crafty, not upright; Duke Huan of Qi was upright, not crafty."

Notes: *Cheng Shude and He Yan both quote Zheng Xuan here:* Jue 譎 *means "crafty"; this refers to his summoning the emperor and causing the feudal lords to have an audience with him. Confucius said, For a minister to summon the ruler cannot be taken as a model. Therefore the "Shujing" ("Book of Documents") says: For the emperor to hunt in Heyang, this was "crafty, not upright." Ma Rong says: To attack Chu in service of common justice, finding fault with their failure to bring their tribute of bundled thatch, and then to ask about why King Shao had not returned when he made his southern expedition—this was "upright, not crafty."*

Comments: Although they were both illustrious hegemons, Confucius repeatedly praises Duke Huan of Qi, while not mentioning Duke Wen of Jin. As to exactly why this is so, commentators disagree, and it remains unclear. Although I have included the note above, it is difficult to know if this is the way it should be understood.

14.16. 子路曰:「桓公殺公子糾, 召忽死之, 管仲不死。」曰:「未仁乎?」子曰:「桓公九合諸侯, 不以兵車, 管仲之力也。如其仁! 如其仁! 」

[Zilu said,] "Duke Huan of Qi killed Prince Jiu. Shao Hu killed himself, but Guan Zhong did not." Zilu [added], "This must be from lack of the virtue of humaneness, right?" Confucius said, "When Duke Huan of Qi repeatedly brought together and united the various feudal lords, without resorting to war, it was thanks to the efforts of Guan Zhong. This is humaneness! This is humaneness!"

Comments: Prince Jiu was the older brother of Duke Huan of Qi, and Shao Hu and Guan Zhong were both ministers of Prince Jiu; this is why this later became a knotty problem. Guan Zhong did not die for his ruler, and in this sense was not loyal. Furthermore, there was the matter of the "Three Returns" (*san gui* 三歸)[3] and so on, which also demonstrated a lack of knowledge of ritual propriety, and did not at all accord with Confucian standards. Mencius heartily denounced and despised Guan Zhong. This was even more true later of the Neo-Confucians, who especially advocated the idea that "inner sageliness leads to outer kingship." So how should we understand Confucius praising him like this? Here again there are myriad explanations. My reading understands Confucius to be affirming Guan Zhong on the basis of the great objective flourishing he achieved on behalf of the people, in the same way that Confucius elevates the "sageliness" of broadly benefiting the people, and thus universally succoring the masses 博施於民而能濟眾 (6.30) over "humaneness." **Inner sageliness is not the aim in itself, and in this respect Confucius is very different from the Buddhist-influenced Song-Ming Neo-Confucians.** After Confucius, Confucianism also gave attention to "outer kingship" in a way that differed from the Song-Ming Neo-Confucian party or its "line." For example, Xunzi's explanation of ritual was close to that of Legalism, and Dong Zhongshu's "humaneness is outer, righteousness inner" 仁內義外, and Chen Liang 陳亮 (1143–1194) and Ye Shi's 叶適 (1150–1223) emphasis on action and achievement—all these constitute quite a separate "line." **Chinese tradition is characterized spiritually by the mutual complementarity of Confucianism and Daoism, and politically by the mutual alternation between Confucianism and Legalism. In both of these mutualities, Confucianism is primary.** Why? There are many reasons, including the fact that both of these mutualities are originally built upon the development of elements internal to Confucianism. Confucianism has Yan Hui and Zengzi, both beloved of Confucius, who could join paths with the Daoists. And it has the side that praises Guan Zhong and approves of Zigong and Zilu—and thus it is not hard for them to join paths with Legalists either. From Dong Zhongshu's deciding cases on the basis of the *Chunqiu* to Zhang Juzheng's remaining in office rather than observing a period of mourning [for his father], many of the famous officials and sagely ministers of Chinese tradition led personal and political lives characterized by both the alternation of Confucianism and Legalism, and the mutual complementarity between Confucianism and Daoism. At the same time, all of them would have self-consciously affirmed Confucianism and the Confucians.

14.17. 子貢曰:「管仲非仁者與? 桓公殺公子糾, 不能死, 又相之。」子曰:「管仲相桓公, 霸諸侯, 一匡天下, 民到于今受其賜。微管仲, 吾其被髮左衽矣。豈若匹夫匹婦之為諒也, 自經於溝瀆, 而莫之知也。」

Zigong said, "Guan Zhong is a man without humaneness, isn't he? When Duke Huan of Qi killed Prince Jiu, he was not able to give up his life, but on the contrary, he became Duke Huan's prime minister." Confucius said, "Guan Zhong assisted Duke Huan, dominating the feudal lords, and unifying and rectifying all under heaven, so that the common people are still enjoying these benefits up to today. Without Guan Zhong, I'm afraid we would be letting our hair loose and wearing robes that open on the left. How could he be expected to kill himself in a ditch for the sake of some small sense of duty, like a petty commoner?"

Notes: *Cheng Shude quotes Gu Yanwu's* 顧炎武 *(1613–1682) "Rizhi lu"* 日知錄*: The status of ruler and minister has to do with a single person, while the protection of China from the barbarians involves the whole world. Thus when Confucius here sides with Guan Zhong, it is because his failure to die for Prince Jiu is weighed against his accomplishments in uniting the nine lords, and the [benefit to] the whole world becomes the core issue.*

Qian Mu explains: This passage has to do with letting go of small scruples in favor of great accomplishments; Confucius's opinion is quite clear. The Song Neo-Confucians all disliked his partiality toward [Duke Huan's] accomplishments, and emphasized that Duke Huan was the younger brother of Prince Jiu, in order to minimize Guan Zhong's crime in failing to take his life. They did not understand Confucius's meaning; there are things higher than [the relations between] ruler and minister, and older and younger brothers. Speaking of how the way of humaneness is easy, Confucius said, "If any person truly desires it, it will come" (7.30). But if we want to speak of the greatness of the way of humaneness, this passage provides an example. To summarize, when Confucius speaks of humaneness, he absolutely does not exclude external accomplishment, nor does he focus solely on the individual's heart—this much is clear. [Qian] remarks again: A previous passage applied the word "upright" 正 *to Duke Huan of Qi, and these two passages apply the word "humane" to Guan Zhong—both are important places to look for Confucius's views on humaneness and on the Way. Beginning with Mencius, it began to be said that Confucius's disciples did not speak of the accomplishments of [Duke] Huan. [Qian] also said: Guan Zhong was what Zeng Xi*[4] *was not willing to emulate. Later Confucians mostly followed Mencius in looking down on these two [Duke Huan and Guan Zhong]. Furthermore, these three passages of the "Analects" have been the subject of contentious dispute; I could not refrain from discussing the matter here.*

Comments: The phrase "letting our hair loose and wearing robes that open on the left" refers to the destruction of Chinese culture, and falling into servitude to backward minority tribes. This passage has to do with another big question of balancing principledness (*jing* 經) and flexibility (*quan* 權), and it basically says that one should look at the larger picture. This is historicism. But at the time (the time of Prince Jiu's death), Guan Zhong's accomplishments were still in the future, he had not yet achieved anything, so how could he so quickly set aside the ethical question? Mencius looked down upon Guan Zhong because by his time the problem of backward peoples entering the central plain no longer existed. What he did face in his time was the issue of the various hegemons of the civilizations and states of the central plain warring in ways that did not accord with the Confucian kingly way. The Song-Ming Neo-Confucians, for their part, were most interested in nature and Principle, and emphasized only ethical relationships; in this regard Qian Mu's critique is very penetrating and straightforward. I do not know how today's New Confucians, who still sing the praises of inner sageliness opening the way for outer kingship, would position themselves in regard to this.

14.18. 公叔文子之臣大夫僎, 與文子同升諸公。子聞之曰: 「可以為文矣。」

Gongshu Wenzi's lower-ranking official Zhuan was promoted together with himself to a position of the same rank. Confucius heard of it and said, "This can truly be called 'civilized' [*wen* 文]."

Comments: To recommend someone who ranks below you to be promoted with you to a position of the same rank was not an easy thing to do in the strictly ranked traditional society (or indeed, even in today's China), so it is no wonder Confucius praised this. Envy of the abilities of others is a common fault both ancient and modern, so Wenzi's willingness to be "civilized" in this manner at least demonstrates a natural graciousness and a suitable degree of refinement. But in contemporary society, this [envy] is a matter of course. We should employ systems to reform these customs and mindsets.

14.19. 子言衛靈公之無道也, 康子曰: 「夫如是, 奚而不喪?」孔子曰: 「仲叔圉治賓客, 祝鮀治宗廟, 王孫賈治軍旅。夫如是, 奚其喪?」

Confucius was speaking of the corruption of Duke Ling of Wei. [Ji] Kangzi said, "Since this is the case, why has he not been destroyed?" Confucius said, "He has Zhongshu Yu to handle his diplomatic affairs, the priest Tuo to manage the sacrifices, and Wangsun Jia leading his army. In this state, how could he be destroyed?"

Notes: *Cheng Shude quotes the "Du sishu cong shuo": The Master at other times has found fault with each of these three people, but here speaks of them in this way; clearly the sage does not throw out someone's strengths due to their shortcomings.*

Comments: The term in the original, *wu dao*, or "without the Way," is too broad, so for now I have rendered it "corruption." This passage says that if one has sagely ministers, even a muddled ruler will be able to avoid failure or destruction—this shows the importance of talent. There will always come the day, however, when these talented individuals are run off or killed; if there are systemic safeguards in place, that will not matter. This shows the importance of systems. The above note is interesting. Clearly, Confucius did not seek perfection, but always picked out people's strengths; those in government have even more need to do the same.

14.20. 子曰: 「其言之不怍, 則為之也難。」

Confucius said, "If one is shamelessly boastful, it will be difficult to do what one says one can do."

Comments: Many fashionable young people today are often of this ilk—they do not keep their word and are not honest, yet they think themselves the most brilliant arbiters of truth, and so their speech is full of braggadocio and they fill up papers with their writings, yet they do not stand the test of time or actual experience.

14.21. 陳成子弑簡公。孔子沐浴而朝, 告於哀公曰: 「陳恆弑其君, 請討之。」公曰: 「告夫三子! 」孔子曰: 「以吾從大夫之後, 不敢不告也。君曰『告夫三子』者。」之三子告, 不可。孔子曰: 「以吾從大夫之後, 不敢不告也。」

Chen Chengzi killed Duke Jian of Qi. When Confucius had fasted and bathed he went to tell Duke Ai of Lu, saying, "Chen Heng has killed his ruler, please send out troops to have him punished." Duke Ai said, "Go tell the [heads of the] Three Great Families."

When Confucius had withdrawn, he came out and said, "Because I have held office before, I could not refrain from reporting this; and here the ruler asks me to go tell those three people."

Confucius went and reported to the three people, but could not get them to agree [to punish him]. Confucius said, "Because I have held office before, I could not refrain from reporting this."

Comments: Here we see Confucius's "pedantic" zeal; because he has served as a high official in the past, according to the ritual system, he "ought to" take an interest in affairs of state. Even if he knows it is in vain, he has to report. [Could] this also in a sense [be said to] reflect the spirit of "knowing something is not possible yet going and doing it" (14.38)?! The reason Duke Ai asks Confucius to go talk to the heads of the Three Families is that true authority is in their hands. Fasting and bathing are remnants of the primitive shamanistic ritual (one could not undertake the rituals before having fasted and bathed). The *Book of Rites* says, "The scholar keeps his person free from stain, and continually bathes (and refreshes) his virtue; he sets forth what he has to say (to his superior by way of admonition), but remains himself in the background" 儒有澡身而浴德, 陳言而伏[5]—this is the traditional ritual system. According to Xu Zhongshu 徐中舒 (1898–1991) in his *Jiaguwen zhong suo jian de ru* 甲骨文中所見的儒 [*Ru in the Oracle Bones*]: Scholars (*ru* 儒) were "needed" (*xu* 需); that is, [they were] those who after fasting and prayer managed the shamanistic or priestly ceremonies.

14.22. 子路問事君。子曰:「勿欺也, 而犯之。」

Zilu asked about how to serve the ruler of a state. Confucius said, "Do not cheat him, but you may offend him."

Comments: Today it is exactly the opposite. Bring good news, not bad, and flattery and toadying will get you everywhere. The cheating of the Great Leap Forward led to the death of tens of millions. From Han times, China had the Censorate and the system of remonstrances, which could be said to be a systematization of this teaching, and was really unprecedented in the world. This positive tradition of Confucian outer kingship can be carried on and be integrated with modern government.

14.23. 子曰：「君子上達，小人下達。」

Confucius said, "The noble person moves upwards, the petty person downwards."

Comments: There are very many interpretations of this passage, most of which take "upwards" and "downwards" to refer to "righteousness" (*yi* 義) and "profit" (*li* 利). It is the same as "The noble person understands ritual and righteousness, the petty person understands profit and loss" (4.16). See also 14.35. Some translate *da* 達 as "accomplishment," that is, "the noble person accomplishes in major things, the petty person in minor things."

14.24. 子曰：「古之學者為己，今之學者為人。」

Confucius said, "In ancient times, scholars were trying to improve themselves; today's scholars are trying to teach others."

Comments: This is another difficult passage, of which interpretations abound. The Song-Ming Neo-Confucians raised this high and dug it deep, none of them failing to preach the superiority of "inner sageliness" over "outer kingship," and so on. This translation is simply a plain explanation that connects with today's reality. Don't you see how many fashionable and trendy young scholars (actually not all necessarily young) set out to win glory for themselves in their scholarly endeavors by stepping on others?

What does it really mean to "study for [the sake of] oneself"? From the point of view of morality alone, it would seem to leave something to be desired. Although the Song-Ming Neo-Confucians praised the idea of "sitting half a day in reading books, half a day in meditation," this "half a day of meditation" did not only entail reflection on morality—what it sought was the mystical realm of a trans-moral union between Heaven and humans. Therefore I think that **the actual core of Chinese philosophy lies in the experience of and quest for [the intersection of] "action" (the Dao/Way)—"emotion"—"realm" (the realm of human life), rather than in the dry discussion of categories like nature, Principle, the heart-mind, and *qi*.**

14.25. 蘧伯玉使人於孔子。孔子與之坐而問焉, 曰: 「夫子何為?」對曰: 「夫子欲寡其過而未能也。」使者出。子曰: 「使乎! 使乎!」

Qu Boyu sent an envoy to see Confucius. Confucius bade him sit, and asked him, "What is the old master up to these days?" The envoy answered, saying "The old master wants to reduce his faults, but he has not been able to."

When the envoy had left, Confucius said, "What a good envoy; what a good envoy!"

Comments: This is the true spirit of Confucius. As in his "gentleness, goodness, respect, simplicity, and modesty" (1.10), **he never thought of himself as a talent, superior to others, or as having the absolute truth. If this is so with the individual, it should be so with the nation and its people as well. The reason for the longevity of Chinese culture is because it upholds this type of unflaggingly diligent spirit that is never self-satisfied.** Even in its most arrogant and stubbornly self-aggrandizing moments, there is always a courageous person who comes forward to criticize it. One of these was Lu Xun, who in his fiercely unsentimental attack on "national purity" made the "spirit of the people" his final judgment. This could not be more different from those "fashionable youth" and "counterfeit scholars" who, thinking they are great talents and others are fools, therefore come up with intentionally astonishing statements. I have raised this repeatedly in my comments on these three passages because I have had profound experience of this in recent years.

14.26. 子曰: 「不在其位, 不謀其政。」曾子曰: 「君子思不出其位。」

Confucius said, "If someone is not in that position, he should not go about strategizing the job of governing [associated with that position]."

Zengzi said, "The noble person in his thoughts does not leave the scope of his own duties."

Notes: *Kang Youwei notes: A position is the name for a set of duties; each has its limits of authority, beyond which one may not go. . . . For example, military officials specialize in military affairs, while agricultural officials specialize in agricultural affairs. They do not go beyond the boundaries [of their positions],* *and thus are able to perfect and excel in them. If a scholar holds no position, then he can apply himself to understanding the principles that underlie anything in all the breadth of the world or the myriad changing things. . . . In fact, scholars and those who hold positions are the exact opposite in this regard; let the reader be careful not to confuse the two.*

Comments: Confucius's words here may arise from many different reasons and may have many different interpretations. Zengzi's words are too conservative. The phrase "in his thoughts does not leave the scope of his own duties" 思不出其位 originates from the *Book of Changes*, but its meaning there is different—it does not refer to a norm or demand. Kang Youwei's note above is very interesting, as it is in keeping with a modern democratic spirit; it is no wonder that he wants to turn Confucius's words, "When the Way is practiced in the world, the people will not be full of opinions," into "When the Way is practiced in the world, the people will be full of opinions," meaning that people will have a right to criticize the government—this is of course completely different from Zengzi's meaning. Thus, "do not go about strategizing the job of governing" is just to say that one should not interfere in an expert's realm of expertise.

14.27. 子曰:「君子恥其言而過其行。」

Confucius said, "The noble person is ashamed of his words surpassing his deeds."

Comments: This passage once again addresses the relationship between speech and action. Language is not only a communication issue, but an issue of its real effects. It is only for this reason that morality demands unity of speech and action, the keeping of promises, and so on.

14.28. 子曰:「君子道者三, 我無能焉: 仁者不憂, 知者不惑, 勇者不懼。」子貢曰:「夫子自道也。」

Confucius said, "The noble person's morality has three elements, which I have not been able to practice. A humane person is not anxious, a wise person does not suffer from confusion, and a brave person is not fearful." Zigong said, "Teacher, this is speaking of yourself!"

Comments: This is a famous passage. Wisdom, humaneness, and courage are the so-called three perfect virtues; this is both morality and psychology, that is, culture sedimented into psychology.

14.29. 子貢方人。子曰:「賜也賢乎哉? 夫我則不暇。」

Zigong often ridiculed and criticized people. Confucius said, "Zigong, are you so great yourself? I don't have that kind of time myself."

Comments: Zigong is probably the disciple in the *Analects* that comes across as the smartest; that he would enjoy ridiculing and criticizing others is only natural. Confucius criticizes him in a mild and roundabout manner, not at all with the severity with which he criticized Ran You and Zai Wo. The character *fang* 方 is elsewhere *bi* 比 ("to compare"), that is, he liked to compare himself with others. This is also something that intelligent people like to do, as through comparison they can understand their own strengths and weaknesses.

14.30. 子曰:「不患人之不己知, 患其不能也。」

Confucius said, "You should not worry about others not knowing about you; only worry about whether you lack talent or ability."

Comments: After all is said and done, it is still the cultivation of inner achievement that is important. Today people usually do the opposite [of what this passage advises]—they fear that they will be overlooked. I often tell authors that they should not fear their works being overlooked. A good work of literature will be excavated after the author's death, while a mediocre one will be forgotten while the author yet lives. Since this is so, what is the use in chasing after the latest fashion, revising, and rushing to publish, out of fear that others will not know you? Therefore, where is the real value of human life? You see, there are many people who while they lived were celebrated by all, and piled high with accolades, but after their death immediately sank into oblivion or were scorned as prostitutes. For oneself to know where the value of one's life lies is enough—there is no need to seek it outside oneself.

14.31. 子曰:「不逆詐, 不億不信。抑亦先覺者, 是賢乎!」

Confucius said, "Not suspecting people ahead of time of cheating you, not planning ahead for people to be untrustworthy, yet being able to sense this when it happens—is this not to have sagely virtue?"

Comments: This probably describes the natural wisdom of a "humane" person, I should think.

14.32. 微生畝謂孔子曰:「丘何為是栖栖者與? 無乃為佞乎?」孔子曰:「非敢為佞也, 疾固也。」

Weisheng Mu said to Confucius, "Kong Qiu, why are you always busily rushing around everywhere like this? Isn't this just trying to gain success through the use of your tongue?" Confucius said, "It is not that I dare to show off my tongue, but that I hate incorrigible obstinacy."

Comments: From the tone of voice it appears that Weisheng Mu is an obstinate old elder, but Confucius answers him pointedly, without giving in.

14.33. 子曰:「驥不稱其力, 稱其德也。」

Confucius said, "A 'thousand-*li* steed' is so called not because of his strength, but because of his quality."

Notes: *Liu Baonan quotes Zheng Xuan:* De 德 *["virtue" or "quality"] means* tiao liang 調良 *[regulating strengths]. . . . If a "thousand-*li *steed" has its strengths regulated, it can attain its quality, and thus be considered a good horse.*

Comments: What does "regulating strengths" 調良 (*tiao liang*) mean? Could it mean training? A "thousand-*li* steed" also needs to be trained and exercised; it is not all due to natural qualities.

14.34. 或曰:「以德報怨, 何如?」子曰:「何以報德? 以直報怨, 以德報德。」

Someone said, "What do you think of responding to enmity and resentment with kindness?" Confucius said, "Then how would one respond to kindness? One should respond to resentment with justice, and respond to kindness with kindness."

Comments: This is an important aspect of Confucian thought, and where Confucianism differs from other teachings like "respond to resentment with kindness" 報怨以德 (*Laozi* 63), "sacrificing oneself to save a tiger" 捨身飼虎 (from the Buddhist scriptures), and "love your enemies" and "turn the other cheek" (from the Bible). It is also a perfect expression of pragmatic reason. **It neither indiscriminately applies emotion, preaching universal love in all circumstances (which is very difficult to put into practice), nor denies human emotions, making profit and loss the standard in all things (like the Legalists); but rather allows reason to penetrate the emotions, so that emotion takes reason as its principle.** In this respect, Confucianism's public social morality (justice and fairness) and its private religious morality (assisting one's generation and saving the common people 濟世救人) are unified.

14.35. 子曰:「莫我知也夫!」子貢曰:「何為其莫知子也?」子曰:「不怨天, 不尤人。下學而上達。知我者, 其天乎!」

Confucius said, "No one can understand me!" Zigong said, "How can there be no one who understands you?" Confucius said, "I do not resent Heaven, nor do I blame other people. Below I have studied human affairs, and above, I have attained the truth. The one who knows me is only Heaven."

Comments: Confucius also has his resentment about others not knowing him (i.e., not making use of or employing him)—but doesn't this conflict with what he just said above? This precisely describes a true picture of Confucius. To express one's depression over having talent and yet not meeting opportunity—this is a common human situation that even Confucius cannot avoid. Although Confucius does not blame Heaven or any person here, he sure has plenty of resentments, as we see repeatedly in the *Analects*. Clearly, Confucius is an ordinary person, and certainly not the kind of transcendent, saintly paragon of perfection and cultivation—the straw man of a "perfect sage"—that Song-Ming Neo-Confucians make him out to be.

14.36. 公伯寮愬子路於季孫。子服景伯以告，曰：「夫子固有惑志於公伯寮，吾力猶能肆諸市朝。」子曰：「道之將行也與？命也。道之將廢也與？命也。公伯寮其如命何！」

Gongbo Liao slandered Zilu to Ji Sun. Zifu Jingbo reported it, saying, "That old Ji Sun has been confused by Gongbo Liao, but I still have the power to get rid of this rotten guy." Confucius said, "Whether the Way and Righteousness can be put into practice comes down to fate; if it can't be put into practice, that also comes down to fate. What can Gongbo Liao do about fate?"

Comments: The concrete historical situation [that gave rise to this exchange] is completely unclear, and so we can do nothing but rely upon the literal meaning to understand the attitude of "inaction" that Confucius seems to be taking here (opposing the notion of using violence to purge those that oppose him). But the phrase "comes down to fate" (or "it is fate") raises a big question. Today, many people still believe in fate, thinking that there is a governing force arranging their life and prospects, and therefore offering prayers and consulting cards to seek blessing or protection. But as I have already explained many times above, "fate" is nothing but "chance"; one should pay attention to, respect, or even reverence this fortuitousness, but one need not worship or submit to it. On the contrary, one should work hard to "build" necessity out of all kinds of fortuitousness—this is what is meant by establishing one's fate (*li ming* 立命), or dominating fate. Because chance governs all of life, if one does not take initiative to establish one's intent or one's fate, leaving everything to be governed by the "will of Heaven" or "luck," without taking any action, then one will completely lose one's subjectivity[6] and accomplish absolutely nothing. This is often the choice of the weak.

14.37. 子曰：「賢者辟世，其次辟地，其次辟色，其次辟言。」子曰：「作者七人矣。」

Confucius said, "Moral people withdraw from society; next are those who withdraw from a [certain] place; after that are those who withdraw because of an expression; and finally, those who withdraw because of an ill-spoken word." Confucius said, "There are already seven people who have done so."

Comments: At the time, "ritual was in decline and music was spoiled" 禮崩樂壞, and there were many types of reclusion due to the chaos of society.

14.38. 子路宿於石門。晨門曰:「奚自?」子路曰:「自孔氏。」曰:「是知其不可而為之者與?」

Zilu passed the night at Stone Gate. In the morning, the man who kept the gate asked, "Where did you come from?" Zilu said, "From where Confucius is." The gatekeeper said, "Is he the one who knows something is not possible, yet goes and does it?"

Comments: From these two passages we can see that Confucianism and Daoism (or reclusion) are not entirely mutually incompatible, but the fact that the core of Confucianism is still "knowing something is not possible, yet going and doing it"—this is stirring and tragic. Is this not the reason this saying has been passed down for thousands of years?

14.39. 子擊磬於衛。有荷蕢而過孔氏之門者, 曰:「有心哉! 擊磬乎!」既而曰:「鄙哉! 硜硜乎! 莫己知也, 斯己而已矣。深則厲, 淺則揭。」子曰:「果哉! 末之難矣。」

Confucius was playing on the stone chimes in the state of Wei, when someone carrying a straw basket passed his doorway and said, "He has something on his mind, playing like that!" A moment later he added, "Why all this stubborn clinking and clanking! Since no one else knows of it, it is enough that you know it yourself. When the water is deep, you cross the river with your clothes on; when the water is shallow, you lift up your garment to cross."

Confucius said, "How resolute! I have nothing to say to refute him!"

Comments: The reference to water being deep or shallow means that one should act according to circumstances or the environment. These several passages all have to do with the perspectives and speech of those that opposed

Confucius. The phrase *bizai* 鄙哉 does not have an exact interpretation, so I have paraphrased here. The word *li* 厲 is elsewhere glossed as *qiao* 橋, so the passage would read, "If the water is deep, you cross by a bridge; if the water is shallow, you gather up your garments and wade across." The last line could also be translated, "Oh is that so? That's not hard at all then."

14.40. 子張曰:「《書》云:『高宗諒陰, 三年不言。』何謂也?」子曰:「何必高宗, 古之人皆然。君薨, 百官總己以聽於冢宰, 三年。」

Zizhang said, "In the *Book of Documents* it says that when Emperor Gaozong of the Yin dynasty observed mourning, he would not speak for three years; what does this mean?" Confucius said, "Why only speak only of Gaozong? The ancients all did this. When an old ruler died, all the officials would stay in their positions and listen to the orders of the Prime Minister for three years."

Comments: Three years of mourning, as I commented in Book 1 [cf. 1.11], has always been a great topic for the historians, and there are many opinions as to whether it actually existed [as a practice] or not. I believe that it originated in primitive ritual ceremony, and as it was passed on through the ages, became part of a ritual system that everyone from the clan leaders to its ordinary members had to carry out. In China, up to the late Qing the regulation was that for the "three years of mourning" one should not carry out one's official duties. A traditional ancient clan practice that has continued so tenaciously and proved so long-lived is certainly something deserving of our attention. I believe the line "listen to the orders of the Prime Minister for three years" originally referred to the new ruler taking office, and being unfamiliar with the affairs of state, therefore he should not speak rashly (especially in giving orders), but rather allow his experienced prime minister to handle the affairs of government and take care of matters. Is this not what it is said that Yi Yin and the Duke of Zhou both did? The real antecedent for this is in the regulations of primitive clan society, as I have already explained above.

14.41. 子曰:「上好禮, 則民易使也。」

Confucius said, "If the leaders take pleasure in the ritual system, the ordinary people will be easy to order."

Comments: This has the same meaning as "when the wind blows, the grass bends" 風行草偃 (12.19), as I have already explained above. Because "ritual" was customary law in ancient times, and was passed down through the ages, it became "easy to order" people with it. It is quite different from the way that written law forces people to comply. But as the generations passed, leaders might "take pleasure in the ritual system," but the people might not necessarily obey them. The historical trend was for the diminishment of the Way under Confucianism to give way to the rise of Legalism. The Legalists rose and then faded away again in favor of the Confucians, in what would become the mutual alternation between Confucianism and Legalism; this is the so-called ritual law. Since the Han dynasty, ritual law has actually entered popular custom. From beginning to end, it emphasizes guidance and admonishment, while placing less emphasis upon force or obedience. This is all the legacy of "when the wind blows, the grass bends," and "the people will be easy to order."

14.42. 子路問君子。子曰:「脩己以敬。」曰:「如斯而已乎?」曰:「脩己以安人。」曰:「如斯而已乎?」曰:「脩己以安百姓。脩己以安百姓,堯舜其猶病諸!」

Zilu asked what a noble person was like. Confucius said, "He cultivates himself, and handles his duties with solemnity and diligence."

Zilu said, "Is that all?" Confucius said, "If you cultivate yourself, it makes others content."

Zilu said, "Is that all?" Confucius said, "If you cultivate yourself, you make the people content. Cultivating themselves and making the people content was not easy even for Yao and Shun."

Comments: Clearly, there were some things that even the sage kings Yao and Shun could not do. How could one use the word easy to speak of making the people content? How could one use the word easy of inner sageliness and outer kingship? Could the teaching of later Neo-Confucians be farther from the truth here?

14.43. 原壤夷俟。子曰:「幼而不孫弟,長而無述焉,老而不死,是為賊!」以杖叩其脛

Yuan Rang received Confucius while squatting. Confucius said, "If one is not modest as a child, one will not know how to behave when grown up, and when old one will not know when to die. This is what is called a disaster." He used his cane to strike his shin.

Comments: Yuan Rang was apparently Confucius's old friend; he was not particularly courteous to Confucius, nor was Confucius very polite to him. But because they were so close, they could joke together. The picture of their interaction comes vividly before our eyes.

14.44. 闕黨童子將命。或問之曰:「益者與?」子曰:「吾見其居於位也,見其與先生並行也。非求益者也,欲速成者也。」

A youth from the village of Que was carrying messages to and from Confucius. Someone asked, "Is this child seeking to make progress?" Confucius said, "I see that he stands in the place of adults, and walks shoulder to shoulder with his teacher. This is not seeking progress, rather it is eagerness to make a name for himself."

Comments: There are students like this today. They have just entered the door and they want to independently set up shop; they arrive in the hall [of a teacher] and want to sit in a position equal to his, or they haven't even entered the room before they think themselves far superior to their teacher. It is rare to find one who "holds to the great reverence appropriate to a disciple" 执弟子礼甚恭. China originally had a tradition of respect for teachers, thus the formulation, "Heaven, Earth, country, parents, teacher" 天地國親師—for teachers to be placed among these objects of worship was a rare thing among other cultures. The reason we have this situation today has to do with several decades of trying to sweep away this culture, placing teachers ninth in the list, and is not unrelated to Mao Zedong's repeated calls for criticism of teachers and old Confucians ("bourgeois" experts and scholars), even developing to the point of events such as the tragedy of the "testing of professors" during the Cultural Revolution.[7] The younger generation has subconsciously been affected by this environment and its messages about "old" customs, leaving us with the situation we have today. It is a pity.

Book 15

15.1. 衛靈公問陳於孔子。孔子對曰:「俎豆之事, 則嘗聞之矣; 軍旅之事, 未之學也。」明日遂行。

Duke Ling of Wei asked about the deployment of troops. Confucius answered, "About ritual matters, I know a little. About military matters, I have not studied." The next day he left the state of Wei.

Comments: Confucius has [elsewhere] remarked, "If one does not undertake military training of the people, this can be called throwing them away," and the like (13.29 and 30). Therefore, this passage should not be read as reflecting a lack of concern for military matters. There must have been a concrete reason for Confucius to have adopted this posture. Perhaps the earlier passage refers to mounting a defense, while the present passage refers to mounting an invasion? In later generations, apart from some pedants, most scholar-officials both opposed the use of troops offensively and upheld the need to resist aggression to the end. Yue Fei and Wen Tianxiang will always be heroes, but unending warmongering always meets with censure. Perhaps this is the "peace and harmony" referred to in the formulation, "loyalty and filiality, humaneness and love, trustworthiness and justice, peace and harmony"?![1] It is usually said that the Chinese people are peace-loving; only Mao Zedong said otherwise. But even Mao did not advocate aggression toward other nations. From its systematization under Dong Zhongshu in the Han dynasty, the "alternation between Confucianism and Legalism" was very apparent in the fact that civil officials outranked military leaders, while the prime minister and the censor mutually checked and contained each other. It is also apparent in the use of recommendations and academies in a system of "advancing the worthy." This was a repetition of neither the pre-Qin

Legalists' wanton military aggression and sole emphasis on agricultural and military strength, nor the familial respect and pure emphasis on humaneness and righteousness of classical Confucianism.

15.2. 在陳絕糧, 從者病, 莫能興。子路慍見曰: 「君子亦有窮乎?」子曰: 「君子固窮, 小人窮斯濫矣。」

Confucius ran out of provisions in the state of Chen, and those following him all became ill to the point of being unable to rise. Zilu angrily came to Confucius and said, "Does even the noble person have times that he is utterly without recourse?" Confucius said, "The noble person, when he is without recourse, perseveres, while the petty person in the same situation turns to wrongdoing."

Comments: Zilu's character is again apparent here. Clearly the disciples could express great dissatisfaction with their teacher to his face. They could express their own opinions directly, and did not need to pretend to be compliant, much less be overly modest to his face while slandering him behind his back. The word *qiong* 窮 means not only poverty but being "utterly without recourse," which includes poverty. Cheng Shude quotes Zhang Yangyuan 張楊園 in his *Beiwang lu* 備忘錄: "[This speaks of] the difficulty of bearing up when one arrives in narrow straits. After stepping carefully one's whole life, one begins unconsciously and gradually to relax; it begins with allowing one or two points of excess, then three or four, then five or six, until when one reaches this sort of situation there is nothing one will not do." Isn't this the case with today's old cadres, who become so covetous? Being careful of this from the start, one will understand [when it happens]. This way of reading the *Analects* begins to prove useful.

15.3. 子曰: 「賜也, 女以予為多學而識之者與?」對曰: 「然, 非與?」曰: 「非也, 予一以貫之。」

Confucius said, "Zigong, do you think I'm someone who studies a lot and remembers a lot?" Zigong answered, "Yes. Isn't it so?" Confucius said, "No. I use a single foundational viewpoint to thread them all together into a unity."

Comments: This is another difficult passage, of which there are numerous interpretations. What does "thread them all together into a unity" mean, and how does one do it? This statement has quite a strong mystical quality. The Han Confucians explained the "one thread" (一貫) with the phrase *jiaxing* 駕行 ["driving action"], emphasizing the superiority of "action" over "knowledge," and using action as the thing that unifies all knowledge into one. The Song Confucians explained the "one thread" as "loyalty and forbearance" (忠恕; see 4.15); and there are even more explanations. It is very difficult to decide which is right. Popularly there is the Yiguandao sect (Way of the One Thread), which is a branch of Daoism, but might not the name One Thread have come from this passage? Actually, the best thing is to read this passage literally: that is, knowledge is just the raw material; what is more important is the basic concept or structure that governs and unifies this knowledge. Without this concept or structure, even if one learns broadly and remembers well, one's learning will still be like coins scattered on the ground. Among the supposedly very learned, are there not some who are like this? But if we connect this with what Zengzi says in 4.15, then the "one thread" should refer to action and virtue, that is, keeping to "loyalty" (private religious morality) and "forbearance" (public social morality), rather than fragmentary moral scruples.

15.4. 子曰: 「由! 知德者鮮矣。」

Confucius said, "Zilu, those who carefully practice virtuous action are very few."

Notes: *Zhu Xi says: Virtue is attaining righteousness and Principle in one's self.*

Comments: What is "virtue" (*de* 德)? The *Laozi* says, "When the way was lost there was virtue; when virtue was lost there was benevolence [*ren* 仁]."[2] "Virtue" is above "humaneness" [or "benevolence"]. How Confucius treats these two terms is not completely clear. "Virtue" (*de* 德) has been glossed as *de* 得 [meaning "to acquire"]. Apparently, it is a kind of result of humaneness, or the highest level of action? In previous works, I have suggested that "virtue" is the regulation of significant action under the customary law of ancient clans (see my *Zhongguo gudai sixiang shi lun* [*On the history of ancient Chinese thought*]). Only later was it defined as an inner quality ("being upright of heart-mind is virtue" *zhi xin wei de* 直心為德),[3] and still later it became a moral norm or standard. As in Zhu Xi's note above, it is "attaining righteousness and Principle in one's self." This "regulation of customary law" itself arises from the internal and external standards required for primitive shamanistic ceremony.

15.5. 子曰:「無為而治者, 其舜也與? 夫何為哉, 恭己正南面而已矣。」

Confucius said, "As for those who can by doing nothing cause there to be peace on the earth, probably there was only Emperor Shun. What did he do? He himself respectfully sat in his place, that is all."

Comments: To "govern by doing nothing" would seem to be something said by a Daoist, yet it is brought up several times in the *Analects* (see, for example, 2.1). When the *Shiji* records Confucius as asking Laozi about "ritual," this is probably based in truth. To do nothing and yet have nothing be left undone is what the Legalists speak of: by maintaining his infinite latent possibility, the Son of Heaven is able to retain his highest position of authority for the long term; this is the art of politics. Later, as Confucianism and Legalism were adopted in alternation, the "sagely ruler" had to have a "worthy minister." You see, the "sagely ruler" could leisurely pass his days in comfort, reading the *Poetry* and *Documents*, and allowing his "worthy minister" to attend to the numerous affairs of state, sparing no effort in the performance of his duties. This is the art of governance, employed by both the Confucians and the Legalists, which originated in Daoism, then from Daoism evolved into Legalism. The alternation of Confucianism and Legalism comes precisely out of the mutual complementarity of Confucianism and Daoism. Its earliest origins, however, are in shamanism: [In the idea of] facing south like the heavenly bodies (being "like the North Star" [2.1]) while silently practicing one's Legalist craft, [we see] how the development of Chinese primitive astronomy was related to shamanism. The direct rationalization of the shamanist-historical [culture] produced the Daoist and Confucian schools. Clearly, part of the history of Chinese philosophy must be explained beginning from these shamanist-historical origins.

15.6. 子張問行。子曰:「言忠信, 行篤敬, 雖蠻貊之邦行矣; 言不忠信, 行不篤敬, 雖州里行乎哉? 立, 則見其參於前也; 在輿, 則見其倚於衡也。夫然後行。」子張書諸紳。

Zizhang asked about how to act effectually. Confucius said, "If you are honest and trustworthy in your speech, and respectful and dependable in your action, then even if you are sent to an uncivilized region, you will be able to act effectually. If you are not honest or trustworthy in your speech, or respectful or dependable in your action, then even if you are serving in your own hometown, how will you be able to act effectually? When you stand up, see these words before you, and when you ride in a carriage, see them on the wood of the carriage front. In this way you will be able to act effectually." Zizhang wrote this down on his sash.

Comments: This point about being able to act effectually even in a so-called uncivilized or barbaric region again stresses the power of "culture." This passage has roughly the same meaning as the [conversation with Zizhang in 12.20] about "eminence" (*wen* 聞) and "reputation" (*da* 達). Zizhang stressed the importance of external affairs, in contrast to Zengzi, who emphasized inner cultivation; this is why Kang Youwei commended Zizhang, while criticizing Zengzi.

15.7. 子曰:「直哉史魚! 邦有道, 如矢; 邦無道, 如矢。君子哉蘧伯玉! 邦有道, 則仕; 邦無道, 則可卷而懷之。」

Confucius said, "How upright was Shiyu! When the country was at peace, he was straight as an arrow; when the country was in darkness and chaos, he was also straight as an arrow. What a noble person was Qu Boyu! When the country was at peace, he held office; when the country was in darkness and chaos, he hid himself away."

Comments: According to the historical record, Shiyu once remonstrated through his corpse, and did so effectively.[4] This is probably one of the reasons that Confucius praises him here. But Confucius was not at all dogmatic, and he praises both varieties of attitude. It may be that he slightly prefers the latter. This is another instance in which we see that the "mutual complementarity between Confucian (engagement) and Daoist (reclusion)" originated with Confucius himself.

15.8. 子曰:「可與言而不與之言，失人；不可與言而與之言，失言。知者不失人，亦不失言。」

Confucius said, "To fail to engage in conversation someone with whom you have a great deal in common is to pass over a talent; to converse with someone with whom you have nothing in common is to waste your speech. The intelligent person does not pass over talent, nor does he waste his speech."

Comments: This is general wisdom for everyday life. Yet it is difficult to manage to neither waste one's speech nor pass over talent; thus these are common failings.

15.9. 子曰:「志士仁人，無求生以害仁，有殺身以成仁。」

Confucius said, "The knight of great intentions and the humane person do not hold on to their lives to the detriment of humaneness, but would rather sacrifice their lives in order to perfect humaneness."

Comments: This is an important maxim that has been passed down to today. It can be understood both in terms of morality, and in supermoral terms. The "supermoral" interpretation refers to the way that "humaneness" begins in a person's inner heart-mind but can communicate with the universe, as in Mencius's supermoral morality "born of accumulated righteousness" 集義所生 (*Mencius* II.A.2), the "flood-like *qi*"[5] 浩然之氣 (*Mencius* II.A.2) "flooding out in an irresistible fashion" 沛然莫之能禦 (*Mencius* VII.A.16). According to the Neo-Confucians, it is the "little spark of intelligence" of the heart-mind that expands and fills it; it is "feeling—*qi*" that has shed common sentiment. When moralists speak of the "upright *qi* of Heaven and Earth," or when adepts speak of *qigong*, this is the *qi* they are speaking of. In the phrase, "sacrifice their lives in order to perfect humaneness," there seems to be this upright *qi*, in an unadulterated form. The word "intention" (*zhi* 志) was glossed in ancient times as "knowledge" (*zhi* 知), so this would refer to a wise person; clearly, the sacrifice of one's life here is not blind sentiment, but self-conscious action. This passage should be read alongside "Kindhearted people naturally return to humaneness, smart people keenly seek humaneness" 仁者安仁，知者利仁 (*Analects* 4.2).

15.10. 子貢問為仁。子曰:「工欲善其事, 必先利其器。居是邦也, 事其大夫之賢者, 友其士之仁者。」

Zigong asked about how to put humaneness into practice. Confucius said, "When a craftsman wants to do his job well, he must first sharpen his tools. When you live in a country, you should serve under a senior officer of sagely virtue, and befriend those intellectuals who display humaneness and virtue."

Comments: This passage should be read alongside 1.15 ("As from the knife and the file, / As from the chisel and the polisher") and 13.28 ("Among friends he should urge them on").

15.11. 顏淵問為邦。子曰:「行夏之時, 乘殷之輅, 服周之冕, 樂則韶舞。放鄭聲, 遠佞人。鄭聲淫, 佞人殆。」

Yan Hui asked how a country's systems could be established. Confucius said, "Use the calendar of the Xia dynasty, drive chariots from the Shang, wear hats from the Zhou, and adopt the music of Shun; discard the melodies of the state of Zheng, and keep a distance from those who speak only sweet words. The melodies of the state of Zheng are excessive, and those who speak only sweet words are dangerous."

Notes: *Qian Mu notes: To "do" [government]* [wei 為 *in line 1] means to create systems, that is, systems of rites and music, with all the revolutionary and innovative implications this contains, in contrast with most inquiries into methods of governance.*

Comments: The original first line should really be translated "how to govern a country," but what is spoken of here is systems, and therefore I have translated it accordingly. Confucius advocated combining the strengths of the governments of all the dynasties, and although this largely meant carrying on what came before, there was also invention. This is also the meaning of "though it may be a hundred generations from now" (2.23)—Confucianism has this broadly inclusive character.

The second period of Confucianism, represented by Dong Zhongshu, incorporated the various schools including the Yinyang school, Daoism, Legalism, and Mohism to create a grand system encompassing the cosmos as well as society. Within it, the idea of "being filial, respecting your elder brothers, and working hard on the land" 孝弟力田[6] already demonstrates the incorporation of Mohist ideals of working hard at agriculture. This was no longer the classical Confucianism that regarded study of agriculture as the province of the petty person; it had incorporated the Five Elements theory of the Yinyang school as the external framework for "humaneness is the heart-mind of Heaven" 仁, 天心也.[7] It had incorporated Daoism (dynamism, processes) and Legalism (the Three Cardinal Guides, order), and melded all these together. In this absorption, the principledness (*jing*) and flexibility (*quan*) of Confucianism are very obvious.

In the third period of Confucianism, Song-Ming Neo-Confucianism, the incorporation of the essence of Buddhism is even more well-known. The transcendent question of "What is the Buddha's teaching" becomes the life-affirming philosophy of "In what did Yanzi rejoice"; insight is substituted for awe in Chan Buddhism, and Neo-Confucianism "rectifies it with respect" (cf. Qian Mu's explanation); spending the whole day in mediation gives way to a half day of "quiet sitting" and a half day of study. In combination with the mystical experience of "without sincerity [*cheng* 誠] one cannot transform all things" that in classical Confucianism arises from shamanism, these become a sort of metaphysical quest or understanding that melds principle with feeling.

Today we are in the fourth period of Confucianism, in which the question of how to incorporate Marx, Heidegger and others to actively meet the challenges posed by Christian and Muslim cultures may be bringing us into a new creative stage.

15.12. 子曰:「人無遠慮, 必有近憂。」

Confucius said, "If a person does not have thought for the long term, he will be sure to have worries close at hand."

Comments: This passage concerns the government of a state, but also makes a great life maxim. This is another way in which people differ from animals. The latter case describes a person who thinks only of the present, never [letting the] considerations of the present inform thoughts of the future, so that when disaster arrives and threatens to destroy him, he is taken unawares. "Thought" is also commonly linked with "worries"; when a person is always worrying and thinking throughout his life, this can also be harmful. Today people say that Chinese culture is characterized by a "suffering consciousness"; a concern for one's country, people, and the world; "worrying first about the worries of the world"; relying upon the concerns of foresight to help avoid the downfall of the homeland or the loss of culture. . . . Could the fact that Chinese tradition has continued for several thousand years without fail be due to this? China's culture of delight (or culture of optimism) has always contained this suffering consciousness—otherwise what need would there be for optimism? I have addressed this above.

15.13. 子曰:「已矣乎! 吾未見好德如好色者也。」

Confucius said, "I'm done! I have never seen someone who likes virtue as much as beauty!"

Notes: *Kang Youwei notes: The sensory effect of beauty upon the eyes involves an electrical attraction, therefore this love is the strongest. . . . Therefore among human loves none is as great as the love of beauty, and even if someone loves virtue, that love will never measure up to it.*

Comments: Food and sex are natural; virtuous action is not natural (in the nature of nature). It is truly as Kang Youwei notes above.

15.14. 子曰:「臧文仲其竊位者與? 知柳下惠之賢, 而不與立也。」

Confucius said, "Zang Wenzhong is probably someone who stole a position to occupy, don't you think? He was well aware of Liu Xiahui's sagely virtue, yet did not give him a position."

Comments: Confucius speaks frequently of Zang Wenzhong, though usually in a positive light, while here he sternly denounces him. Zang must have been an important figure, but unfortunately today we do not know any more details about him.

15.15. 子曰:「躬自厚而薄責於人, 則遠怨矣。」

Confucius said, "If you have strict demands on yourself, yet seldom blame others, naturally resentments will be few."

Comments: The *Analects* is full of these sorts of simple yet incisive life maxims that Hegel derided for being inadequately philosophical, ignoring the fact that this is precisely where China's spirit of pragmatic reason lies. [This spirit] must necessarily find expression in everyday life and in many of these practical behaviors that "attain true accomplishment by way of solid action" 以實事程實功.[8] It does not seek to create an ingenious abstract system of thought, for that would not solve the concrete problems or real difficulties of life. Ethics, after all, is gray, while the tree of life is always green.

15.16. 子曰:「不曰『如之何如之何』者, 吾末如之何也已矣。」

Confucius said, "I don't know what to do with a person who does not ask, 'What should I do? What should I do?'"

Comments: The language here is vivid, and it is not said in jest; we again see how Confucius's style of speaking is not the least bit sanctimonious. A person who says "no problem, no problem" to everything usually has a lot of problems and is not dependable. This is still true today. In the face of such a person, even the sage does not know what to do.

15.17. 子曰:「群居終日, 言不及義, 好行小慧, 難矣哉!」

Confucius said, "If a bunch of people is together for a whole day without speaking about serious things, rather preferring to play around with petty cleverness, this is difficult to handle."

Comments: This can be said to be true of some kinds of meetings today: "difficult to handle"!

15.18. 子曰:「君子義以為質, 禮以行之, 孫以出之, 信以成之。君子哉!」

Confucius said, "The noble person makes righteousness the essence, puts it into practice by way of the ritual system, expresses it in humble language, and completes it by maintaining trust. Only this is truly a noble person!"

Comments: This passage seems to be best interpreted from the point of view of social morality and systems, which are quite distinct from the private religious morality of self-cultivation. Political systems today must deal with modern economic development, such as principles of contract relations, individual freedoms, fair competition, social justice, and so on—all these are public, social norms of today's life, and do not necessarily need to find their origins in the tradition. The various cultural traditions differ greatly, but share this direction and trend toward the inevitable modernization of material life and the provision of food, shelter, clothing, and work. Therefore, even though each tradition has its particularities, public social norms have a tendency to become more unified, in what has been called overlapping consensus (see John Rawls's *Political Liberalism*). Thus, the various cultural traditions only play the role of regulative principles, causing slight differences in public social morality and in the principles governing political systems in the public sphere. The doctrines of Confucianism are no exception. For instance, they attempt to create a more human flavor in modern life with a stronger emphasis on a spirit of harmony, mutual understanding, collaboration, mutual aid, and so on. It is emphatically not a matter of moving "from inner sagehood to outer kingship," or starting from individual self-cultivation to open up today's democratic freedoms. In the final analysis, I believe that today's democratic freedoms are built upon the foundation of modernized life (on the basis of modern economics), and do not originate in the cultural tradition. This point should be very clear. This is also the reason that I emphasize the separation of public social and private religious morality in this book, for the former should be of help for today's social systems, while the latter concerns only individual self-cultivation. "Completes it by maintaining trust" originally belonged to private religious morality, having its origins in the "sincerity" (*cheng* 誠) of shamanistic ritual (*cheng* can be glossed as "speaking [*yan* 言] and accomplishing [*chenggong* 成功]"); today, however, it refers to keeping one's word in contracts and promises, and thus belongs to public social morality. But the private religious morality of classical Confucianism can also function as a regulative principle for today's public social morality. Looking at it from another angle, today's social morality should also gradually influence and reform the private religious morality of traditional Confucianism. The two exist in a dialectical relationship of mutual interaction.

15.19. 子曰:「君子病無能焉, 不病人之不己知也。」

Confucius said, "The noble man is concerned about his own lack of ability, not about whether others know about him or not."

Comments: See 1.16, 4.14, and 14.3; these passages all teach that one should not fear that others do not know or give enough importance to oneself. This is a common problem for intellectuals ancient and modern; the masses of workers and peasants do not seem to have this problem. The character 知 (*zhi*, "to know") can also be glossed as 舉 (*ju*, "to raise up"), in which case this would mean one should not worry about not being recommend for an official position. [Similarly,] in the first passage of the *Analects*, "to find that no one understands you, and yet feel no frustration or resentment" (1.1) would mean not feeling resentment over failing to be recommended for official position.

15.20. 子曰:「君子疾沒世而名不稱焉。」

Confucius said, "The noble person hates this dark world [in which] name does not accord with reality."

Comments: Many commentators and translations understand this to mean "The 'noble person' [*junzi*] hates to live in this dark age, when he is unable to obtain a name for himself." This would seem to be in direct contradiction to the previous passage, and does not entirely resemble the "noble person" that Confucius so praises. For this reason, differing interpretations have proliferated. Some say the "noble person" does love reputation, for he "regards a glorious name as his treasure" 榮名以為寶.[9] Kang Youwei in particular emphasizes the importance of "leaving behind a good name" 身後之名, otherwise one will "decay like the grass and trees." In his commentary on the *Analects*, he notes that "if one's name remains, then it is as if the person remains . . . whether they were traveling or at rest, we feel strongly about and yearn for them; we compile their timelines and research their daily lives." He goes further, attacking the Song Neo-Confucians for being "misled by the Daoists' attacks on reputation, to the end that they get the whole world to regard reputation as unworthy, so that people do not love reputation but instead love profit, to the great harm of customs." But the Song-Ming Neo-Confucians' theory of Heavenly Principle and human desire is a cut above Kang's naturalistic humanism as a theory.

15.21. 子曰:「君子求諸己, 小人求諸人。」

Confucius said, "The noble person makes demands upon himself; the petty person makes demands of others."

Comments: Here again is "be stringent with yourself, and lenient with others." This is a life maxim, as well as a description of virtuous action and cultivation. The verb *qiu* (求, "to seek" or "demand") can also be understood here to mean "depend upon," in which case this would be translated "the noble person relies upon his own hard work; the petty person relies upon the help of others."

15.22. 子曰:「君子矜而不爭, 群而不黨。」

Confucius said, "The noble person is solemn and not contentious, and gets on well with others while avoiding partiality."

Comments: Mao Zedong once received democratic representatives of the people and was asked about someone who had no party affiliation; he laughed and said, "The noble person gets on well with others while avoiding partiality" [*dang* 黨 means "party"]. He also once said that his relationship to the Communist Party was "forming a clique to pursue personal interests" 結黨營私. In China such sayings as "forming a clique to pursue personal interests" and "unite with those with similar views, alienate those who differ" 同黨伐異, and so on, all have very negative connotations. However, today's society has come to depend upon a multitude of parties all seeking their "personal interests" so as to check and balance each other, in the service of society's greater good.

15.23. 子曰:「君子不以言舉人, 不以人廢言。」

Confucius said, "The noble person does not recommend someone based upon the ability to speak well, nor does he deny the validity of what someone says because he is a bad person."

Comments: In today's China it is very common to act in a diametrically opposite way, to [our] great loss. Only in modern times has it been so common to find people who lack personal integrity but excel in scholarship, or who are poor in character yet gain great fame—is this not what it means to not "deny the validity of what someone says because he is a bad person"? Thus the antinomy between history and ethics appears yet again. Yet the words of Qin Hui 秦檜 (1090–1155) and Yan Song 嚴嵩 (1480–1567), and the poetry of Ruan Dacheng 阮大鋮 (1587–1646) and Wang Jingwei 汪精衛 (1883–1944) have died away without being passed along. The ethical imperative is paramount, is this not a fearful thing? Let the one who studies think thrice.

15.24. 子貢問曰:「有一言而可以終身行之者乎?」子曰:「其恕乎! 己所不欲, 勿施於人。」

Zigong asked, "Is there a single word that one can follow one's entire life?" Confucius said, "That would be consideration [*shu* 恕]: what you do not want, do not give [or do] to others."

Comments: The New Testament says, "Do unto others what you would have them do unto you" (Matthew 7:12); these are different paths to the same end (see also 4.15). In this book I interpret "loyalty" (*zhong* 忠) in terms of "personal religious morality" ("loyalty" originally being related to "respect" [*jing* 敬]); and [I interpret] "consideration" (*shu* 恕) in terms of "public social morality" (reciprocity usually appears in negative formulations, such as "what you do not wish," and can precisely stand in for something like the idea of "negative freedoms" in today's social morality). But because both "loyalty" and "consideration" are established within the psychological emotions, if we continue to understand "consideration" in the traditional terms of what "pleases the heart" (*ruxin* 如心),[10] then it is private religious morality. If we today regard "consideration" as related to public social morality, we must leave aside psychological principles and take the modern rational social contract as its foundation. Only in this way can we practice "Chinese application of Western substance" 西體中用. "Loyalty" makes demands upon the self, while "consideration" has to do with the treatment of others; if we seek a single strand to "string things together into a unity" [see 4.15], then "loyalty" (private religious morality) can only function as a sort of regulative principle for "consideration." Otherwise there would be no way to distinguish between reason and emotion, public and private, political and religious. But as the public social morality of "consideration" has undergone a long process of sedimentation, it has been able to transform into a new private religious morality and cause it to develop.

15.25. 子曰: 「吾之於人也, 誰毀誰譽? 如有所譽者, 其有所試矣。斯民也, 三代之所以直道而行也。」

Confucius said, "In speaking of others, whom did I criticize? Whom did I praise? If there are people I have praised, it is only after having undertaken an investigation of the facts. These kinds of ordinary people were the measure of the upright action of the three dynasties of the Xia, Shang, and Zhou."

Comments: This would seem to refer to some concrete circumstance that we do not understand fully.

15.26. 子曰: 「吾猶及史之闕文也, 有馬者借人乘之。今亡矣夫! 」

Confucius said, "I can still see places in the ancient histories where there are omissions or mistakes in the documents. Today it seems you no longer see someone who has a horse and lends it to someone else to ride!"

Comments: It seem there may be a mistake or omission in the original here. There are many explanations, none of which makes sense. Actually it is not necessary to force an interpretation, so here I have simply made a literal translation, which has no significance.

15.27. 子曰: 「巧言亂德, 小不忍則亂大謀。」

Confucius said, "Flowery language and clever sayings create confusion for morality. If one does not exercise restraint in small matters, one will ruin great stratagems."

Comments: This phrase, "If one does not exercise restraint in small matters, one will ruin great stratagems," is both well-known and true, as well as useful for tactics and statecraft. Pragmatic reason as [a form of] reason, just like speculative reason, always has its instrumental, neutral aspect.

15.28. 子曰:「衆惡之, 必察焉; 衆好之, 必察焉。」

Confucius said, "If everyone hates a person, you should definitely investigate; if everyone likes a person, you should definitely investigate."

Comments: The meaning of this passage is very close to 13.24 ("If all the people in a village like someone") with only slight differences.

15.29. 子曰:「人能弘道, 非道弘人。」

Confucius said, "People promote the truth; it is not the truth that promotes people."

Comments: This passage has been a major topic for later Neo-Confucians (like Wang Yangming) and New Confucians (like Mou Zongsan). It is simply speaking of how in China the "substance of the Dao" 道體 and "substance" 本體 are both related to the human heart-mind (*xin* 心) and human nature (*xing* 性), without having any other object. The "substance" is found in the "heart-mind" and "nature" of humans, and therefore the Dao relies upon people (i.e., of course, the "Dao mind" 道心) for increasing its brilliance, while people cannot rely upon any external thing, even the Dao, in order to increase their own brilliance. This explains, from a metaphysical standpoint, the self-reliant (自力更生) and striving (自強不息) spirit of Confucian humanism, with its lack of a personal god. As I have noted above, I believe that for China (including both Confucians and Daoists, due to their common origin in "shamanism") the way of Heaven is established through an elevation of the way of humanity, and the way of everyday life is elevated to become the "Dao" of the "profound will of Heaven" 於穆天命. Of course, this "elevation" is a kind of hypothesis and an agreed-upon convention. But on the other hand, we actually cannot say it is a hypothesis or a convention—on the contrary:

because of its sacredness and dignity, we must say it is "a priori" and "innate." It does not require inference, but is experienced or known by way of the conscience or enlightenment, yet still it is not a personal god. It follows that I believe the most important thing to emphasize is how this kind of "hypothesis," this "convention," causes this substance, this human life, to have a strongly tragic character. **Because human life does not have a root or origin, but is cast upon this earth through chance, it has nothing to rely upon or support it (because there is no personal god), but people must establish a support and basis for themselves. Compared to having an external god, is this not more bitter, desolate, and sorrowful—does it not present more hardship and difficulty? China's culture of delight, full of humanistic spirit as it is, actually has this sort of deeply tragic foundation,** and is not at all a "happy-go-lucky" "merging of sorrow and pleasure" 憂樂圓融. This crucial point, however, has never been thoroughly explicated. This tragic aspect is often attributed to the quasi-personal god of an awe-inspiring "will of Heaven," or to the politico-social so-called suffering consciousness. Only in the inimitable laments about life found in the "Nineteen Old Poems of the Han" and similar works do we find some level of expression given to this deep ontological sorrow about life without a basis of support.

In face of this tragedy, Confucians demonstrate a forced fighting spirit and a forced smile, [the spirit of] "knowing it is impossible yet still doing it," purposely endowing the universe and human life with active significance, and expressing it in an emotional manner. As I have said many times, **passages like "The Creative works sublime success, / Furthering through perseverance" 乾, 元亨利貞,**[11] **"The movement of heaven is full of power" 天行健,**[12] **"It is the great virtue of heaven and earth to bestow life" 天地之大德曰生,**[13] **"As begetter of all begetting it is called change" 生生之謂易,**[14] **and so on are not provable or arguable using reason—they simply require the universe to be deliberately endowed with an emotional warmth in order to make it serve as an "ontological" support or basis. This is what is meant by an "emotional [or benevolent] view of the universe" 有情宇宙觀** (see my *Zhexue tanxun lu* 哲學探尋錄). In the face of this tragedy, the Daoists maintain a calm posture of investigation, while summarizing and demonstrating how people can effectively handle their own lives and respond to all the things on earth. "The Dao that can be spoken of is not the constant Dao" 道可道非常道, "Something and Nothing produce each other" 有

無相成, "The high and the low incline towards each other" 高下相傾,[15] and so on are [examples of] this type of emotionless dialectic on change and movement (again, see my *Zhexue tanxun lu*).

Both the Confucians and the Daoists proceed from the "way of humanity" to the "way of Heaven," begin from function in their construction of reality, regard the will of Heaven from the standpoint of human affairs, and take aesthetics as their compass. The former employ emotion, the latter wisdom, but both are manifestations of pragmatic reason and the culture of delight. Therefore, aesthetics here is not "mindfulness" (as in Greece) or lust (as in a modern Dionysian spirit). Because aesthetics arises from the entire body and mind and exerts an effect upon the entire heart and spirit, it can be transformed into a sedimentation that realizes all kinds of human potential, qualities, and characteristics, and thus can allow the individual to become a creative subject. What I have elsewhere spoken of with such formulations as "perceiving truth through beauty" 以美启真 (see my *Zhutixing lungang* [*An outline of subjectality*]), or "aesthetics is the realm of Heaven and Earth" (see my *Huaxia meixue* [*The Chinese Aesthetic Tradition*]), are all explorations of this kind of individual creativity. Because its characteristic is precisely to differ from ordinary intellectual knowledge or the usual laws of morality, it becomes a true pathway for the full realization of individual subjectivity[16] or uniqueness. This Confucian view that "People promote the truth; it is not the truth that promotes people" is the key to what sets Confucianism apart from many other philosophies or religions. From this we understand that the meaning of aesthetics is here in the shaping of emotions, **to enable people, to the fullest extent possible, to manifest their individuality, uniqueness, and subjectivity, so as to play the leading role in history (the "Dao," or the Way).** Lu Xun remarked that the world originally had no roads, but roads are made when people walk on them (to paraphrase); this is also the legacy of "people promote the truth." **"People" here refers both to the historical collective and to actual individuals.**

15.30. 子曰: 「過而不改, 是謂過矣。」

Confucius said, "To have faults and not correct them, this is truly a fault."

Comments: As I have commented above, this is also a life truth of pragmatic reason; to make mistakes and fail to correct them is dangerous. Once corrected, the mistake is gone. This demonstrates the spirit of tolerance in Confucianism. Otherwise, one will have no way to learn from one's mistakes, and in keeping a record of wrongs, one will accumulate enemies, in an endless cycle of retribution—and how does that benefit either oneself or others? Whether on the grand scale of government or the small scale of everyday life, is this not always the case?

15.31. 子曰:「吾嘗終日不食, 終夜不寢, 以思, 無益, 不如學也。」

Confucius said, "Once I went a whole day without eating, and a whole night without sleeping, in order to think, but to no avail; it is better to study."

Comments: This passage means the same thing as "To think without studying is dangerous" 思而不學則殆 (2.15). After all, "study" [in Chinese tradition] usually encompasses behavior and practice, not the pursuit of empty thought apart from practice. This no doubt has its positive aspects, but its fault is that pure speculation remains too undeveloped [in China], to the point that it has no true philosophy to speak of, to its great loss. How to maintain the strengths of this tradition while reflecting upon and rectifying its faults requires careful thought.

15.32. 子曰:「君子謀道不謀食。耕也, 餒在其中矣; 學也, 祿在其中矣。君子憂道不憂貧。」

Confucius said, "The noble person thinks about his work, not about eating. If one pursues a living from the land, one may often suffer hunger; if one studies, on the other hand, one can obtain a salary. The noble person is concerned about his work, not about poverty."

Comments: This passage speaks of the reality at the time, and has been bitterly criticized by farmers at the time as well as those today who praise the "laboring masses." The word *dao* 道 [here translated "work"] could also be rendered "virtuous action," "morality," "the truth," and so on. But Song-Ming Neo-Confucians, in making much of their intelligent discussions of moral life, actually concealed the importance of eating and making a living—this is also a big problem.

15.33. 子曰:「知及之, 仁不能守之; 雖得之, 必失之。知及之, 仁能守之。不莊以涖之, 則民不敬。知及之, 仁能守之, 莊以涖之。動之不以禮, 未善也。」

Confucius said, "What one attains by relying upon intelligence, but does not have the humaneness of heart to maintain, even though one may have obtained it, one will certainly lose it. If one attains it with intelligence, and has the humaneness of heart to maintain it, but does not handle it with a dignified attitude, then one will not have the respect of the people. If one can attain it with intelligence, maintain it with humaneness of heart, and handle it with dignity, but one's actions do not accord with ritual, this is still not good enough."

Comments: The problem here is whether "humaneness" (*ren* 仁) should be understood as "perfect or complete virtue" or "the highest virtue." In the *Analects*, "humaneness" is much more prominent than ritual, righteousness, wisdom, trustworthiness, and so on, and it is ranked much higher. Yet here we see expressed the fact that although "humaneness" may be the most important, it cannot substitute for all these others. This seems to show yet again that the foundational meaning of humaneness has to do mostly with the inner emotions, and that it cannot claim not to need anything else. What exactly is being "obtained" or "maintained"? This has usually been understood to be an "official position," or "post." In this translation I have followed the literal text and left it unspecified.

Secondly, this passage calls to mind the famous passage from the "Xicizhuan" in the *Yijing* that reads:

> It is the great virtue of heaven and earth to bestow life. It is the great treasure of the holy sage to stand in the right place. How does one safeguard this place? Through men. By what are men gathered together? Through goods. Justice means restraining men from wrongdoing by regulation of goods and by rectification of judgments.[17]
>
> 天地之大德曰生, 聖人之大寶曰位。何以守位曰仁, 何以聚人曰財。理財正辭, 禁民為非曰義。

The Mawangdui manuscripts read:

> The great thought of heaven and earth is called life. The great expenditure of the sage is called establishing posi-

> tion. What is used to maintain position is called man. What is used to gather men together is called resources. To bring order to resources and to make upright the statements, to love the people and to pacify actions is called propriety.[18]
>
> 天地之大思曰生，聖人之大費曰立立（位）。何以守立（位)曰人，何以聚人曰財。理財正辭愛民安行曰義。

The character *ren* 仁 [translated "men" in the *Yijing* passage] was glossed very early on as *ren* 人 (meaning "person"), and this passage demonstrates [the connection] even more strongly. Beginning with the Song-Ming Neo-Confucians, people have enjoyed discussing "It is the great virtue of heaven and earth to bestow life," but few have discussed the rest of the passage. From the Mawangdui manuscripts it appears that "propriety" [*yi* 義 "righteousness"] was superior to "humaneness." It was Confucius who first emphasized "humaneness" as the "complete virtue" or first of all virtues. The *Analects* speaks of "humaneness" a hundred times, but as to exactly what "humaneness" is or what should be considered "humane," it never lays this out very clearly. The reason for this is that **the origin [of humaneness] remains tied to a particular type of human emotion, that is, the rationalization of higher psychological modalities that originated in shamanistic ritual. Its range is broad and ambiguous, and not determinable through conceptual knowledge, which is why it has come to carry the mystical, all-transcending sense of "perfect virtue." However, it seems beyond doubt that its core is caring for others and integrity of personality,** and this also can be traced to its origins in the psyche of shamanism.

15.34. 子曰：「君子不可小知，而可大受也；小人不可大受，而可小知也。」

Confucius said, "The noble person does not have petty smarts, but can take on great responsibilities. The petty person cannot take on great responsibilities but may have petty smarts."

Comments: Every person has some talent, and strengths and weaknesses co-exist; therefore one should not look for perfection [in anyone]. A "petty person" will have some sort of strength, and a "noble person" will also have all kinds of faults and weaknesses.

15.35. 子曰:「民之於仁也, 甚於水火。水火, 吾見蹈而死者矣, 未見蹈仁而死者也。」

Confucius said, "The people find 'humaneness' more important than water or fire. I have seen people die from walking into fire or water, but have not seen anyone die from putting 'humaneness' into practice."

Comments: This passage seems to have mistakes or omissions, and only a forced translation can be made.

15.36. 子曰:「當仁不讓於師。」

Confucius said, "If you seek 'humaneness,' you need not defer even to your teacher."

Comments: "Seek humaneness" could also be rendered "in face of humaneness." If one dies to achieve virtue, then the pupil can surpass the master, and take the right of way. Unfortunately, today it is a case of "if you seek reputation, you need not defer to your teacher." People think that they are number one in the world, unrivaled by anyone, and much less do they have their teachers anywhere in view.

15.37. 子曰:「君子貞而不諒。」

Confucius said, "The noble person is resolute and upright, and does not insist upon keeping small promises."

Notes: *Zhu Xi notes:* Zhen 貞 *means upright and resolute*. Liang 諒 *means insisting upon keeping one's word regardless of right and wrong*.

Comments: Zhu Xi's note is most apt. This is how this passage differs from "In his speech he keeps to his word, in his behavior he is dependable" 言必信, 行必果 (13.20). Mencius says the same: "A great man need not keep his word nor does he necessarily see his action through to the end. He aims only at what is right" 大人者, 言不必信, 行不必果, 惟義所在.[19] However, this is also problematic, in that there is too much flexibility, so that one loses the respect for objective standards. This is where corruption may show up within pragmatic reason, with its lack of religious faith; for it lacks the doctrinal tradition of law that is absolute and inviolable due to its having been handed down by God. It is precisely because of this [aspect of] pragmatic reason that such massive, thoroughly anti-traditional ideological trends have arisen beginning with the May Fourth movement.

15.38. 子曰:「事君, 敬其事而後其食。」

Confucius said, "In serving a ruler, be diligent in your work, and only then take your salary."

Comments: Clearly, as I have said above, among ministers of this time period there was already a condition that one would first finish one's work before collecting one's salary. Thus presumably if one does not collect a salary, one can refrain from working—and return to being a carefree person?! Although Confucius did not have this meaning in mind, perhaps this teaching was simply directed toward those contemporaries who collected a salary without doing their work diligently.

15.39. 子曰:「有教無類。」

Confucius said, "In teaching students, one should not make distinctions."

Comments: This passage has become an aphorism. To what does "distinctions" (*lei* 類) refer? It may refer to clan, rank, status, or natural gifts and endowments. In the "Yaodian" chapter of the *Shangshu*, Confucius notes that "*Lei* 類 means *zu* 族 [clan]." For the ancients, this meant primitive kin groups, clans, or tribes, that is, the "kind" of "If it is not my kind, it must differ from me in mindset" 非我族類, 其心必異 [*Zuozhuan*, Duke of Cheng, year 4]. For Confucius to break these types of clan boundaries was a major step forward.

15.40. 子曰:「道不同, 不相為謀。」

Confucius said, "If people are walking different paths, then they need not discuss plans with each other."

Comments: To translate *dao* 道 here as "walking" is perfect. If people's direction, road, or path is different, it is certainly not good for them to make plans with each other. This is also the case in politics, in life, and in work.

15.41. 子曰:「辭達而已矣。」

Confucius said, "If the language is adequate for expressing meaning, that is good enough."

Comments: Unfortunately, today's standard is exactly the opposite: what is sought in "language" is not expression but lack of expression. Don't you see what a great volume of scholarly papers are tortuous and winding, full of difficult and unpronounceable words, seeming to make sense yet not making sense, and so extremely difficult to read, they often make people dizzy and their brains feel like exploding, as if they had fallen into a thick fog, so that by the end of the thing one is still uncertain of what it is trying to say. Apparently, this is how to be really deep and true—this is a masterpiece, good writing, and "postmodern." I really don't understand, and this is why I would rather listen to stubbornly conservative Confucius, rather than subscribing to today's fashionable critics. Since the vernacular May Fourth movement, a great number of new Western ideas, concepts, and research have entered China through plain, clear, and fluent written language that is as understandable as speech, and have exercised a huge influence. In it, the concise and lucid character of Chinese writing has been maintained (e.g., by reducing the number of compound or complex sentences), while paying attention to balance, parallelism, and exquisite tone (even to the extent that it is beautiful to read aloud). This is an example of successful Chinese application of Western substance (西體中用), in stark contrast to the kinds of writing we find today. It is possible that I am moving against the current of the times, but I believe I am actually upholding the May Fourth tradition. This tradition is the same as Confucius's tradition of "If the language is adequate for expressing meaning, that is good enough." It is enough for writing to express the thought or concepts, and thus it is utterly unnecessary to follow the pattern of today's "scholarly" articles, constructing lengthy and tedious essays and huge systems to express what is actually a very small idea. According to this type of "scholarly standard," neither historical commentaries nor the recorded sayings [of scholars] from the Song and Ming can be considered "scholarly." But I would rather the Comments in the present work reflect the kind of simple concision of the old manner of traditional annotation than to create a brilliant, specialized work. Even if it is judged as "non-scholarly," or "of a very low level of scholarship," still I would prefer this, without any hesitation.

Furthermore, "If the language is adequate for expressing meaning, that is good enough" should also be read in connection with "By working on his words, so that they rest firmly on truth, he makes his work enduring" 修辭立其誠.[20] It is not simply a question of adequacy of expression, but also of sincerity or truth [*cheng* 誠]. To be loyal and dependable, allowing one's true feelings to be manifest, all these belong to "sincerity." "Sincerity," as I have argued in this work, is the extension and rationalization of the emotions of shamanism (i.e., the breaking of a curse), but [the idea that] "sincerity breeds effectiveness" (誠則靈) has persisted through today. If sincerity can move Heaven and Earth and affect the gods and spirits, it can certainly have an effect on people. And "If the language is adequate for expressing meaning," then that effect will be all the greater.

15.42. 師冕見, 及階, 子曰: 「階也。」及席, 子曰: 「席也。」皆坐, 子告之曰: 「某在斯, 某在斯。」師冕出。子張問曰: 「與師言之道與?」子曰: 「然。固相師之道也。」

Music Master Mian came to visit. When he had arrived at the steps, Confucius said, "Here are the steps." When he had arrived near the mat, Confucius said, "Here is the mat." When all had been seated, Confucius said to him, "So-and-so is here. So-and-so is here."

After the music master had gone out, Zizhang asked, "Did the way you spoke to the music teacher accord with the ritual system?" Confucius said, "Yes, this was originally the ritually correct way to help a blind person."

Comments: The word *dao* 道 (here translated "accord with the ritual system") can be translated as "principle," "morality," and so on, but here *dao* means "ritual" (*li* 禮), that is, "humaneness" (*ren* 仁), meaning to make sense and accord with human feeling, like today's humanism that governs how we treat disabled persons. It goes to show that "ritual" is the same as "humaneness." This passage is extremely vivid and is still applicable today. From the perspective of historical origins, "humaneness" arises from "ritual"; from the perspective of later individuals, "ritual" arises from "humaneness." There is therefore no contradiction. In this manner we can bring Mencius and Xunzi together within the fold of Confucianism.

Book 16

16.1. 季氏將伐顓臾。冉有、季路見於孔子曰:「季氏將有事於顓臾。」孔子曰:「求! 無乃爾是過與? 夫顓臾, 昔者先王以為東蒙主, 且在邦域之中矣, 是社稷之臣也。何以伐為?」冉有曰:「夫子欲之, 吾二臣者皆不欲也。」孔子曰:「求! 周任有言曰:『陳力就列, 不能者止。』危而不持, 顛而不扶, 則將焉用彼相矣? 且爾言過矣。虎兕出於柙, 龜玉毀於櫝中, 是誰之過與?」冉有曰:「今夫顓臾, 固而近於費。今不取, 後世必為子孫憂。」孔子曰:「求! 君子疾夫舍曰欲之, 而必為之辭。丘也聞有國有家者, 不患寡而患不均, 不患貧而患不安。蓋均無貧, 和無寡, 安無傾。夫如是, 故遠人不服, 則修文德以來之。既來之, 則安之。今由與求也, 相夫子, 遠人不服而不能來也; 邦分崩離析而不能守也。而謀動干戈於邦內。吾恐季孫之憂, 不在顓臾, 而在蕭牆之內也。」

The head of the Ji clan was preparing to attack Zhuanyu; Ran You and Zilu came to see Confucius and said, "The head of the Ji clan is going to use troops against Zhuanyu."

Confucius said, "Ran You, isn't this your fault? The ruler of the former dynasty allowed this Zhuanyu to become the lord over the Dongmeng area, which lies within the borders of the state of Lu, making it an important vassal of the state. Why do they want to go attack it?"

Ran You said, "Our lord wants to do this—neither of us is in favor of it."

Confucius said, "Zhou Ren once said, 'Do your utmost in order to obtain a rank; if you cannot, then you should resign.' If you cannot hold firm when faced with difficulty, if you cannot support your ruler when he is tottering, what use does he have for your help? Furthermore, what you say is not correct; if a tiger or a wild ox escapes its cage, or if a piece of tortoiseshell or jade is destroyed it its case, whose fault is that?"

Ran You said, "Today Zhuanyu's strength has grown great and it is also near the stronghold of Bi. If he does not take it now, it is certain to become a problem for his sons and grandsons."

Confucius said, "Ran You, a noble person hates it when people don't say what they want, but find a pretext. I have heard it said that a country or a family does not fear scarcity, but rather fears lack of fairness; it does not fear poverty, but fears a lack of stability. Because where there is fairness there will not be poverty; where there is harmony there is no need to fear scarcity; where there is stability there will not be a downfall. Thus if a far-off people does not submit, they should be attracted through properly enacting a system of rites and music. Once they have come, then they can be made to settle down. Currently, with Ran You and Zilu helping the head of the Ji clan, those afar off do not submit, and cannot be attracted; the state will shortly collapse; he cannot maintain his rule over it, yet he is planning to use troops within his own borders. I'm afraid the head of the Ji clan should be worried not about Zhuanyu, but about what is happening within the gates of his own home."

Comments: This is one of the longest and most famous passages in the *Analects*. The lines "it does not fear scarcity, but rather fears lack of fairness; it does not fear poverty, but fears a lack of stability" have become part of our common parlance. This may have made sense in the context of ancient clan and agricultural societies, but beginning with later Confucians' advocacy of "reviving the nine squares system"[1] through the implementation of large collectives during the contemporary period, all the distribution-oriented agricultural socialist and egalitarian systems that have tried to put these words into practice have only created disasters. Actually, the word *jun* 均 does not mean "fair" here, but should be understood to mean *fen* 分 (meaning "portion"). Kang Youwei in his *Lunyu zhu* notes: "*Jun* means that each receives his portion." In other words, according to the rank or status of each, there will be a different distribution. The two lines beginning "does not fear" may also be corrected to read "it does not fear poverty, but fears lack of fairness; it does not fear scarcity, but fears a lack of stability," but this simple mistake has been passed along for so long now that it does not pay to correct it any longer.

16.2. 孔子曰:「天下有道, 則禮樂征伐自天子出; 天下無道, 則禮樂征伐自諸侯出。自諸侯出, 蓋十世希不失矣; 自大夫出, 五世希不失矣; 陪臣執國命, 三世希不失矣。天下有道, 則政不在大夫。天下有道, 則庶人不議。」

Confucius said, "When there is peace in the land, then rules governing the rites and music and decisions about wars will be made by the Son of Heaven. When there is no peace in the land, rules governing the rites and music and decisions about wars will be made by the various feudal lords. If the feudal lords are in charge, within ten generations all will be lost. If the clans are in charge, within five generations all will be lost. If the officials of the clans hold the reins of government, this will last only three generations. When there is peace in the land, the governmental power will not be in the hands of the leaders of the family clans. When there is peace in the land, the people will not be endlessly expressing their opinions."

Notes: *Kang Youwei notes: The "Hongfan" [chapter of the "Shangshu"] says, "Consult with the common people"* 謀及庶人, *and "If . . . the common people are in agreement, this is called the Great Concord"* 庶人從, 謂之大同. *. . . If we consider the line "the people will not be endlessly expressing their opinions"* 庶人不議, *then would the authoritarian King Li of Zhou who suppressed dissent be considered to have had the Way?*

Yang Bojun notes: Confucius's words here may come from his conclusions from a study of history, especially the history of contemporary affairs. The line "made by the Son of Heaven" 自天子出 *Confucius would have applied to Yao, Shun, Yu, Tang, and the Western Zhou. "When there is no peace in the land"* 天下無道 *[would have referred to the time] after Duke Huan of Qi, when the Zhou rulers no longer had the power to issue or enforce commands. From the time that Duke Huan became hegemon of Qi, there were established Duke Xiao, Duke Shao, Duke Yi, Duke Hui, Duke Qing, Duke Ling, Duke Zhuang, Duke Jing, Duke Dao, and Duke Jian—ten dukes, until Duke Jian's assassination by Chen Huan, which Confucius personally witnessed. In Jin, from the time that Duke Wen became hegemon, there were established a total of nine dukes—Duke Xiang, Duke Ling, Duke Cheng, Duke Jing, Duke Li, Duke Ping, Duke Zhao, and Duke Qing, and when the Six Hereditary Families (*liu qing 六卿*) subsequently took control, Confucius also personally witnessed this. This is why he says "within ten generations all will be lost." In the state of Lu, beginning with the ascendency to power of Ji You, Prince Wen, Prince Wu, Prince Ping, and Prince Huan were established in turn, following which Yang Hu took control, which again Confucius personally witnessed. This is why he says "within five generations all will be lost." As for how long it took for the Ji clan steward Nan Kuai, facing the revolts of Gongshan Furao and Yang Hu, to personally suffer defeat, this was no more* *than three generations. At the time, all the states had power in the hands of clan stewards; when Confucius speaks of it lasting only "three generations" he is likely speaking broadly. This also demonstrates the inexorability of historical change; the closer the change of eras, the more intense the struggle for the re-distribution of power.*

Comments: The "Son of Heaven" (*tianzi* 天子) at the time would have corresponded to the leader of a clan alliance, while the feudal lords would have corresponded to the tribe or clan, and the *daifu* 大夫 would have corresponded to the clan or family. As to why each would endure for ten or five generations, and so on, see Yang Bojun's note above.

In Kang Youwei's annotations, he insists on deleting two *bu* 不 characters [in the last two lines]; he notes, "Today's edition has the character *bu*, which is redundant"; "this redundant misprint was probably a rash addition by some later person." Thus the original would read, "When there is peace in the land, the governmental power *will* be in the hands of the leaders of the family clans," and "When there is peace in the land, the people *will* be expressing their opinions." He explains: "When the government is in the hands of the leaders of the clans, the ruler will be able to establish laws. When the Way is in the land [or there is peace in the land], then this means the promotion of peace. The ruler does not take responsibility; therefore the clan leaders take on the duties of government." "If there is 'great concord,' then all under heaven is for the public, and the government benefits from the public comments of the citizens. This is peaceful government, the epitome of having the Dao. What this passage is saying when it speaks of three generations has to do with the *Spring and Autumn Annals*. It is only appropriate to that particular time, and should not be applied inappropriately, which would be dangerous. When it is appropriate, all will be ruled by the Dao."

This can really be said to be Kang Youwei's attempt to extricate himself from China's middle ages, by actually forcing a traditional sage to preach bourgeois reformism (see "Kang Youwei sixiang yanjiu" ["Studies on Kang Youwei's thought"] in my *Zhongguo jindai sixiang shilun* [*A history of modern Chinese thought*]). **Dong Zhongshu had respect for Confucius, so his discussion of the *Spring and Autumn Annals* praises the idea of the mutual interaction of Heaven and humans. Zhu Xi in his discussions of Confucius and editing of the *Four Books***

was setting up his theories of Heavenly Principle and human desire. Kang Youwei's discussion of Confucius emphasized the reformation of systems, and principles of improvement and reform. This is Chinese hermeneutics, always developing. The idea of allowing "the classics to comment on me" (六經注我) falls within this same tradition. It has a great deal of political significance, and also has to do with [the relationship between] Heaven and humans (cosmology) and ancient and modern (conceptions of history).

Kang's interpretation, of course, takes inspiration from modern Western democracy. For this reason Zhang Zhidong 張之洞 (1837–1909) and Chen Baozhen 陳寶箴 (1831–1900) and their followers all blamed Kang for using Confucius's name to advocate "reform of the system" and vilified him for "using the foreign to change China" 以夷變夏. Actually what is "using the foreign to change China" is using Western modernization to change China, a change that is not merely technological but also affects thought and ideas, political dogmas, and systems; this is what is known as "Chinese application of Western substance" 西體中用. Kang Youwei was the chief advocate of this kind of change. But Chen Yinke's idea of "independent spirit and free thought," today so widely acclaimed, also comes from the modern West and is by no means "home-grown." Then there are those like Yan Fu, who said, "This word freedom is actually something that the true Chinese sages of old feared most deeply, and it is being taught by those who have never succeeded in establishing it" 夫自由一言，真中國歷古聖賢之所深畏，而從未嘗立以為教也 (*Lun shibian zhi ji* 論世變之亟 [On the speed of world change]). Clearly, freedom and such are not the same as Chen's "Chinese substance, Western function" teaching. On the contrary, [they] do not attain to the far-reaching and wide-ranging foresight of Kang's "Chinese application of Western substance." (Kang's *Datong shu* 大同書 takes individual freedom as the foundation of a world characterized by Great Concord.) As for the criticisms of Kang for setting up an unachievable utopia that serves only to throw order into chaos, that is not necessarily so; actually having an ideal as a far-off goal can not only arouse people's excitement and a lofty ethical spirit, so as to give people something to aim for and rely on, it can also help to avoid the satisfaction with the status quo and loss of direction common to the sycophantic idealization of everything foreign (爬行主義). There is nothing wrong with holding up a utopia as a long-term goal; the key is that one must not construct a blueprint for its implementation. Creating a blueprint is not utopian. Kang would seem not to have had this fault, unlike Mao.

16.3. 孔子曰:「祿之去公室, 五世矣; 政逮於大夫, 四世矣; 故夫三桓之子孫, 微矣。」

Confucius said, "It is already five generations that the government of the state of Lu is not in the hands of the ruler; it is already four generations that governmental authority has resided in the various families; therefore the descendants of the Lu ruler are already on the decline."

Comments: In both of these passages, Confucius is using historical interpretation to conjecture about the future. The first line means that rank and emoluments (positions and salary) are no longer determined by the ruler, authority has already been continually migrating downward, the original clan system has already collapsed, and real power has gradually been turned over to newly arisen figures and families of non-aristocratic background. It is true that everything changes with the passage of time.

In the previous passage, I spoke of how Chen Yinke's notion of "independent spirit and free thought" actually came from the modern West (Chen had studied abroad in America and Europe, where he imbibed their influence for months and years). But actually Confucianism itself also has a very inclusive spirit; in Mencius's rejection of Yangism and Mohism, Han Yu's prohibition of Buddhism, as well as in Zhu Xi's differences with Lu Jiuyuan or his arguments with Chen Liang, the intensity of discussion did not have the kind of intensely divisive flavor or destructive attacks of some religious sects. Even though this is the case, in general Chinese tradition's general condition was still characterized by the domination of a single school (Confucianism) that unified the people with the school of names and the Bonds and Virtues,[2] so that no one could oppose it, as in Tan Sitong's words: "We must not only close their mouths, so that they cannot complain; but we must also imprison their hearts, so they do not dare begin to think." What do freedom and independence mean [in this context]? Therefore as I said in the previous passage, the things that Chen Yinke advocated actually came from the West and were put to use in China, so that what he advocated as "Chinese substance, Western function," was actually "Western substance, Chinese function." This is even true of Chen Yinke's historical knowledge and historiographical methods. It is just that because of Chen's personality and level of cultivation, it is difficult to distinguish between substance and function in his blending of West and East.

16.4. 孔子曰:「益者三友, 損者三友。友直, 友諒, 友多聞, 益矣。友便辟, 友善柔, 友便佞, 損矣。」

Confucius said, "There are three types of beneficial friends, and three types of harmful friends. If friends are frank, trustworthy, and well-informed, they will be beneficial. Friends who are superficial, smooth and evasive, or who indulge in exaggeration will be harmful."

Comments: The Way of making friends is the Way of being human viewed from the point of view of the other party. In the *Analects*, Confucius often uses these types of concrete beneficial generalizations of experience to teach his disciples; this is the teaching method and content of Confucianism's religious morality. It could not be more different from the approach of today's "modern New Confucians" to teaching Confucian religiosity by using only authoritative explications of passages. I believe this is also the reason that today's so-called modern New Confucians (or modern Neo-Confucians) are but a pale reflection of the Song-Ming Neo-Confucians and are not capable of constructing (or leading us into) a new era. They aim to attain to the outer form of the Song-Ming Neo-Confucians (and their analytical strength, categories, and level do not in the slightest go beyond those of the Song and Ming) while they leave behind its religious pragmatic spirit. Therefore, what is left is only a pile of philosophical essays, which would seem to be full of abstruse thoughts and ingenious ideas, but which actually have no relationship with practice. When compared with people like Chen Yinke, Qian Mu, and Yu Jiaxi 余嘉錫 (1884–1955), who would not easily speak into these types of philosophical issues but rather demonstrated their traditional spirit through their physical actions, the question of which are better embodiments of Confucius and Confucianism is worth some thought and discussion.

16.5. 孔子曰:「益者三樂, 損者三樂。樂節禮樂, 樂道人之善, 樂多賢友, 益矣。樂驕樂, 樂佚遊, 樂宴樂, 損矣。」

Confucius said, "There are three types of happiness that are beneficial, and three types that are harmful. To enjoy using the rites and music to regulate oneself, to enjoy discussing other people's good points, or to enjoy making more good friends—these are beneficial. To enjoy being arrogant and wanton, to enjoy wandering or idle strolling about, or to enjoy eating and drinking and putting on big banquets—these are harmful."

Comments: Today, putting on banquets and idle strolling or wandering have come to [be seen as] having great benefits. This is especially true of the enjoyment of traveling, which today has become a necessity of life.

16.6. 孔子曰:「侍於君子有三愆: 言未及之而言謂之躁, 言及之而不言謂之隱, 未見顏色而言謂之瞽。」

Confucius said, "There are three mistakes it is easy to commit in serving a noble person. To speak when it is not yet one's time to speak—this is called impatience; to remain silent when one should speak—this is called holding back or concealment. To speak without first regarding the countenance or the situation—this is called blindness."

Comments: Although in speaking one must select the time and person and decide what to say based upon circumstances, is this a philosophy of how to conduct oneself in society? The implication here is that a person must be conscious of self and must live in these types of concrete situations; it is not a question of an abstract, empty existence or Dasein. All of Confucius does not depart from concrete situations; its metaphysical significance lies here.

16.7. 孔子曰:「君子有三戒: 少之時, 血氣未定, 戒之在色; 及其壯也, 血氣方剛, 戒之在鬬; 及其老也, 血氣既衰, 戒之在得。」

Confucius said, "The noble person watches out for three things: As a youth, when his energies are unstable, he must guard against self-indulgence in his sex life. In his strong middle years, when his energies are in their prime, he must guard against contention and aggression. In his older years when his energies are waning, he must guard against conservatism and greed."

Notes: *Zhu Xi notes: The blood and vital energies [*xue qi 血氣*], are what the body relies upon for life; blood is yin and vital energy (*qi*) is yang. Fan Ziyu* 范祖禹 *(1041–1098) says: The sage is like other people in his blood and vital energies; he differs from other people in his aspirations (*zhiqi 志氣*). The blood and vital energies sometimes wane, but aspiration does not wane with time. During youth, they are not settled; in one's prime, they are strong; in old age they wane. The warnings against lust, fighting, and greed have to do with aspiration. The noble person cultivates his aspirations and therefore is not moved by his blood and vital energies.*

Comments: Zhu Xi's note is very good here. The "vital energies" or "energies" include both body and mind. This is especially seen in older people who are loathe to leave behind the position and emolument they already have, worrying about personal gain or loss, pandering to the current dynasty, and displaying their buffoonery—today we have numerous examples of how even the most famous and sanctimonious white-haired scholars cannot avoid this. The word translated "greed" here can also mean "satisfied," so the line would mean that older people should not be satisfied with what they have already achieved, but rather can continue to propel themselves forward.

16.8. 孔子曰:「君子有三畏: 畏天命, 畏大人, 畏聖人之言。小人不知天命而不畏也, 狎大人, 侮聖人之言。」

Confucius said, "The noble person has three fears: fear of the will of Heaven, fear of rulers and great men, and fear of the words of the sages. The petty person does not understand the will of Heaven, so has no fear of it; he looks down upon great men, and laughs at the words of the sages."

Comments: This is one of the problems under discussion today: Is Confucius's "fear of the will of Heaven" a submission to fate? Is Confucius a courageous knight, or a coward? Didn't Mencius openly say we should look down upon "great men"? Yet Confucius "fears great men." Isn't this a sharp contradiction? Apparently, the only resolution is a historical one: the times were different. In Confucius's time, although the "rulers and great men" had already ceased to act virtuously, they still held an awesome position seemingly bestowed upon them by "Heaven," and were endowed with a sacred duty and responsibility, therefore they were worthy of fear and awe; this is the tradition that unites the shaman and the ruler. The "will of Heaven" is the same—it is a concept that comes from the traditional rites of shamanism. The *taotie* inscriptions on the bronzes of the Yin and Zhou are all manifestations of this "fear." With the advent of culture, this type of primitive emotion changed form and became rationalized to become Confucian "reverence." "Reverence" is a humanistic emotional state. The three "fears" here can all appropriately be read as "reverence." Fear is an attitude of extreme reverence. **The reason that Confucian ethics always seem to carry a certain latent metaphysical religious flavor can be traced to this "fear."** Once it had shed the concrete forms and activities of primitive shamanism, miracles, commandments, and so on, leaving behind solemn and deep "religious" feelings, this became an important characteristic of Confucianism beginning with Confucius. Therefore, the "will of Heaven" in this passage, as in 2.4 ("At fifty I understood my own fate" [literally "knew the will of Heaven"]), is by no means a specific external transcendent object, but rather may be understood as a profound self-consciousness of one's own existence and its finitude. Thus **reverence, or fear, refers to the greater appreciation of the value, meaning, and mission of existence in its finitude.**

16.9. 孔子曰:「生而知之者, 上也; 學而知之者, 次也; 困而學之, 又其次也; 困而不學, 民斯為下矣。」

Confucius said, "To be born knowing is the highest level; to study and then obtain knowledge is the next level; to encounter difficulties and then pursue learning is the next level; to encounter difficulties and still be unwilling to learn—this type of person is really low level."

Notes: *Zhu Xi quotes Yang Shi (楊時 1053–1135): Those who are born knowing, those who study to obtain knowledge, and those who encounter difficulties in their studies, although they are of different quality, are united in that they do obtain knowledge. Therefore the noble person regards only study as precious.*

Comments: Zhu Xi's note emphasizes study. Of course, there is no such thing as being "born knowing." Confucius denies that he himself belongs to this level: *Analects* 7.20 denies the possibility of omniscience or omnipotence ("I wasn't born with knowledge; rather, I obtained it through a love for antiquity and by diligently seeking"), and 9.6 ("It is Heaven that wanted him to be a sage") **points out that any person or thing can be marred by fault. This is the fundamental spirit of Confucianism.**

16.10. 孔子曰:「君子有九思: 視思明, 聽思聰, 色思溫, 貌思恭, 言思忠, 事思敬, 疑思問, 忿思難, 見得思義。」

Confucius said, "The noble person has nine types of thoughts: When he looks, he thinks of whether or not he has seen clearly. When he hears, he thinks of whether he has understood. About his expression, he thinks about whether or not it is gentle and mild. About his attitude, he thinks about whether it is respectful. In speech, he thinks about whether it is loyal and sincere. In carrying out affairs, he thinks about whether he is honest. If he has a problem, he thinks about whether he has consulted [adequately] with others. In anger, he thinks about whether he will cause annoyance. If he sees that he can gain something, he thinks about whether it is legitimate."

Comments: This passage deals out extremely concrete guidelines for living; this, too, is "ritual" (*li* 禮). Indeed, "ritual" seems to exercise too broad and strict control, even of one's speech and countenance. It is no wonder that both modern Chinese people and Westerners dislike Confucius and instead incline their hearts toward the Daoists, who give full play to nature. However, even Freud has pointed out that only with regulation and constraints can there be civilization. One of the reasons that Chinese civilization matured extremely early is the "three hundred greater ritual rules, three thousand lesser ritual rules" from the shamanist ceremonial system that governed people's everyday life, their eating, drinking, living, speech, behavior, and deportment, with all sorts of very specific concrete rules like those that have been preserved in the ancient records of the Han dynasty *Yili* 儀禮 (Rites and Ceremonies). All of these concrete ritual systems and ceremonial forms and standards have changed and evolved with time, so that the people of today need not carefully observe traditional ceremonies, regulations, or concepts (including Confucian doctrine); but **the fundamental emphasis of Confucius and the Confucians on "ritual" as the norm of existence**

of the social collective must not be discarded—it is "known across a hundred generations." In this book I have previously quoted Kang Youwei's commentary, which has been fairly well-received. In sum, I believe Kang Youwei is the "worst offender" of the modern period in using the foreign to change China and taking Western substance for Chinese application. His "Western substance" is reflected in his *Datong shu* 大同書, his "Chinese application" in *Kongzi gaizhi kao* 孔子改制考, *Chunqiu bixiao weiyan dayi kao* 春秋筆削微言大義考, *Chunqiu Dongshi xue* 春秋董氏學, and various other commentaries on the classics. **Kang hoped that by way of transformative creation within the Chinese tradition, he could find a modern way out.** Despite his many subjective assertions (which even Zhu Xi was unable to avoid, as for example in giving primacy to Zhou Dunyi in his formation of Confucian orthodoxy) and the many flaws in his scholarship, Kang still accomplished a lot, in great contrast to the way those who came after him would twist their own scholarship to suit the tastes of the times.

16.10. 孔子曰:「見善如不及, 見不善如探湯。吾見其人矣, 吾聞其語矣。隱居以求其志, 行義以達其道。吾聞其語矣, 未見其人也。」

Confucius said, "To see goodness, and seek it as if you were trying to catch up to it, to see evil and avoid it as if you had touched your hand to boiling water—I have seen such people, and heard them speak. To take up seclusion in order to maintain one's intention, then on coming out, to successfully practice righteousness—I have heard such things spoken of but have not yet seen such a person."

Comments: This was probably said in response to some concrete event. As to who "such people" might have been, it is impossible to know. Given his travels all around the various states, anxiously rushing about, could the Master not be speaking about himself?

16.12. 齊景公有馬千駟, 死之日, 民無德而稱焉。伯夷叔齊餓于首陽之下, 民到于今稱之。[「誠不以富, 亦只以異」] 其斯之謂與?

Duke Jing of Qi had four thousand horses, but when he died, there was not one among the people who spoke well of him. Bo Yi and Shu Qi starved to death at the foot of Mount Shouyang, yet to this day the people still praise them. The saying ["Truly it is not because of his riches, but because of the extraordinary uprightness of his character"] can be said to refer to this, right?

Notes: *Zhu Xi quotes Hu Anguo 胡安國 (1074–1138): Cheng Yi believes that the bamboo strip containing the phrase "Truly it is not because of his riches, but because of the extraordinary uprightness of his character"[3] was mistakenly placed in 12[.10], and should have been at the beginning of this passage. Looking carefully at the language of the passage today, it seems that it should be at the beginning of [the last] line. It says that a person's reputation is not in riches but in uprightness of character. I believe this explanation is close to the mark, and also that this passage should begin with the phrase "Confucius said," which was probably omitted by mistake.*

Comments: For an unknown reason, this passage does not start with the usual "Confucius said." Reputation is spread by one's "virtue," not one's "wealth" or "position." It is no wonder that industrialists as well as high ranking officials the world over jump over each other to donate money to establish schools. Apart from avoiding taxes, spreading their reputation is also one of their goals.

16.13. 陳亢問於伯魚曰:「子亦有異聞乎?」對曰:「未也。嘗獨立, 鯉趨而過庭。曰:『學詩乎?』對曰:『未也。』『不學詩, 無以言。』鯉退而學詩。他日又獨立, 鯉趨而過庭。曰:『學禮乎?』對曰:『未也。』『不學禮, 無以立。』鯉退而學禮。聞斯二者。」陳亢退而喜曰:「問一得三, 聞詩, 聞禮, 又聞君子之遠其子也。」

Chen Gang asked Kong Li [Confucius's son, Boyu], "Have you heard anything in particular?"

Boyu answered, "No. Once he was standing alone in the courtyard, and I was walking lightly across the yard. He asked me, 'Have you studied the *Book of Songs?*' I said, 'No.' He said, 'If you do not study the *Songs*, you will not be able to speak.' When I had departed, I went and studied the *Songs*. One day, when he was standing there alone again, I was walking across this same courtyard. He asked, 'Have you studied the ritual system?' I said, 'No.' He said, 'If you do not study the ritual system, you will not be able to stand up.' When I had departed, I went and studied the ritual system. Just these two things."

When Cheng Gang returned, he was very happy, saying, "I asked one thing, but learned three things: I learned about the *Songs*, about ritual, and I learned that the noble person does not give his own son special treatment."

Comments: Confucianism has no secret tradition, nor does Confucius himself show partiality. The word *yuan* 遠 [in the last line], meaning to be at a distance, does not of course imply keeping one's son far away, but rather refers to not being particularly close or familiar. Actually fathers and sons are often like this. In the "Qu li shang" chapter of the *Liji*, it says, "The noble person embraces his grandson, but not his son." The ancient sayings "Father and son do not share a mat," and "A father does not teach his son," and so on, along with the *zhao-mu* 昭穆 system (from the "Cha li" chapter of the *Liji*) according to which "grandfather and grandson are close, father and son distant" are all vestiges of primitive clan systems of marriage and succession.

16.14. 邦君之妻，君稱之曰夫人，夫人自稱曰小童；邦人稱之曰君夫人，稱諸異邦曰寡小君；異邦人稱之亦曰君夫人。

[Yang Bojun's translation:] The wife of a ruler is called *furen* 夫人 ["Madame"] by the ruler, and refers to herself as 小童 *xiaotong* ["little child"]; the people within the state call her *jun furen* 君夫人 ["Madame Ruler"], but when referring to her to those outside the state they call her 寡小君 *gua xiaojun* ["diminutive little ruler"]; people of other states also refer to her as *jun furen* ["Madame Ruler"].

Comments: This passage is quite different from the others. Liang Qichao believed that these were ritual terms of address that were added later to the empty space on the bamboo slips, but some have disagreed with and issued retorts to this view. In my opinion, it can be regarded as unrelated to the record of Confucius's sayings, and it does not merit further research. Quite a few of the passages of the *Analects* can be said to be relatively "doubtful." For example, the content, thought, and wording of 16.10, 17.8, 17.16, 20.2, and other passages are all different from the other things "Confucius said," and can be considered almost certainly not to have originated with Confucius. There are also the very famous and influential passages like 11.25 and 17.21 that also differ from the rest of the book in terms of their length and language. There are yet many instances of such things. Many earlier [commentators] have also questioned and argued about these. In this reading, however, in accordance with the scope laid out in the introduction, I regard the *Analects* that have been passed down to us as a whole and do my best to elucidate it. Even if this "whole" is constructed, it has, after all, been passed down for over two thousand years, and as such already has a certain integrated value. Its function and meaning in the Chinese cultural tradition already have a sedimented historical existence.

Book 17

17.1. 陽貨欲見孔子，孔子不見，歸孔子豚。孔子時其亡也，而往拜之，遇諸塗。謂孔子曰：「來！予與爾言。」曰：「懷其寶而迷其邦，可謂仁乎？」曰：「不可。」「好從事而亟失時，可謂知乎？」曰：「不可。」「日月逝矣，歲不我與。」孔子曰：「諾。吾將仕矣。」

Yang Huo wanted to meet Confucius, but Confucius would not see him. Subsequently he sent Confucius a steamed suckling pig.

Confucius went to visit him at a time when he would not be home. As a result, they met on the road.

Yang Huo said to Confucius, "Come, let me speak with you." He continued, "If one is full of capabilities, and yet allows the country to remain in a state of confusion, is this what is called having a heart of humaneness?"

Confucius said, "It is not."

"If one wishes to serve yet repeatedly allows opportunities to pass, is this what is called intelligence?"

"It is not."

"The days go by one by one; the passing years do not spare a person!"

Confucius said, "You are right. I will come out and take office."

Comments: Yang Huo was the person who held real authority over the Ji clan. That Confucius "would not see" him meant that he was avoiding him. Yet according to ritual Confucius was required to make a return visit. As apparently this was not a man to be trifled with, Confucius found a time that Yang Huo was away from home to make this return visit. But in an unlucky coincidence, he ran into him on the way, and in his awkward position could not avoid smiling cringingly and putting on an obsequious manner as he was forced to respond. Does Confucius calmly bite his tongue here in order to preserve his life and avoid suffering harm? It is impossible to know. Or perhaps this shows Confucius's expedient (or flexible) quality (*quan* 權)? This is also impossible to know. If this were Zilu, he would not have done the same. As for those who insist on defending the "sage," saying, "[He was] both dignified and unflappable, and upright and unyielding; this is what made [the Master] the wonder of his age" (Hu Bingwen's 胡炳文 *Sishu tong* 四書通), this is a great stretch.

17.2. 子曰:「性相近也, 習相遠也。」

Confucius said, "People are originally very close in nature; it is their practice and habits that set them far apart from one another."

Notes: *Kang Youwei notes: Later many would comment upon nature. Most of the world believes that nature includes both good and evil. If people's good nature is cultivated to perfection, then goodness is stronger, while if one's evil nature is cultivated to perfection, then evil is stronger. The disciples Fu Zijian* 宓子賤, *Qi Diaokai* 漆雕開, *and Gongsun Nizi* 公孫尼子 *all thought nature was both good and evil, but Mencius thought nature was good, and Xunzi that it was evil. Gaozi said nature was neither good nor not good; Yangzi said that good and evil were mixed. All of these were stuck in [the categories of] good and evil. Confucius did not speak in terms of good and evil, but rather of closeness and distance.*

Cheng Shude quotes Huang Kan: Nature is that with which people are endowed at birth. "Practice" means those hundred rites and habits that one puts into practice after birth. People are all endowed with the qi *of Heaven and Earth at birth, and despite the differences in degree of their endowment, all share the same* qi*, and thus it says they are close together. As one grows in knowledge, if one encounters good friends then the result of their concourse will be goodness, while if one encounters bad friends, then the result of their concourse will be evil. Good and evil thus grow apart, and this is why it says they are far apart from one another.*

Comments: In all of the *Analects*, only twice does it address *xing* (性 "nature"). The first is [where it says we are not allowed to listen to the Master's views on] "nature and the Way of Heaven" (5.13), and the second is here. But do these two references to "nature" actually mean the same thing? About this question, commentators have had disagreements from ancient times to the present. In my opinion, at the very least we can say that "nature" here is neutral; it has no "good" or "evil," and thus differs from Mencius's view that "human nature is good." Confucius only addressed "humaneness," and considered further that ritual had its origins in humaneness. Mencius, by contrast, traced the roots of humaneness to the "four beginnings" (*siduan* 四端), which amounted to an a priori good nature. Later, the Commentaries on the *Book of Changes* and the *Doctrine of the Mean* returned to cosmology (external) and ontology (internal), that is, "The movement of Heaven is full of power"[1] 天行健 (*tian xing jian*) and "What Heaven decrees is called nature" 天命之謂性 (*tianming zhi wei xing*) (*Doctrine of the Mean*), and in doing so further systematized both "nature" and "fate" to form the framework and backbone of Confucianism. The yinyang and Five Elements theories of the Han and Song-Ming Neo-Confucian psychology developed these further. Mencius's student Gaozi thought "Appetite and lust are nature" (*Mencius* VI.A.4). Jiao Xun 焦循 (1763–1820) also said, "Nature is none other than the appetite for food and sex. Drinking and eating, male and female—in these people are just like animals." This view can be developed into modern naturalistic humanism, such as that of Kang Youwei. Of course, Kang was influenced by the West, but ever since the late Ming school of Wang Yangming and based upon its theoretical logic, we can also find the beginnings of a naturalistic humanism in which "desire is Principle" 欲即理 (*yu ji li*) (see my *On the History of Modern Chinese Thought*). Naturalistic humanism must be innately connected with modern societal life (a prosperous and developed material life) in order to develop fully. In China, for thousands of years and up to the present, the mainstream is still some variation on a "theory of Heavenly Principle and human desire," which was even able to reemerge in Marxist form and run rampant in the Cultural Revolution. The idea of "Human nature is good" and that of [Mao's poem that reads], "China's six hundred million can fill the shoes of Yao and Shun"[2] are not far removed from each other.

The word *xi* 習 ("practice") is quite worth discussing. "Practice" here refers primarily to the "practice of ritual." "Ritual" must be "often practiced" (時習之, *Analects* 1.1). This "practice" does not refer to recitation or thought but to behavior and action. It is because of this that Robert Eno believes Confucianism is a system of skills, a set of norms put into practice, and Confucians are "masters of dance."[3] Although this is a bit of an overstatement, it actually makes sense. The words "shaman" 巫 (*wu*) and "dance" 舞 (*wu*) were originally the same character and share the same origin in practices of ancient ritual and ceremony. **Chinese pragmatic reason, which was established through the activities of the rites and music, is very different from Western analytical reason, which was established through argument and logic.**

17.3. 子曰: 「唯上知與下愚不移。」

Confucius said, "It is only the most intelligent and the most foolish that do not change."

Notes: *Cheng Shude quotes Wang Yangming's "Chuan xi lu"* 傳習錄: *In what sense are the most intelligent and most foolish unable to change? The Master says, it is not that they cannot change but that they do not want to change.*

Comments: The "most intelligent" are those who "are born knowing," that is, supermen, or great talents, which, as we saw in an earlier chapter, Confucius says he himself is not. The "most foolish" probably refers to idiots? Actually, the most important word here is "only." In other words, apart from supermen and total idiots, all other people can and should be educated; this is all. There is no need to read too much into it, or to let the words interfere with the sense. Wang Yangming's explanation emphasizes self-conscious study.

The meaning of this passage is the same as the previous one, and it can also be taken to explain the use of "nature" in the previous passage.

17.4. 子之武城, 聞弦歌之聲。夫子莞爾而笑, 曰: 「割雞焉用牛刀? 」子游對曰: 「昔者偃也聞諸夫子曰: 『君子學道則愛人, 小人學道則易使也。』」子曰: 「二三子! 偃之言是也。前言戲之耳。」

Confucius went to Wucheng, and heard the sound of someone playing the *qin* and singing. Confucius smiled and said, "If you want to kill a chicken, why use an ox-butchering knife?"

Ziyou answered, saying "Teacher, in the past I have heard you say that if the noble person has studied the rites and music, he will love people, and if common people study the rites and music, they will easily obey commands."

Confucius said, "Students, Ziyou is correct in what he says. In what I just said, I was only joking with him."

Comments: Actually Confucius was not joking; it is true that for killing a chicken there is no need to use a butcher's knife, and that a minor official has no need to aspire to great acts. But it would be difficult for Confucius to say this seriously, and we can easily imagine his expression here. The word *dao*, here translated as "rites and music," could also be translated "education," or "morality," and so on.

17.5. 公山弗擾以費畔, 召, 子欲往。子路不說, 曰: 「末之也已, 何必公山氏之之也。」子曰: 「夫召我者而豈徒哉? 如有用我者, 吾其為東周乎? 」

Gongshan Furao was occupying the town of Bi as a base for revolt. He wanted Confucius to go there, and Confucius was planning to.

Zilu was unhappy, and said, "If we have nowhere to go, let it be! Why should we go to join Gongshan?"

Confucius said, "He had a reason for inviting me to go; how could my going be in vain? If someone makes use of me, will I not be able to revive the Zhou dynasty in the east?"

Comments: This passage and 17.7 once again raise the contradiction between principledness (*jing* 經) and expediency or flexibility (*quan* 權). Confucius teaches people to act according to principledness, while himself practicing no end of flexibility. No wonder Zilu was upset! Exactly how to grasp the balance between normativity and expediency has been the subject of many writings. To sum up from a few passages, the reasons Confucius spoke of going were: (1) he is able to enter the mud without getting dirty, [and so] he need not be afraid of dirt or chaos; and (2) a life should not be lived in vain, so he is always hoping to find an opportunity to accomplish something great. These several passages engage in objective and quite realistic description so that we are able to see that Confucius was also an ordinary man. The words he spoke were true, and in the face of questioning, he can do nothing but say he was only joking. He wants to hold office and accomplish things, and in the face of questioning can only force himself to come up with a rationalization.

17.6. 子張問仁於孔子。孔子曰:「能行五者於天下, 為仁矣。」請問之。曰:「恭、寬、信、敏、惠。恭則不侮, 寬則得眾, 信則人任焉, 敏則有功, 惠則足以使人。」

Zizhang asked Confucius what humaneness was like. Confucius said, "If, in the world, one can put into practice five types of moral behavior, then one can be said to be humane."

"May I ask what five types?"

Confucius said, "Respect, generosity, honesty, diligence, and kindness. If you are respectful, you will not insult people; if you are generous, you will receive everyone's support; if you are honest, you will obtain people's trust; if you are diligent your work will be effective; and if you are kind, you will be able to direct and move others."

Notes: *Zhu Xi notes: If one practices these five, then one's heart-mind will be steady and one will grasp Principle.*

Comments: It is possible that there may be an error in the text here: "The calligraphy in this passage is different from that of the surrounding passages, and the Master's answer is more like his answers to questions about government than the way he usually answers questions about humaneness" (Cheng Shude quoting [Zhou Yingzhi's] *Lunyu shuyao*). I believe that because in the *Analects* as a whole Zizhang is one of the disciples most besotted with politics, Confucius answers him here in terms of the "outer kingship" aspect of humaneness, which is very different from how he would have answered Yan Hui or Zengzi. He is tailoring his teaching to the strength of the student. Furthermore, there has always been a great deal of disagreement regarding the authenticity or dating of the various passages of the *Analects*, all of which the present book has ignored. As for Zhu Xi's insistence in his Note above on treating "outer kingship" as "inner sageliness," that's Neo-Confucianism for you.

17.7. 佛肸召, 子欲往。子路曰:「昔者由也聞諸夫子曰:『親於其身為不善者, 君子不入也。』佛肸以中牟畔, 子之往也, 如之何!」子曰:「然。有是言也。不曰堅乎, 磨而不磷; 不曰白乎, 涅而不緇。吾豈匏瓜也哉? 焉能繫而不食?」

Bixi invited Confucius, and Confucius planned to go.

Zilu said, "In the past I have heard the Teacher say that the noble person does not associate with those who themselves do bad things. Bixi is rebelling in Zhongmou; how is it that you want to go?"

Confucius said, "You are correct, I have said this. Haven't I said that if something is hard, grinding it will not make it thin? Haven't I said that if something is pure white, dying it will not make it black? Am I really nothing but a bitter-tasting gourd? How can I always be hanging there not being eaten?"

Comments: The meaning of this passage is the same as 17.5.

17.8. 子曰: 「由也, 女聞六言六蔽矣乎? 」對曰: 「未也。」「居! 吾語女。好仁不好學, 其蔽也愚; 好知不好學, 其蔽也蕩; 好信不好學, 其蔽也賊; 好直不好學, 其蔽也絞; 好勇不好學, 其蔽也亂; 好剛不好學, 其蔽也狂。」

Confucius said, "Zilu, have you heard of the six virtues and the six faults?"

Zilu answered, "I have not."

Confucius said, "Have a seat, and I will tell you. If you like kindness but do not like learning, that fault is foolishness. If you like intelligence but do not like learning, that fault is being undisciplined. If you like trustworthiness but do not like learning, that fault is narrowness. If you like frankness but do not like learning, that fault is rashness. If you like courage but do not like learning, that fault is courting disaster. If you like strength but do not like learning, that fault is arrogance."

Comments: These six are all good qualities, but if one does not reinforce them with learning and is not good at applying them, they will still have major drawbacks. Pure kindness can turn into foolishness, showing off one's intelligence can lead to a careless lack of restraint, placing too much emphasis on trust can be a bad thing, and so on. This is purely experiential and extremely practical; it is practical guidance about realistically handling interpersonal relationships and cultivating the human condition. This is the spirit of Confucianism and can also explain the importance of "learning": **learning here means learning how to grasp the appropriate "degree,"** that is, what I have repeatedly spoken of as "A ≠ A ±." **If not in the appropriate degree, any good quality can be a great fault. Also note that "learning" here is not analytical but pragmatic learning.**

17.9. 子曰:「小子何莫學夫詩? 詩, 可以興, 可以觀, 可以群, 可以怨。邇之事父, 遠之事君。多識於鳥獸草木之名。」

Confucius said, "Why do young people not study the *Book of Songs*? Through the *Songs* one can inspire thought, observe things, unify a community, and express one's griefs. Nearby, it can be used to serve one's father, and afar to serve one's ruler. It can also help in recognizing and remembering the names of all kinds of animals and plants."

Comments: These four principles—inspiring, observing, uniting, and grieving—have been directly adopted as the major principles of traditional Chinese artistic and literary criticism. "Inspiring" refers to the associative power of art. "Grieving" is the theoretical basis for how all kinds of sorrowful and resentful feelings would later find their expression. But Confucian theories like "gentle and sincere" and "resenting without anger" also severely restricted the true development of "grieving," so that it remained controlled by the imperative to "begin in the feelings and end at [the boundaries of] ritual propriety," and never had any possibility of heading off in the direction of a Dionysian spirit. Chinese arts and letters have very little revelry, romanticism, or intense emotion, preferring to keep to the peaceful and moderate; this is both a strength and a weakness. For more on this see my book *The Chinese Aesthetic Tradition* (*Huaxia meixue*).

Why would one want to "recognize and remember the names of all kinds of animals and plants"? Is this for the sake of knowledge of the natural world, or for some other purpose? Perhaps these "names" are either shamanistic or totemic symbols or signs? Is there a historical "reality" to all these "names"? Is that why Confucius, who "transmits and does not create" 述而不作 (*Analects* 7.1), would say this? It is impossible to know.

17.10. 子謂伯魚曰:「女為《周南》、《召南》矣乎? 人而不為《周南》、《召南》, 其猶正牆面而立也與? 」

Confucius said to [his son] Kong Li, "Have you studied the Zhounan and Shaonan odes in the *Book of Songs*? If someone does not study the Zhounan and Shaonan odes, it will be as though he is standing facing a wall!"

Comments: The meaning of the phrase "as though standing facing a wall" is that one is unable to proceed forward. As I have said before, the function of the *Book of Songs* in ancient times was not only to express feelings; rather, it had broad pragmatic value and scope of use. It was especially invoked as a source in the study of the ritual system or when carrying out diplomatic duties. Because the *Book of Songs* was regarded as a classic at the time, it had great authority. Without studying it, it would have been difficult to move forward a single step or to accomplish anything. In the ancient ritual system, the relationship between husband and wife was primary,[4] and only after that came the relationships between father and son and minister and ruler. The Zhounan and Shaonan odes are the first two sections of the *Book of Songs*.

17.11. 子曰:「禮云禮云, 玉帛云乎哉? 樂云樂云, 鐘鼓云乎哉?」

Confucius said, "Ah, ritual! Ritual! Is it only presenting jade and offering silks? Ah, music! Music! Is it only ringing bells and striking drums?"

Comments: This passage is of course especially important. It points out that the "rites and music" are not simply a matter of externals—external forms, expressions, or sounds—but rather a matter of the entire system, and especially the inner emotions. In other words, it traces "ritual" back to "humaneness." This is something that the *Analects* emphasizes over and over again.

17.12. 子曰:「色厲而內荏, 譬諸小人, 其猶穿窬之盜也與?」

Confucius said, "To be stern on the surface and weak-willed underneath is perhaps—to use an analogy from the common people—like a petty thief who digs a hole in the wall."

Notes: *Cheng Shude quotes Huang Kan: This says it is like a petty person who is stealing something. A petty person who is a thief either enters through the wall of someone's chamber or over a person's wall, and as he does so, on the outside he is focused on carrying out the theft, while on the inside he is afraid of the people and constantly aware of the route of his retreat. His outer form is moving forward, but his heart is retreating, so that inner and outer balance themselves out, like someone whose appearance on the outside is proud and upright but whose heart on the inside is weak and sycophantic.*

Comments: This is a very apt analogy. Do we not have many such people today, on the outside creating great and glorious writings and making a great show of earnestness in criticizing others, while inside being as panic-stricken as a petty thief? In my translation of the term *xiaoren* [as "petty thief" instead of "petty person"], I have not followed the Note above.

17.13. 子曰:「鄉原, 德之賊也。」

Confucius said, "Your harmless Mr. Nice Guy is a scourge upon virtue."

Comments: The term *xiangyuan* means a yes-man, someone who is afraid of offending anyone; his yea and nay are always ambiguous. Whichever way he turns he meets with smooth sailing; he may wobble but he does not fall. His reputation is good, his relationships with others are good, everyone likes him, and he is happy with himself. Are there not many such among today's "top scholars"?! "I have seen such people, and heard them" [cf. 16.11].

17.14. 子曰:「道聽而塗說, 德之棄也。」

Confucius said, "To pass along what we hear of on the road is to cast away virtue."

Comments: To "cast away virtue" here means to lack a sense of responsibility. Today, people hear a smattering of Western learning spoken of on the road and loudly broadcast it all over the country, flaunting each other's various "posts" and "isms"—are these not also many?

17.15. 子曰:「鄙夫! 可與事君也與哉? 其未得之也, 患得之; 既得之, 患失之。苟患失之, 無所不至矣。」

Confucius said, "Is it possible to serve one's ruler alongside vulgar people? When they have not yet obtained something, they are scared to death of not obtaining it; when they obtain it, they are scared to death of losing it; if they are scared to death of losing it, then they are willing to do anything [to keep it]."

Comments: The phrasing "scared of obtaining or losing" (*huan de huan shi* 患得患失) is extremely vivid and accurate to the point that it has become an idiomatic saying. Do we not have many today of these as well, who will stop at nothing in pursuit of fame or profit?

17.16. 子曰: 「古者民有三疾, 今也或是之亡也。古之狂也肆, 今之狂也蕩; 古之矜也廉, 今之矜也忿戾; 古之愚也直, 今之愚也詐而已矣。」

Confucius said, "The ancients had three types of faults; today, possibly even these faults are no longer to be found. The 'wildness' of the ancients was hastiness; today it is dissipation. The 'reserve' of the ancients was pointedness; today it is overbearing imperiousness. The 'foolishness' of the ancients was frankness; today it is nothing but putting on an act in order to cheat people."

Comments: In summary, this is A ≠ A ± in concrete detail; one must not stray from this in the slightest. In action, if one does not correctly emphasize established customs and appropriacy; if one goes on about the mind, nature, Principle, and *qi* while practicing gluttony in private; or claims that ancient and modern are one and the same—this would seem to be in harmony with the true Confucian tradition while actually being completely at variance with it.

17.17. 子曰: 「巧言令色, 鮮矣仁。」

[This is a repetition of 1.3].

17.18. 子曰: 「惡紫之奪朱也, 惡鄭聲之亂雅樂也, 惡利口之覆邦家者。」

Confucius said, "I deplore the way that purple has usurped the position of red; I deplore the way that the tunes of the state of Zheng have destroyed proper music; I deplore those that overturn the kingdom with their careless words and sharp tongues."

Comments: At the time and in later years, purple was the color of nobility worn by the ruler; this may not have been the same as the ancient tradition, which is why Confucius deplored it. However, customs had already changed, and "It's no longer the old make-up styles of the Tianbao period"—it is never possible to revive the ancient ways, even in personal adornment. The same is true of the music of Zheng and proper music.

17.19. 子曰:「予欲無言。」子貢曰:「子如不言,則小子何述焉?」子曰:「天何言哉? 四時行焉, 百物生焉, 天何言哉? 」

Confucius said, "I do not wish to speak anymore." Zigong asked, "If you do not speak, then how will we young people pass along [your teachings]?" Confucius said, "Does Heaven speak? The four seasons are set in motion, and the myriad things are born and grow—does Heaven speak?"

Comments: This is another very important passage. Historians of philosophy have attempted to use this passage to argue that Confucius was an atheist, and so on—attempts that are truly groundless. What is important is how this passage shows once again that China's "In the beginning was the Deed" 太出有為 or "In the beginning was the Way" 太出有道 (as in walking) is different from "In the beginning was the Word" 太出有言, in which God says "Let there be light" and there is light. Precisely because they transcend language, people and the myriad things are not created, and therefore there can be a unity between Heaven and humans, and human affairs can be united with the Way of Heaven. They share the same quality (*qi*) and the same virtue ("begetting and being begotten without end" 生生不已), differing only in form. I have emphasized that "Heaven's movement is full of power" and "Human nature is good" share the same origin and mutually follow from one another, which is why the emotional ("sincerity" 誠) is the highest realm. "Heaven" is not a moral code; "Heaven" is life itself, carrying on without ceasing, begetting and being begotten without end. It is because of this "Deed" and "Way" that we have these "feelings" and this "realm." Zhu Xi says, "The heart-mind of Heaven, Earth, and all living things is humaneness; it is only through being naturally endowed with this heart-mind of Heaven and Earth that people can have life, and therefore the sense of pity in people is also life" (Zhu Xi, *Collected Works*, *juan* 44). Xiong Shili says that one must perceive the universe in the midst of life, for Heaven is in people, and we must not leave people behind in the service of emphasizing Heaven (preface to *Yuan Ru*). Qian Mu criticized Buddhists for "having a body and not being useful," and so on. All of these follow the same train of thought—that Heaven and humans are unified and not separated. Further, since form and function share the same origin, and there is not the smallest distance between them, then humans are an extension of Heaven. It is only thanks to Zhu Xi's insistence on raising "humaneness" to the level of Heavenly Principle that people get imprisoned within "just and rational nature" (*yili zhi xing* 義理之性) and lose the vitality of human life that is connected with Heaven and Earth. That is why in this work I emphasize the need to describe the unity of Heaven and humans using feeling in place of nature and Principle, and aesthetics in place of religion.

Due to Heaven's inexorable movement, China never had a sense of the extinction of human life, or of original sin, but instead had more a sense of the inconstancy of human life, and thus an emphasis on sorrow and regretful emotion. There is no aspiration toward a life to come or absolute transcendence; instead, people strive to find eternity in the regulation of the seven emotions (the emotions of the human world), the pleasure of Heaven and humans (the mystical experience of the interaction of Heaven and humanity), and in the unbroken continuity of generations of descendants. In sum, "Heaven's movement is full of power," and whatever acts in continuity with it is good, that is, human nature. This kind of optimistic consciousness comes from the assumption of the non-existence of any transcendent external supporting power, and thus is even more desolate. This is where China gets its expectation of hardship, respect for virtue and [emphasis on] study, cautiousness, and continual self-examination. **This is the notion of "relying upon oneself and not on the other" (Zhang Taiyan [Zhang Binglin (1869–1936)]), which is quite distinct from the human-divine dichotomy of Christianity's tradition of original sin.**

17.20. 孺悲欲見孔子，孔子辭以疾。將命者出戶，取瑟而歌。使之聞之。

Ru Bei wished to see Confucius. Confucius declined, saying he was sick. When the person transmitting this message had gone out the door, Confucius began playing the *qin* and singing, so that Ru Bei would hear it.

Notes: *Kang Youwei notes: This is what Mencius called [instructing someone by] "disdaining to instruct" him ["Mencius" VI.B.16], and thus giving him a deep lesson.*

Comments: Many commentators, like Kang Youwei in the above Note, say that Confucius did this to let Ru Bei know that actually he was not sick but simply did not want to see him, in another sort of "educational method." Really? Would that not be purposeful lying? I believe that there must have been some other concrete circumstance or reason for this which is impossible for us to know more about.

17.21. 宰我問:「三年之喪, 期已久矣。君子三年不為禮, 禮必壞; 三年不為樂, 樂必崩。舊穀既沒, 新穀既升, 鑽燧改火, 期可已矣。」子曰:「食夫稻, 衣夫錦, 於女安乎?」曰:「安。」「女安則為之! 夫君子之居喪, 食旨不甘, 聞樂不樂, 居處不安, 故不為也。今女安, 則為之!」宰我出。子曰:「予之不仁也! 子生三年, 然後免於父母之懷。夫三年之喪, 天下之通喪也。予也, 有三年之愛於其父母乎?」

Zai Wo asked, "Keeping three years of mourning for parents is truly too long. If the noble person refrains from participating in ritual ceremonies for three years, ritual will grow unfamiliar. If he does not practice music for three years, music will be forgotten. As the stored up grain is eaten up, the new grain comes to market, and the seasonal tinder woods have already gone through a full cycle;[5] one year should be enough."

Confucius said, "Would you be at ease eating good grain and wearing good clothing?"

Zai Wo said, "I would be at ease."

"If you would be at ease, then do so. The noble person in mourning for a parent cannot taste his food, and when he listens to music takes no joy in it. Rising or sleeping he is not at ease; this is why he does not do these things. But if as you say you would be at ease, go ahead and do them."

When Zai Wo had walked out, Confucius said, "Zai Wo truly lacks humaneness! Sons and daughters leave the embrace of their parents only after three years. This system of three years of mourning is a general norm honored by everyone. Did Zai Wo not receive three years of love and care from his parents?"

Comments: I believe this is the most crucial passage of the entire *Analects*. I have addressed it many times already and will not repeat myself here. To summarize, Confucius builds "ritual" (the three-year mourning period) upon the principle of the psychological emotions (feeling "at ease"). Therefore the first principle of Confucianism is human emotion. The question of "three-year" or "one-year" is really not important. The stipulation of three years was probably in line with the practice of the ritual system of ancient clan tradition, and actually had no rational basis or explanation. This is exactly why, when Confucius gives his explanation, he takes the psychological emotions as the ultimate basis. Actually three years is of course too long, and very early on became impracticable.

Confucius's contribution lies in taking external ritual (norms) and turning them into internal psychology (feeling). But this core emotion is not a religious "fear," "reverence," or "solemnity," and so on, but rather the "filiality and love" that lies at the center of the parent-child relationship. The Han dynasty saw the systematization and even legalization of this train of thought, and subsequently it gradually sedimented into a deeply rooted cultural-psychological formation. In both the alternation of Confucianism and Legalism and the mutual complementarity of Confucianism and Daoism, Confucianism has always been primary, precisely because it takes this core emotional psychology of "filiality and love" as primary. It was supported over the long term by the societal foundations of the small-scale production of the agricultural family.

When the first draft of this book was already finished, I came upon the recent works of A. C. Graham, David Hall, Roger Ames, Robert Eno, and Chad Hansen, and discovered places where they lay very close to my own line of thought, in that they all gave attention to the vast differences between Chinese and Western traditions. David Hall and Roger Ames discuss the distinction in terms of transcendent (Western) and inner (Chinese) and logic (Western) and the aesthetic order (Chinese), while when it comes to the distinction between "this-worldly" (Chinese) and "other-worldly" (Western), their language happens to coincide (before this I was unaware of Roger Ames's English translation of the *Sunzi binfa*). For this reason I have done my best to supplement this work using their writings. Where we differ is largely as follows: I give more emphasis to Chinese tradition's social origins and historical foundations (the patriarchal ties of clan blood relations) and its appearance amid rationalized shamanism, and for this reason I regard "emotional psychology" as a key link, which I summarize as "pragmatic reason" and "a culture of delight." At the same time, I pay a lot of attention to how the binary of ethics (which is related to private religious morality) and history (which is related to public social morality) is manifest in both traditional and modern thought; this is also, I believe, beyond the scope of their field of vision. In my estimation, the emphasis of Ames et al. on the differences between China and the West is too extreme, and does not accord with China's traditional spirit of seeking common ground while preserving differences. In this book I cannot expound on these differences in full detail, but simply let these few preliminary words suffice as an impetus toward opening up further scholarly thought in the twenty-first century.

17.22. 子曰:「飽食終日, 無所用心, 難矣哉! 不有博弈者乎, 為之猶賢乎已。」

Confucius said, "It's hard to know what to do with those who eat their fill all day long and don't apply their minds to anything. Aren't there those who play chess? Doing this type of thing is a little better."

Comments: People must always use their intelligence and work their brains, otherwise they live in vain. This is in great contrast to the Daoist notion of "renouncing sagehood and discarding wisdom" 絕聖棄智 (*Laozi* I.19).

17.23. 子路曰:「君子尚勇乎?」子曰:「君子義以為上。君子有勇而無義為亂, 小人有勇而無義為盜。」

Zilu asked, "Does the noble person esteem courage?" Confucius said, "The noble person esteems ritual righteousness above all. If a noble person is courageous but does not pay attention to ritual righteousness, there will be chaos; if a petty person is courageous and does not pay attention to ritual righteousness, he will become a robber."

Comments: Zilu always gave free rein to his courage, which is why Confucius repeatedly warned him about it.

17.24. 子貢曰:「君子亦有惡乎?」子曰:「有惡: 惡稱人之惡者, 惡居下流而訕上者, 惡勇而無禮者, 惡果敢而窒者。」曰:「賜也亦有惡乎?」「惡徼以為知者, 惡不孫以為勇者, 惡訐以為直者。」

Zigong said, "Does the noble person also have hatreds?" Confucius said, "Yes. He hates those who speak badly of others; he hates those who, being lowly themselves, malign those above them; he hates those who are courageous yet do not understand the ritual system; he hates those who are decisive and yet wilful."

He then asked, "Zigong, do you also have things you hate?" [He answered,] "I hate those who copy others in order to falsely claim to be intelligent; I hate those who use modesty to pretend to courage; I hate those who uncover people's secrets and call it frankness."

Comments: Confucius is no yes-man, nor does he love everyone indiscriminately. **He has loves and hates, and by no means "loves all people."** This is what makes him a living person rather than a make-believe sage or hypocrite. Student and teacher here are engaging in a cozy question and answer, exchanging their thoughts. What both of them hate is for the most part A ≠ A ±.

17.25. 子曰:「唯女子與小人為難養也, 近之則不孫, 遠之則怨。」

Confucius said, "It is only wives, concubines, and servants who are difficult to know how to treat: if you draw near, they do not obey; if you pull away, they are resentful."

Comments: This passage has been the most criticized by modern women. Many essays have been written in criticism or explanation, but actually neither is necessary. On the contrary, I believe this saying quite accurately describes some characteristically feminine dispositions. If you are close to them, they sometimes become overly comfortable, and laugh or curse or fight at will. But if you keep a distance from them, they will complain unendingly. This characteristic of their psychological disposition is not necessarily good or bad; it simply reflects a difference that is born of sex difference; it is a kind of psychological fact. As for [the way this passage] draws a connection between women and servants, this is difficult to make sense of. Whether we understand "petty person" [小人

("servant")] here as an ordinary person or as a less cultivated intellectual (see 13.20), both lead to plausible readings. Unfairness toward women is universal all over the world, so of course Chinese tradition is also very unfair and very unreasonable toward women, and Confucianism is no exception. In the modern period both Kang Youwei in his *Datong shu* and Song Shu 宋恕 (1862–1910) in his *Liuzhai Beiyi* 六齋卑議, among others, all have exposed this in depth and concrete detail. But compared with the Christian teaching of the European Middle Ages that women had no soul, or the serious harm caused by the large-scale rounding up of "witches," and so forth, this is still slightly better. Alternatively, one could say that this saying is addressed to the ruler and is speaking of ladies in waiting and servants of the ruler.

17.26. 子曰:「年四十而見惡焉, 其終也已。」

Confucius said, "For someone to reach forty years of age and still be hated by others—that is it [for him]."

Notes: *Zhu Xi notes: This is to urge people to improve their strengths and correct their faults. Mr. Su [Shi 蘇軾 (1037–1101)] notes: This was spoken about someone; who that was is not known.*[6]

Comments: It is probably the case that this refers to a concrete situation, as suggested by Mr. Su in the Note above. Its general meaning is that time waits for no one, and one should be diligent in good time to avoid great tragedy when one is old. This is true both of study and of knowing how to conduct oneself as a person. Of course, there is nothing special about the age of forty, but [Confucius's] saying "At forty I was no longer confused" (*Analects* 2.4) is commonly taken to mean that forty is the "age of perfect virtue," the stage at which a person has matured and taken his or her final form.

Book 18

18.1. 微子去之，箕子為之奴，比干諫而死。孔子曰：「殷有三仁焉。」

Weizi departed, Jizi became a slave, and Bigan was put to death because of his remonstrances. Confucius said, "The Yin had three humane men."

Comments: Because King Zhou of the Yin [Shang] "lacked the Way," these three all either left, were killed, or were punished with servitude. "Humaneness" or "being humane" does not necessarily gain one a good fate or reward; this has always been the case from ancient times until the present. But how can "good fortune" and "virtue" be united? Where is this "perfect goodness" to be found? Since we cannot trace it back to God as in Kant's moral theology, we can only seek to unite it with the whole of humanity, with its unbroken string of descendants. For more on this see my *Zhexue tanxun lu* 哲學探尋錄 [A *record of philosophical inquiries*].

18.2. 柳下惠為士師，三黜。人曰：「子未可以去乎？」曰：「直道而事人，焉往而不三黜？枉道而事人，何必去父母之邦。」

Liu Xiahui was serving as a judge, and three times was relieved of his post. Someone said, "Why do you not leave?" He answered, "If one carries out one's duties in legitimate ways, wherever one goes will one not be repeatedly removed from office? If one carries out one's duties in illegitimate ways, then why would one ever leave one's own country?"

Comments: "Floodwaters inundate everything everywhere" [18.6]; the administrations of Lu and Wei were held by brothers. Since "everywhere it is the same," it is better just to serve in one's own home country.

18.3. 齊景公待孔子，曰:「若季氏則吾不能，以季、孟之閒待之。」曰:「吾老矣，不能用也。」孔子行。

Duke Jing of Qi said of the standard according to which he would treat Confucius: "I cannot treat him as I would the Duke of Ji; I can treat him somewhere between the Duke of Ji and Duke of Meng." He also said, "I am old, and cannot make use of him anymore." Confucius then departed.

Comments: Confucius also wanted to address value and status. A "beautiful jade" ought to bring a good price.

18.4. 齊人歸女樂，季桓子受之。三日不朝，孔子行。

The people of Qi sent some singing girls. Ji Huanzi received them, and for three days did not hold court. Confucius then departed.

Comments: This is an example of when [Confucius] knew something was not possible and decided not to do it, [instead] taking his leave. **It was not the case that in every place and at every time he would "know something is not possible, yet go and do it"** [14.38]; that would be to be a hypocrite. A hair's breadth of deviation can take you a thousand miles off course. Neither "humaneness" nor "wisdom" should be emphasized at the expense of the other.

18.5. 楚狂接輿歌而過孔子曰:「鳳兮！鳳兮！何德之衰？往者不可諫，來者猶可追。已而，已而！今之從政者殆而！」孔子下，欲與之言。趨而辟之，不得與之言。

The madman of Chu drew near to Confucius's carriage and passed him, singing, "The phoenix! The phoenix! How can virtuous doings bring on such decline! It doesn't pay to speak of the past, there's still enough time for the future. Forget it! Forget it! Those who govern today are really awful."

Confucius got out of his carriage and wanted to talk with him, but he quickly ran away, and Confucius was unable to speak with him.

Comments: The phrase *jie yu* 接輿 has a meaning, and is not a person's name [as some commentators have suggested]; it means he passed Confucius's carriage. In sum, the words of the song mean that nothing can be done, government is dangerous, and one would do better to retire from the world. There is no need to rush around. Clearly the Daoists were around before Confucius, and there were recluses early on.

18.6. 長沮、桀溺耦而耕, 孔子過之, 使子路問津焉。長沮曰: 「夫執輿者為誰? 」子路曰: 「為孔丘。」曰: 「是魯孔丘與? 」曰: 「是也。」曰: 「是知津矣。」問於桀溺, 桀溺曰: 「子為誰? 」曰: 「為仲由。」曰: 「是魯孔丘之徒與? 」對曰: 「然。」曰: 「滔滔者天下皆是也, 而誰以易之? 且而與其從辟人之士也, 豈若從辟世之士哉? 」耰而不輟。子路行以告。夫子憮然曰: 「鳥獸不可與同群, 吾非斯人之徒與而誰與? 天下有道, 丘不與易也。」

Changju and Jieni were plowing side by side when Confucius passed them and asked Zilu to go ask them about where to ford the river.

Changju asked, "For whom are you driving?"

Zilu answered, "It is Confucius."

He asked, "Confucius of the state of Lu?"

"Yes," he said.

Changju said, "Then he knows the ford."

Zilu turned and asked Jieni.

Jieni asked, "Who are you then?"

He said, "I am Zilu."

He asked, "The disciple of Confucius of Lu?"

Again he answered, "Yes."

He asked, "Floodwaters inundate everything everywhere; who can change them? You—and they that follow those who avoid bad people—would do better to follow those who avoid the affairs of the world." He continued plowing, without stopping to rest.

Zilu returned to report all this to Confucius.

Confucius sighed deeply and said, "It has never been possible to live with flying birds or moving animals. If I am not to be with people, then with whom shall I be? If all under heaven were at peace, I would not need to go seek to change it."

Comments: This is about the difference between Confucians and Daoists (or recluses), between avoiding government (i.e., avoiding bad government) and avoiding the world (not even inquiring about worldly affairs). Later scholar-officials would "live by rivers and lakes, while their heart remains at the court of Wei";[1] it was always difficult for them to forget their interest in the great affairs of state, and they always remained connected with government. This is the Confucian tradition, and a characteristic of the cultural psychology of Chinese intellectuals. Furthermore, government (its theory, concepts, thought, and attitudes) usually formed an important aspect of or content of their philosophy, arts, and literature; those who could thoroughly and completely free themselves from it were few indeed. From Qu Yuan to Lu Xun, from the pre-Qin philosophers and sages to modern New Confucians, all are the same.

This type of attitude often expresses itself in heartfelt sighs, as in this passage of the *Analects*. Clearly, Confucius's feelings are different from those of the recluses. This difference definitely arises from differences in how they view their situations as well as differences in their moral ideals. Therefore **they take a different attitude toward human life and have different feelings about life**. Clearly, emotion is without substance; each person must construct substance for themselves. **The substance Confucius constructed was "humaneness," that is, the elevation of this emotion ("If I am not to be with people, then with whom shall I be?"), and therefore "If I am not to be with people, then with whom shall I be," rather than being a sort of theoretical proof is actually better described as a deep exclamation in which reason is melded into emotion. This is the meaning of [my] historico-anthropological ontology. The existence and persistence of human substance is the source of the absolute imperative of moral will, and any sense of mission or sense of duty arises from this.**

Religions and philosophies of salvation abound, some emphasizing the salvation of the soul even to the point of entering darkness, seeking suffering, eschewing the body or embracing pain in order to obtain salvation. Some first save the soul, then the body, with the former being a necessary condition for the latter. Confucianism is different. At the very least, the body and soul are of equal importance, therefore [there are such expressions as] "delivering them from being hung upside down" and "saving the people from flood and fire." First one saves one's own soul, then one saves the people's bodies, and then one benefits them with education—these are also a matter of the salvation of the soul. Confucianism is not only a religious doctrine but also has a political character; **this is why China's so-called history of philosophy must always include political thought.**

18.7. 子路從而後，遇丈人，以杖荷蓧。子路問曰：「子見夫子乎？」丈人曰：「四體不勤，五穀不分。孰為夫子？」植其杖而芸。子路拱而立。止子路宿，殺雞為黍而食之，見其二子焉。明日，子路行以告。子曰：「隱者也。」使子路反見之。至則行矣。子路曰：「不仕無義。長幼之節，不可廢也；君臣之義，如之何其廢之？欲潔其身，而亂大倫。君子之仕也，行其義也。道之不行，已知之矣。」

Zilu was following Confucius, and fell behind. He met an old man, who was using a pole to carry hay-cutting implements.

Zilu asked, "Have you seen my teacher?"

The old man said, "Your four limbs do not labor, and you do not know the five grains. Who is your teacher?" He put down his pole and began cutting hay.

Zilu stood, respectfully making obeisance.

The old man kept Zilu for the night in his home, killed a chicken and made food for him to eat, and even introduced him to his two sons.

The next day, Zilu continued hurriedly on his way, and told Confucius.

Confucius said, "This was a hermit." He wanted Zilu to go back and find him. When Zilu got there, the old man had left.

Zilu said, "It does not make sense to refuse to serve in office. Since one can't discard the order of precedence between old and young, how can one discard the relation between ruler and minister? In order to keep oneself pure, one destroys important social relationships. For the noble person to come out and serve as an official is to fulfill his obligation; but as for the impossibility of putting the righteousness of the Way into practice, we knew this long ago."

Notes: *Zhu Xi notes: The major relationships of humankind are five: between father and son there is kinship, between ruler and minister there is righteousness, between husband and wife there is distinction [of roles], between elder and younger there is deferential order, and between friends there is trustworthiness. This is why an official practices the righteousness [that governs] between ruler and minister, and why, although he knows the impossibility of putting the righteousness of the Way into practice, he will be unable to give up on it.*

Kang Youwei notes: Now, humans share the same qi *with Heaven. All of the human race are brothers, and righteousness should be their salvation. The officials who anxiously surround the ruler to do his bidding are there to put his righteousness into practice for the salvation of the people, and to carry out his compassionate heart. It is like when a relation is sick, although one knows he will not get better, one will still rush about after the medicine to cure him.*

Comments: These three passages are very well known. Each has to do with recluse critiques of Confucius's spirit of "knowing something is not possible and yet going and doing it" [14.38] and Confucius's responses. Confucius had great respect for these people, for the decision to flee the world and live as a hermit, preserving one's own purity. At the same time, these passages also explain his reasons for actively seeking to enter society. "If I am not to be with people, then with whom shall I be?" [18.6]. One could say that this comes out of his sincere feeling and depth of affection (清真意深). **To "know something is not possible" refers to knowledge, while "and yet doing it" means doing it without any regard for success or failure, cause or effect. For by doing it one demonstrates that the ethical "substance" is higher than the knowledge of the phenomenal realm, and one demonstrates the dignity of humans in their freedom to not submit to cause and effect.**

The fact that Zhu Xi's "Five Relationships" have not been discarded in China for these thousands of years has to do with this social construction or social concept. Ruler and minister, or today the relations between lower and upper classes, are governed by the principles of "righteousness," that is, fairness, integrity, respect for the law, not showing favoritism in order to profit oneself, neither cheating those above nor oppressing those beneath. The distinction between husband and wife is a "family value";[2] it is not limited to love but includes the grace and mutual care and support for each other over many years, forgiveness and tolerance, respect for the old and care for the young—none of this is easy. As for the sense of kin between father and son, in the animal world this is limited to motherly love; here it demands that the father love his son and the son be filial to his father. In comparison to today's single-parent families that are primarily led by the mother, this is something to sigh over. **All of these Five Relationships, once given a new interpretation, should still be beneficial to the present age.**

18.8. 逸民: 伯夷、叔齊、虞仲、夷逸、朱張、柳下惠、少連。子曰: 「不降其志, 不辱其身, 伯夷、叔齊與! 」謂: 「柳下惠、少連, 降志辱身矣。言中倫, 行中慮, 其斯而已矣。」謂: 「虞仲、夷逸, 隱居放言。身中清, 廢中權。」「我則異於是, 無可無不可。」

Recluses: Bo Yi, Shu Qi, Yu Zhong, Yi Yi, Zhu Zhang, Liu Xiahui, and Shao Lian. Confucius said, "Those who neither abandoned their ideals nor humiliated themselves are Bo Yi and Shu Qi." He believed that "Liu Xiahui and Shao Lian abandoned their ideals and humiliated themselves, but spoke in a manner that accorded with norms and acted based upon consideration; that's all." He believed that "although Yu Zhong and Yi Yi lived in reclusion, they spoke unreservedly and had brilliant views; they kept themselves pure yet still conducted themselves nimbly in society. I am not like any of these people; there is nothing I am allowed and nothing I am disallowed."

Comments: Confucius compared himself with these noble personages to demonstrate that his flexibility was greater, that he could not be rigidly conformed to one type or pattern. As I have said above, flexibility (*quan* 權) manifests an individual's initiative and uniqueness; it is the core content of subjectivity,[3] and is of great importance.

18.9. 大師摯適齊, 亞飯干適楚, 三飯繚適蔡, 四飯缺適秦。鼓方叔入於河, 播鼗武入於漢, 少師陽、擊磬襄, 入於海。

Grand Music Master Zhi went to the state of Qi, while Second Music Master Gan went to the state of Chu, Third Music Master Liao went to the state of Cai, and Fourth Music Master Que went to the state of Tai. Fang Shu who played the large drum went to the banks of the Yellow River; Wu who played the small drum went to the banks of the Han; Yang the accompanist and Xiang who played the stone chimes went to the seaside.

Comments: This passage is purely a record of facts, and contains none of the words of Confucius. It is about the way that these musicians wandered around and dispersed to the four directions, in what was truly the "collapse of the rites and music." In speaking of "music," what is meant is not only music but also the collapse of traditional systems.

18.10. 周公謂魯公曰: 「君子不施其親, 不使大臣怨乎不以。故舊無大故, 則不棄也。無求備於一人。

The Duke of Zhou said to the Duke of Lu, "The noble person does not relax or slight the relationships of clan or family, nor does he allow grand officials to complain of not being paid enough attention. Among old friends and old relationships he does not cast anyone off who has not committed any great fault. He does not want to expect perfection from anyone."

Comments: The word 施 (*shi*) was originally 弛 (*chi*); Ruan Yuan 阮元 (1764–1849) in his *Lunyu jiaokan ji* says: "*Shi* and *chi* were used interchangeably in ancient times." This passage very clearly explains how the clan system emphasized blood relations and other "old relationships." This is the origin of Confucianism, and the vestiges of its influence are still present now after over three thousand years.

18.11. 周有八士: 伯達、伯適、仲突、仲忽、叔夜、叔夏、季隨、季騧。

The Zhou dynasty had eight personages: Bo Da, Bo Kuo, Chong Tu, Chong Hu, Shu Ye, Shu Xia, Ji Sui, and Ji Gua.

Comments: This passage is quite impossible to explain. It also never claims to have been said by Confucius. These people's historical traces are impossible to find. Bo, Chong, Shu, and Ji are birth order terms, and would seem to indicate that these are brothers in the same family.

The eleven passages of this chapter for the most part speak of the "recluses" who differ from or disagree with Confucius. As time went on and the world became more chaotic, many aristocrats one by one left the towns and politics. Confucius remained immersed in worldly duties, and thus became an opposing reflection to them. Actually, the reason that people can "participate with Heaven and Earth and help with the transformations" 參天地贊化育 is precisely because the order [of things] is not fixed and the role of chance is great, so only in this way can one know or establish one's fate or struggle for anything. This was different from the recluse's submission to Heaven and peace with his fate, and in this respect Confucius was superior to all recluses.

Book 19

19.1. 子張曰:「士見危致命, 見得思義, 祭思敬, 喪思哀, 其可已矣。」

Zizhang said, "When an intellectual meets with a crisis, he gives up his life; when he meets with profit, he thinks of ritual propriety; when he offers sacrifices, he is sincere and solemn; in mourning, he is sorrowful. This is what makes him acceptable."

Notes: *Zhu Xi notes: These four are the major components of establishing oneself. If someone does not practice them perfectly, then he is not worthy of our attention. This is why he says that if an intellectual can be like this, then he will be acceptable to him.*

Comments: Zhu Xi says about this chapter, "The passages in this chapter are all the sayings of Confucius's disciples. Among them, the largest number belongs to Zixia, and the second largest to Zigong. It seems that after Yan Hui, Zigong is the cleverest of Confucius's disciples; after Zengzi, none was as sincere as Zixia. This is why they are recorded in detail."

At this point, near the end of the *Analects*, looking back over the foundational concepts and categories that Confucians preached (e.g., humaneness, ritual, study, filiality, respect for elders, loyalty, compassion, wisdom, and virtue), as well as those raised in this passage (righteousness, respect, mourning, and fate), when compared with the fundamental concepts and categories of Christianity (lordship, love, faith, redemption from sin, salvation, hope, original sin, omniscience, omnipotence, etc.), Greek philosophy (idea, form, qualities, atoms, being, etc.), and modern philosophy (anxiety, isolation, fear, ennui, and nothingness), its characteristic pragmatic reason and culture of delight seem very obvious.

19.2. 子張曰:「執德不弘, 信道不篤, 焉能為有? 焉能為亡? 」

Zizhang said, "If one practices virtue without broadness, if one trusts in morality and justice but lacks perseverance, then how can one be considered to have it, and how be considered not to have it?"

Notes: *Zhu Xi says: If one has accomplishment and keeps to it too narrowly, then one's virtue remains alone; if one has reputation and fails to keep faith with it, then the Way is lost.*

Kang Youwei says: Later people mistakenly revered Zengzi, and therefore put down Zizhang, but this was to mistake black for white and high for low. This was to misunderstand the Way of Confucius.

Comments: Yang Bojun notes that *hong* 弘 ["broad"] should read *qiang* 強 ["strong"], and quotes Zhang Binglin [Zhang Taiyan] in his *Guang lunyu pianzhi* 廣論語駢枝 as reading "practicing virtue without broadness" to mean putting virtue into practice without firmness. My interpretation follows Zhu Xi's note. Virtue is not composed of being obstinate in small virtues; only the virtue that seeks breadth is adequate to meet the demands of the world. This is also why Kang Youwei in his note honors Zizhang over Zengzi. Zizhang liked to ask about government and sought to take on political duties, so his "virtue" naturally needed to be broader, and did not limit itself to the small accomplishments of individual self-cultivation. Thus, the question "How can one be considered to have it?" can be interpreted to mean that only one who "saves the world and relieves the people" can be said to truly possess it—that is, one with broad and far-reaching ambition.

19.3. 子夏之門人問交於子張。子張曰:「子夏云何?」對曰:「子夏曰:『可者與之, 其不可者拒之。』」子張曰:「異乎吾所聞: 君子尊賢而容眾, 嘉善而矜不能。我之大賢與, 於人何所不容? 我之不賢與, 人將拒我, 如之何其拒人也? 」

Zixia's disciples asked Zizhang how one should make friends.

Zizhang answered, "How did Zixia say one should?"

They answered, "Zixia said, those you ought to befriend, do; those you ought not befriend, refuse to make friends with."

Zizhang said, "This is different from what I have heard. The noble person respects those of sagely virtue and accepts the masses; he praises good people and pities those who are not good. Am I a very good person? Then what is there about people that I cannot tolerate? Am I a bad person? Others will distance themselves from me; how can I then distance myself from others?"

Notes: *Cheng Shude quotes Cai Yong's* 蔡邕 *(133–192) "Zheng jiao lun"* 正交論: *The disciples of Zixia were asking Zizhang about friendship, but the two disciples each had heard something from the Master. However, [Confucius] was using [the example of] friendship to instruct him; because [Zixia] had a wide sphere [of relations], therefore he told him to refuse [certain] people; while [Zizhang]'s [relations] were narrow, so he told him to accept the masses.*

Comments: What he has "heard" of course refers to what he has heard from Confucius. It is possible that, as the note says, Confucius answered Zizhang and Zixia differently because of their different situations, and the two of them therefore promulgated their own versions, which led to different interpretations, opinions, and finally schools of thought. In the previous passage, Zhu Xi's note says that Zixia was closer to Zengzi, and placed a greater emphasis on individual self-cultivation; if on "seeing evil" one should "avoid it as if you had touched boiling water" (16.11), then what if one does not succeed in avoiding it? This is why one should refuse friendship with those one "ought not befriend" 不可交. Zizhang was in government, and naturally had to relate with many different kinds of people, including bad people that one "ought not befriend." But based on historical facts like Zixia's living at Xihe, it would seem he was not so close to the "inner sageliness" school of Zengzi.

19.4. 子夏曰:「雖小道, 必有可觀者焉; 致遠恐泥, 是以君子不為也。」

Zixia said, "Even a minor skill can definitely be taken up in some situations; yet one who wishes to accomplish great things must not get bogged down in such things, and therefore the noble person does not take them up."

Notes: *Zhu Xi says: A minor skill is something like farming, gardening, medicine, or divination.*

Comments: This passage is like 2.12, "The noble person is not a tool." Perhaps this has to do with the difference between an "expert" and a "thinker," "philosopher," or "politician"? The latter are not "experts." But the former are not necessarily only "minor skills"; they also have significant value, and are by no means inferior to thinking, philosophy, or government. It is just that because government touches on the mass of households and the whole of society and state that it seems to be a great enterprise. This passage also demonstrates that Zixia did emphasize the enterprise of outer kingliness.

19.5. 子夏曰:「日知其所亡, 月無忘其所能, 可謂好學也已矣。」

Zixia said, "Every day, to learn some new knowledge, and every month, to not forget the old knowledge one has learned—this is what can be called the love of study."

Comments: Study must always rely upon accumulation. It is only through daily accumulation and monthly storing up [of knowledge] that one can either suddenly see something clearly, or make a name for oneself. These are absolutely not the work of a single step. When Gu Tinglin 顧亭林 (1613–1682) named his great work completed over many decades the *Ri zhi lu* 日知錄 [*Record of Daily Knowledge*], this is what he meant.

19.6. 子夏曰:「博學而篤志, 切問而近思, 仁在其中矣。」

Zixia said, "Broad study, a resolute ambition, sincere questioning, and diligent thought—'humaneness' is to be found in these."

Notes: *Zhu Xi notes: These four are all aspects of study and argument, and do not rise to the level of doing one's utmost to practice or act with humaneness. However, if one pursues these in this manner, then one's mind will not stray afield and what one retains will mature by itself; this is why he says that humaneness is to be found in these. . . . Mr. Su [Shi]*[1] *says: If one studies broadly yet one's intention is not serious, one will be great but without true accomplishment; if one asks in generalities and lets one's thoughts range all over, then one will labor but without achievement.*

Comments: The word *qie* 切 should be read as *jiqie* 急切 ("eager"). Along with Huang Kan's *Yishu* and others, I am following Liu Kai's *Lunyu buzhu*:

The *qie* in *qiewen* ("sincere questioning") is the *qie* of *qieqie sisi* 切切偲偲 [see 13.28], and "it means sincere consideration." Zhu Xi brings up the fact that "humaneness" originally had to do with practice and action, and although here, unlike in Confucius's answers, this does not seem to be emphasized, it is interesting that Zhu Xi still argues for this view.

19.7. 子夏曰:「百工居肆以成其事, 君子學以致其道。」

Zixia said, "Every workman of every trade accomplishes his work in the workshop; the noble person should diligently study in order to accomplish his enterprise."

Comments: Each has his or her own job. To be a "noble person" and not study, consuming food for nothing—would this not produce shame vis-à-vis the various tradespeople? Later, many Confucians roundly denounced themselves, often speaking of feeling ashamed in the face of laboring people. This is the traditional precedent for Mao's policy of sending down to the countryside to labor for thought reform, and why intellectuals as a group were the targets. But the meaning of this passage is exactly the opposite: the "noble person" should apply himself to accomplishing his great enterprise of governing the state and bringing peace to the world.

19.8. 子夏曰:「小人之過也必文。」

Zixia said, "Having committed an error, the petty person will always gloss it over."

Comments: The phrase "Glossing over mistakes, concealing faults" 文過飾非 has already become an idiom.

19.9. 子夏曰:「君子有三變: 望之儼然, 即之也溫, 聽其言也厲。」

Zixia said, "The noble person has various changes: he appears very stern, but when approached he is gentle, and his speech is correct and incisive."

Comments: The two phrases "when approached he is gentle" and "his speech is correct and incisive" are to be read in a moderate and complementary fashion. Otherwise, one will either keep people at a great distance, or one will be sullied by improper familiarity.

19.10. 子夏曰: 「君子信而後勞其民, 未信則以為厲己也; 信而後諫, 未信則以為謗己也。」

Zixia said, "Only when the noble person has obtained the trust of the people will he order them about. Before he has obtained their trust, the people will feel they are being harmed. Only when he has obtained the trust of the ruler will he attempt to remonstrate with him. Before he has obtained his trust, the ruler will believe he is being maligned."

Comments: The first half of the passage emphasizes the importance of trust vis-à-vis the people, the second half vis-à-vis the ruler.

19.11. 子夏曰: 「大德不踰閑, 小德出入可也。」

Zixia said, "In great matters one may not cross the line; in small matters a little crossing back and forth is permissible."

Notes: *Zhu Xi notes: Great virtue and small virtue refer to great matters and small matters. . . . Mr. Wu [Wu Yu 吴棫] says: There will certainly be no lack of those who abuse what is said in this passage.*

Cheng Shude quotes the "Fanshen lu": This speaks of how people are different in how they manage their affairs; when observing them, one should observe them in great matters, for if in great matters they are acceptable, their small faults will be missing. If in one's management of one's affairs, one does not overstep the line in great matters, will one really allow any "crossing back and forth" in small ones? When once one allows any crossing of the line, then one lets one's mind go, and one will not be diligent in small matters of behavior, so that in the end [one's conduct in] great matters will also be involved.

Comments: What are referred to here as "great matters" of course have to do with major matters of principle related to enterprise, direction, the nation, society, and so forth. "Small matters" refer to everyday life and matters of daily living and relationships. As the notes suggest, Song-Ming Neo-Confucians did not approve of the idea that in small matters "a little crossing back and forth is permissible." Here, again, it is a question of two types of morality. Actually it is only public social morality that should be considered a "great matter," while private religious morality belongs completely to individual duty and can admit a variety of choices. Thus, individual faith and lifestyle choices, interests, and hobbies, and so on, all should be considered "small matters." Whether or not an individual pursues self-cultivation, nothing is impermissible, as long as there is no violation of public laws. This type of modern viewpoint is of course greatly at variance with traditional systems, including the Way of Confucius and Mencius. The Way of Confucius and Mencius can today function only as individual religious morality that serves to suggest or guide; it cannot serve as the universal public law of society. Thus, what we consider to be great or small matters has certainly evolved with the passage of time, and is now quite different from before.

19.12. 子游曰:「子夏之門人小子, 當洒掃、應對、進退, 則可矣。抑末也, 本之則無。如之何?」子夏聞之曰:「噫! 言游過矣! 君子之道, 孰先傳焉? 孰後倦焉? 譬諸草木, 區以別矣。君子之道, 焉可誣也? 有始有卒者, 其惟聖人乎!」

Ziyou said, "The disciples of Zixia are ok in matters of sweeping and cleaning, receiving guests, and advancing and retreating. But these are tiny matters. They don't have the fundamental things. How can this be?"

When Zixia heard it, he said, "What! Ziyou is mistaken! In the learning of the noble person, the things that are taught first and those that are taught after are each of a different type, like trees, flowers, and grasses. How can the learning of the noble person be so mischaracterized? It is only the sage who can master it from head to tail."

Notes: *Cheng Shude quotes the "Lunyu shuyao": The character* juan 倦 *here should mean the same as the character* jiao 教. *It is saying that some things should be transmitted first, and some taught later, depending on the quality of the student and what they are able to receive (just as grasses and trees are cultivated in different ways, and must not all be treated the same).*

Comments: The most difficult to understand is the last line, "Who can master it from head to tail." What does this mean? There are many interpretations. There are those who emphasize that there is no such thing as "roots and branches"—the branches are the roots, sweeping and receiving guests should be seen as part of the essential, as when the Wang Yangming school regards a child serving tea as a sage. It is in everyday life and ordinary behavior that one can recognize substance, observe the heart-mind and nature, and perfect wisdom. All are understood to be one. But this view in fact bears the influence of Chan Buddhism. Most interpretations read the passage as addressing the need for a certain order in education; it should begin with small matters and move on to greater ones, begin with practical and move on theory, begin with the branches and move on to the trunk or substance. Others understand the passage as relating to the need to teach people according to their capacities, to cultivate different plants differently, as in the note above. Zixia is credited with the transmission of the classics, and his influence on the Han dynasty was very great. His school is the direct successor to Confucius's teachings.

19.13. 子夏曰:「仕而優則學, 學而優則仕。」

Zixia said, "When a person is done holding office, he should seek to study; when his study is complete, he should hold office."

Comments: This is a famous passage, and is often attributed to Confucius because it comes from the *Analects*. Actually, this chapter is entirely the words of Confucius's disciples, and especially the Zixia school. "When his study is complete, he should hold office" is a way of life for intellectuals in traditional Chinese society; this is why the words *shi* 士 [meaning "scholar"] and *daifu* 大夫 (meaning "someone with an official position") are always linked. This is an important phenomenon in the history of world civilization. On the one hand, China was the earliest to establish a systematized structure of civil government linking administration and education, such that society benefited from having intellectuals as its important pillars. On the other hand, the individual life values of intellectuals and their ultimate concerns became subsumed under "aiding the world and saving the people" and "all men are brothers," seeking to establish the "Heavenly kingdom" in this world (whether that took the form of "Reviving the Flourishing of the Three Dynasties" 夏三代

之盛 or "Understanding the Three Sequences and Extending the Three Ages" 通三統張三世).[2] This aspect is what led to the Chinese-style unity of government with education and its pan-moralism, while at the same time avoiding contradictions and disputes among many religious faiths. This is both historical fact and psychological reality; there is no need to engage in endless debates in order to come to a value judgment—the important thing is to try to understand and analyze this phenomenon in order to explore the possibilities moving forward.

19.14. 子游曰: 「喪致乎哀而止。」

Ziyou said, "Funerals should be devoted to the emotion of sorrow, but not to excess."

Comments: There are two meanings: first, you want there to be sorrow, otherwise you will lose the meaning of funeral rituals. Secondly, you don't want sorrow to be excessive to the point of damaging the body or the mind, which would also amount to being unfilial. But Confucius sometimes also "wept excessively sorrowfully" (11.9), [suggesting that] this is also a question of grasping the *jing* ("principledness") and the *quan* ("flexibility").

19.15. 子游曰: 「吾友張也, 為難能也。然而未仁。」

Ziyou said, "My friend Zizhang is such a person as is hard to come by. But he is not 'humane.' "

Comments: This chapter is critical of Zizhang in many places. Could it be that, as Kang Youwei has said, it is the work of the followers of Zengzi's school?"

19.16. 曾子曰: 「堂堂乎張也, 難與並為仁矣。」

Zengzi said, "Zizhang certainly is imposing. It is difficult to carry out humaneness and virtue alongside him."

Notes: *Zhu Xi notes:* Tangtang 堂堂 *means "magnificent in appearance." It means that because he was so aloof and self-possessed, one could not assist him toward humaneness, nor could he assist others in humaneness. Fan Zuyu* 范祖禹 *(1041–1098) says: Zizhang exceeds the mark on the outside but is insufficient on the inside, therefore none of the disciples join with him in working on humaneness together. Confucius says that being strong and resolute is close to humaneness; to be able to achieve humaneness it is better to seem insufficient on the outside while exceeding the mark on the inside.*

Kang Youwei quotes Zheng Xuan: Zizhang's appearance and bearing was magnificent. In the "Confucius" chapter of the "Liezi" it says: Zizhang's appearance was more sagely than that of Confucius. It also says: Zizhang could be serious but could not join with others; because of his conceit and aloofness, it was difficult to pursue humaneness alongside him. Zengzi was reserved, the opposite of Zizhang, and therefore did not approve of him. . . . Confucius approved of Zizhang, and often compared him with Yan Hui, from which we can conclude that in evaluating people we should be led by Confucius's spirit of compromise. Those who wrote down the "Analects" were followers of Zengzi's school, and not disciples of Zizhang, and therefore when they were recording their own teacher's sayings, as when Xunzi refutes the [various] thinkers[3] *and Mencius, these cannot be relied upon for evidence. Zhu Xi wrongly has too much respect for Zengzi, and therefore does not question [this statement], but takes it as pitying Zizhang for being too lofty in action and having too little honesty—this is a great mistake.*

Comments: See above. Zizhang's image in the *Analects* is also quite distinctive. Because he likes politics, tends to be talkative, favors action, and often displays changeability or partiality, he is less "strong and resolute" (13.27); therefore he is on the receiving end of criticism and disapproval from people like Zengzi. Among the disciples these types of situations are certainly very common and should not surprise us. Zhu Xi's note supports Zengzi, while Kang Youwei's supports Zizhang. This is probably explicable as the difference between traditional and modern viewpoints. Wang Kaiyun (1833–1916) in his *Lunyu xun* takes this passage as praising Zizhang, which is very strange.

19.17. 曾子曰:「吾聞諸夫子: 人未有自致者也, 必也親喪乎!」

Zengzi said, "I have heard the Master say that if one has not been able to fully give oneself over to the expression of one's own feelings, surely it will only be when one loses father or mother that one will be able to do so."

Comments: This passage explains how, because Chinese culture gives attention to ritual and emphasizes control and moderation, the feelings are often suppressed and hard to give natural expression to, so that it is only when one loses a parent that one can forget all restraint, let it all out in loud sobs, and the like.

19.18. 曾子曰:「吾聞諸夫子: 孟莊子之孝也, 其他可能也; 其不改父之臣, 與父之政, 是難能也。」

Zengzi said, "I heard from the Master that Meng Zhuangzi's filial piety can be matched in everything but this: he did not change his father's ministers or his father's policies. This is very difficult to match."

Notes: *Kang Youwei notes: If this were not so, then Yu in his controlling of the floodwaters would have been limited to the methods of his father Gun. . . . The reader can easily choose what is permissible.*

Comments: "New dynasty, new policy"—in later generations this was always the practice, and this included many "sagely rulers." Kangxi's policies were lenient, Yongzheng corrected them with cruelty, and Qianlong rectified them yet again—this had nothing to do with being filial or unfilial. Because Confucianism was still in the grip of clan ritual systems, it still emphasized "for three years not changing his father's ways" (*Analects* 1.11), [a practice] which both at the time and into later years had become quite senseless. The Legalists criticized Confucians early on for not realizing the need to adapt with the times, but rather obstinately clinging to old systems, which naturally would not work. The major contribution of Zengzi's school, including later Song-Ming Neo-Confucians, was in preaching the major role of private religious morality in establishing human nature and human character, both in ethical and pragmatic respects. But in terms of establishing public social morality and upholding traditional Chinese society's long-lasting governmental-educational system, they do not compare to the many politicians and thinkers that taught that learning should serve the practical needs of the state, from Zigong and Zixia to Xunzi and Dong Zhongshu. **This latter thread has been far too little studied, to the point that the**

former is allowed to monopolize the limelight. Of course, these two threads are always mutually interweaving and intersecting with each other, even intermixing to the point of being difficult to distinguish from one another (e.g., in Huang Zongxi, Wang Fuzhi, and others). But in terms of their theoretical logic it should still be possible to analyze them clearly. Kang Youwei's note above arguing that it is acceptable to change one's father's policies reflects this later trend, but as Kang Youwei is a modern person, this is of course to be expected.

19.19. 孟氏使陽膚為士師, 問於曾子。曾子曰: 「上失其道, 民散久矣。如得其情, 則哀矜而勿喜。」

Meng Shi wanted Yang Fu to serve as a judge, and Yang Fu asked Zengzi's opinion. Zengzi said, "When those above have lost the meaning of the Dao, the people's hearts will stray and they will disperse. If you truly understand the circumstances in which a crime was committed, you should feel sorrow and pity, rather than being happy."

Comments: This is saying that one should not rejoice in one's own ability to solve a case and pass judgment. This is surely "the speech of a humane person"—Zengzi's strong point. Zengzi is associated with compassion, steadfastness, and pedantry. People's characters have strong and weak points, and no one should be expected to be perfect. The tendency to overly praise [him] (as Zhu Xi's commentary does) or to demean [him] (as Kang Youwei's does) are both totally uncalled for.

19.20. 子貢曰: 「紂之不善, 不如是之甚也。是以君子惡居下流, 天下之惡皆歸焉。」

Zigong said, "The tyrant Zhou's wickedness was not as excessive as it is said to have been. Therefore the noble person hates to settle in an unfavorable location, where all the crime and evil can be pushed onto him."

Comments: King Zhou of Yin [also known as tyrant Zhou] was originally a very capable ruler with many historical accomplishments—of this, there is irrefutable evidence. Because he lost his kingdom and died, he has been reviled in history as a villain, and has been a special target of concerted attack by Confucians. [In this context] it would have taken courage for Zigong to speak out this truth. Zigong's intelligent character is apparent throughout.

19.21. 子貢曰:「君子之過也, 如日月之食焉: 過也, 人皆見之; 更也, 人皆仰之。」

Zigong said, "When the noble person makes a mistake, it is like a solar or lunar eclipse: when he makes a mistake, everyone sees it; when he corrects himself, everyone reveres him."

Comments: This is a smart analogy. Clearly, even the Duke of Zhou and Confucius made mistakes; it is not as the Song-Ming Neo-Confucians would have it.

19.22. 衛公孫朝問於子貢曰:「仲尼焉學?」子貢曰:「文武之道, 未墜於地, 在人。賢者識其大者, 不賢者識其小者, 莫不有文武之道焉。夫子焉不學? 而亦何常師之有?」

Gongsun Chao of Wei asked Zigong: "Where did Confucius study?" Zigong said, "The ritual systems of King Wen and King Wu of Zhou have not been lost, but have been passed down among the people. Those of sagely virtue understand the greater parts, while those without sagely virtue understand the lesser parts; there are none that do not preserve King Wen and King Wu's moral system. Where did Confucius *not* study? And why would he have had a particular teacher?"

Comments: This is related to [Confucius's saying,] "I transmit, I do not create" (7.1). Confucius is the preserver, protector, and interpreter of the Zhou ritual tradition; it is on this basis that he teaches students and calls disciples, and Zigong is his important successor. In all of the *Analects*, Zigong always presents a smart, lively, and likable figure. This chapter records an exceptionally large number of Zigong's sayings. Tradition says that when Confucius died, Zigong alone maintained his grave for six years. The *Shiji* records that of all Confucius's disciples, Zigong left behind the greatest, most well-known, and most celebrated achievements; this is not a coincidence. Some say that it is because of Zigong's illustriousness that Confucius's reputation spread so far around the world. Is it so, is it really so?! (14.13).

19.23. 叔孫武叔語大夫於朝, 曰:「子貢賢於仲尼。」子服景伯以告子貢。子貢曰:「譬之宮牆, 賜之牆也及肩, 窺見室家之好。夫子之牆數仞, 不得其門而入, 不見宗廟之美, 百官之富。得其門者或寡矣。夫子之云, 不亦宜乎!」

Shusun Wushu said to his officials at court, "Zigong is more brilliant than Confucius."

Zifu Jingbo told it to Zigong.

Zigong said, "It is like a wall; my wall only comes up to shoulder height, so you can look over it to see how good the house is inside. My teacher's wall is many stories high, so if you cannot find the door to enter, you will be unable to see the magnificence and grandeur of the temple inside, or its rich and colorful buildings. Those who have entered through this great gate are perhaps very few. What Master Wushu said is only natural, isn't it?"

Comments: It is said that Zigong in his later years served at court in the state of Lu, and was very accomplished, which is why he was thought to have been superior to Confucius. But Zigong strenuously refuted this, believing that should Confucius have had the opportunity to govern, he would have been much better than himself. This is the reason for the things he says here, which so fully display Zigong's feelings of sincere loyalty to Confucius. I have always found Zigong to be the most lovable character in the *Analects*; he is not as greedy as Zai Wo, nor as obtuse as Fan Chi, nor as overcautious or conscientious as Yan Hui or Zengzi, nor as keen on politics or as concerned about surface reputation as Zizhang, nor yet as apt to flaunt his superiority as Zilu. Yet the Song-Ming Neo-Confucians practically refused to say anything about Zigong.

19.24. 叔孫武叔毀仲尼。子貢曰:「無以為也, 仲尼不可毀也。他人之賢者, 丘陵也, 猶可踰也; 仲尼, 日月也, 無得而踰焉。人雖欲自絕, 其何傷於日月乎? 多見其不知量也!」

Shusun Wushu was maligning Confucius. Zigong said, "Do not do this. Confucius is someone who cannot be maligned. Other people's sagely virtue is like a little hill that can be stepped over; Confucius is like the sun or moonlight, which cannot be surpassed. If a person wants to put himself on the road to ruin—what harm can that do to the sun or the moonlight? It will only display how much he overestimates himself."

Notes: *Cheng Shude quotes the "Fanshen lu": A sage like Confucius could not avoid being disparaged by Shusun Wushu. Did not the ancients say, "What is the problem with not being accepted? It is only after not being accepted that the noble person becomes apparent."*[4] *Therefore, if one is not accepted by the mass of petty people, it is then that one can become manifest as a sage or scholar. If one is so unlucky as to meet with this, then one should strengthen one's resolve and harden one's bones, stand tall and have confidence in oneself. If disparagement comes from without, it is better to learn forbearance and allow obstacles to have their benefit, so that in the fiercest flames the brilliance of one's gold should not [prove to] be pale.*

Comments: Despite having many times seen Zigong's way with words, in these sayings his agility, intelligence, and wisdom are on display—this is something that Zengzi and others just cannot equal. They also express Zigong's loyalty and esteem for Confucius. Can today's students have a good conscience in face of this? Not only would they be silent in the face of a wave of disparagement, they would even pick up stones themselves and take part in the action. The note above is also very interesting—it points out how even a sage is unable to avoid meeting with disparagement—or perhaps it is because he is a sage that he meets with it. This should encourage us to determined action and to strengthen our conviction, so that even in the face of dogs barking or donkeys braying, we can continue to proceed on our path.

19.25. 陳子禽謂子貢曰:「子為恭也, 仲尼豈賢於子乎?」子貢曰:「君子一言以為知, 一言以為不知, 言不可不慎也。夫子之不可及也, 猶天之不可階而升也。夫子之得邦家者, 所謂立之斯立, 道之斯行, 綏之斯來, 動之斯和。其生也榮, 其死也哀, 如之何其可及也。」

Chen Ziqin said to Zigong: "You are too modest. How can Confucius be better than you?"

Zigong said, "The noble person in speaking one sentence displays his intelligence, and in one sentence can also display his ignorance; in speech one must not be imprudent. The impossibility of equaling my master is like the impossibility of reaching the heavens by climbing up a ladder. If my master could have been given the government of a country, then he would have used the rites and music to establish that state's foundation; he would have used guidance to put righteousness into practice; he would have used appeasement to gain the allegiance of the people; through action he would have caused the people to obtain harmony. While alive he would have been respected by the people, and in death they would have mourned him. How can this be equaled?"

Comments: This is like 19.23. Of course, in this passage we have an additional large chunk in which Zigong addresses various aspects of how Confucius would have "governed."

Among Confucius's disciples, apart from Zigong, it is Zixia, mentioned so often in this chapter, who must be considered the key character in the continuation of the legacy of Confucius. Not only did Zixia "pass on the classics," and thus greatly influence later generations, while "living at Xihe" he cultivated a whole generation of major governmental reformers related to the Legalists, such as Wu Qi 吳起, Li Ke 李克, and so on.[5] Zixia can probably be seen as one of the first to initiate the "alternation of Confucianism and Legalism." Zigong, Zixia, and even Xunzi must be regarded as the main line of transmission of the Confucian school.

Book 20

20.1. 堯曰:「咨! 爾舜! 天之曆數在爾躬。允執其中。四海困窮, 天祿永終。」舜亦以命禹。曰:「予小子履, 敢用玄牡, 敢昭告于皇皇后帝: 有罪不敢赦。帝臣不蔽, 簡在帝心。朕躬有罪, 無以萬方; 萬方有罪, 罪在朕躬。」周有大賚, 善人是富。「雖有周親, 不如仁人。百姓有過, 在予一人。」謹權量, 審法度, 修廢官, 四方之政行焉。興滅國, 繼絕世, 舉逸民, 天下之民歸心焉。所重: 民、食、喪、祭。寬則得眾, 信則民任焉, 敏則有功, 公則說。

Yao said, "Ah! Shun! The mandate of Heaven above has already landed upon you; you should carefully keep to the Way of the Mean. If all the common people in the world are poor and in difficulty, then your position will also come to an end."

Shun also ceded to Yu in this way.

Tang said, "Little me dares to take a black ox and openly report to the great and glorious Heaven above: If I have sinned, I don't dare to ask for forgiveness; if the ministers of Heaven above have faults, Heaven will understand that in its heart. If I have sin, don't punish people everywhere. If there is sin everywhere, then I will take the responsibility!"

Under the feudal lords of the Zhou dynasty, good people were all rich. [As it was said,] "Even being a relation of the Zhou is not as good as being a person of humaneness and virtue. If the common people have made mistakes, the responsibility is all mine."[1]

Be very careful in establishing weights and measures, and examine every law, regulation, and system; resurrect the offices that have been abolished—do all this and the government of the world will be done right. Revive the clan states that have been destroyed; allow the peoples and tribes that have been cut off to continue; promote people who have been in reclusion or hiding; and all the people under heaven will return to follow you with their whole hearts.

The important things are the people, food, funerary rites, and the sacrifices.

If you are generous, you will receive the support of the people. If you keep your word, you will be employed by the people. If you do your work with alacrity, you will have success. If you are fair, all will rejoice.

Notes: *Cheng Shude quotes the "Chengzi yishu": Before the word "spoke"* (yue) *the character "Tang"* 湯 *is missing. He Yan notes: Mr. Kong [Kong Anguo (156–74 BCE)] says: Giving importance to the people is the foundation of the state. Giving importance to food [controls] the fate of the people. Giving importance to funerary rites allows [them to] fully vent their sorrow. Giving importance to the sacrifices is in order to perfect reverence. The "Sishu bianyi" notes: From "Yao said" to the end of the passage, the language is disjointed and without order, nor is the name of the subject indicated, so that we do not know who said these things. Commentators ancient and modern have never been able to come up with a clear explanation. Su Shi said that this passage mixes random passages about Yu's plans, Tang's mandates, Tai's oaths, and Wu's perfection; they are all upside down and out of order, and impossible to restore to their original sense.*

Qian Mu explains: The "Analects" as a collection of the sayings and actions of Confucius ends at the "Weizi" chapter [Book 18]. The "Zizhang" chapter [Book 19] records the sayings of the disciples, and the "Analects" as a book can actually be said to have finished after the four passages in which Zigong praises Confucius with which it ends. This chapter lists the main aspects of how Yao, Shun, Yu, Tang, and King Wu governed the world, and continues with the words of Confucius. Beginning with "Be very careful in establishing weights and measures, and examine every law, regulation, and system" in order to govern the world, Han Confucians believed these were the words of Confucius, and [reflected] the law of the last king of Chen. They explained that, as this is the afterword of the "Analects," like the "Mencius" it also uses the continuity of Yao, Shun, Tang, King Wen, and Confucius to function as the afterword for the entire book. However, in this passage it nowhere says "Confucius says," so whether or not it records the words of Confucius is impossible to know. . . . Below I will discuss how this chapter was modeled after Book 10.

Comments: Benjamin Schwartz, in his *The World of Thought in Ancient China,* does a systematic comparison of the *Analects* with Plato's *Republic,* and concludes that Confucius has a traditional

background while Plato does not. This is actually precisely the meaning of Confucius's own statement about himself, that he expounds rather than creates [7.1]. The *Analects* concludes with the warnings of the ancient sage kings revered by Confucians, as explained in the Notes above. Confucius "revered Yao and Shun and modeled himself on Kings Wen and Wu";[2] he "revived" the "destroyed" and "continued" what had been "cut off," in an overall return to "ritual." This passage explains this very well. Yet despite the efforts of many commentators, it is very difficult to ascertain the concrete historical circumstances in which these words were said, or what concrete events they addressed. Nor are these very important or necessary to find out. What we should pay attention to is how these words all express the primitive democracy of tribal or clan society. In the phrase "Carefully keep to the Way of the Mean," as I have mentioned many times above, the basic meaning of the "mean" seems to be to "Keep levies moderate so the people will draw near to you" (see my *Zhongguo gudai sixiang shilun*), so that the people will not "be poor and in difficulty." "Revive the clan states that have been destroyed; allow the peoples and tribes that have been cut off to continue" means that because the governing authority of many of the original clans, tribes, and families had been destroyed during the Spring and Autumn period, Confucius wished to revive them. In summary, he wanted to revive the ancient ritual system, to emphasize caring for the people (members of the clan), to demand that leaders take responsibility including for mistakes—this is Confucian or Confucianist "democracy," the "governing of the people" (治人) by "being a ruler for the sake of the people" (為民做主). This does not at all correspond to the modern "rule of law" in which "the people rule." To speak of them as the same thing or to think that it is possible to transform the former into the latter is completely wrongheaded. However, we must not underestimate the importance of the fact that the former was emphasized by Confucians and remained in place as a concept for three thousand years, and is influential still to this day. The problem is how, in the process of establishing our modern laws and government, to incorporate aspects of the former in order to avoid as much as possible the faults associated with modern government, such as fiscal corruption, callousness, indifference, "moral depravity," and the continual emergence of scandals and vice, and so on. This is also a question of "Chinese application of Western substance"—that is, in establishing modern economic and political systems, how can Chinese cultural elements be incorporated in such a way as to be able to move forward along a new path that is of universal significance to the world? This is where the crux and the "mission" lies.

It is interesting that I have advocated "Chinese application of Western substance" ["Western substance, Chinese function"],[3] as opposed to what traditionally and today has been called "Chinese substance, Western function." However, "substance" refers to the technology, methods, and forces of production, and thus because those who speak of "Chinese substance, Western function" allow and promote "Western function," **their "Chinese substance" must become unsustainable, as it will gradually change, whether or not this is conscious or voluntary.** Chin Yinke's "independent spirit and free thought" discussed above in my comments on 16.3 is an example. And this gradual change (reform rather than revolution) is exactly what is advocated by the idea of "Western substance, Chinese function." Therefore, **"Western substance, Chinese function" can realize itself by way of "Chinese substance, Western function," while surprisingly, "Chinese substance, Western function" gets turned around by the "Chinese function" in "Western substance, Chinese function." Isn't this paradox precisely what Hegel called "the trick of history," and a tragic case of historical hide-and-seek?**

Actually, the whole variety of traditional characteristics—constant transformation, renewal day by day, harmony and complementarity, [an emphasis on] real facts and real accomplishments, proceeding in an orderly step-by-step manner, and [seeking] the stability of the whole (i.e., the important spirit of pragmatic rationality) all developed from within the framework of "Chinese application of Western substance." Since this is so, why should we fear that "Chinese application of Western substance" will lead to the loss of tradition? In fact, the opposite is the case; it is exactly suited to the development of tradition, so that tradition is illuminated and magnified so as to influence the world.

In this final book of the *Analects*, how should we define the Confucian tradition, determine its character, or position it? Should we *define* it as a philosophy? Or as a religion? Neither seems exactly right. Is its *character* that of studying inner sageliness? Or outer kingliness? It is clear that the *Analects* favors "inner sageliness." How should we *position* it with regard to other religions and philosophies? The statement "To attack heterodox schools that are different from yours—it is just there that the danger lies" 攻乎異端, 斯害也已 (see 2.16), suggests that the important thing is to absorb and embrace them all. The second and third periods of Confucianism both practiced this, and the present fourth period of Confucianism should do so as well (see comments on 15.11).

20.2. 子張問於孔子曰:「何如斯可以從政矣?」子曰:「尊五美, 屏四惡, 斯可以從政矣。」子張曰:「何謂五美?」子曰:「君子惠而不費, 勞而不怨, 欲而不貪, 泰而不驕, 威而不猛。」子張曰:「何謂惠而不費?」子曰:「因民之所利而利之, 斯不亦惠而不費乎? 擇可勞而勞之, 又誰怨? 欲仁而得仁, 又焉貪? 君子無眾寡, 無小大, 無敢慢, 斯不亦泰而不驕乎? 君子正其衣冠, 尊其瞻視, 儼然人望而畏之, 斯不亦威而不猛乎?」子張曰:「何謂四惡?」子曰:「不教而殺謂之虐; 不戒視成謂之暴; 慢令致期謂之賊; 猶之與人也, 出納之吝, 謂之有司。」

Zizhang asked Confucius, "How should one govern?"

Confucius answered, "If you honor the five virtues, and eliminate the four wicked actions, then you can govern."

Zizhang asked, "What are the five virtues?"

Confucius said, "The noble person practices generosity, but is not wasteful; he commands the people, but is not resented; he has desires, but is not greedy; he is solemn, but not proud, awe-inspiring but not terrifying."

Zizhang asked, "What does it mean to practice generosity without being wasteful?"

Confucius said, "If you act in accordance with what will benefit the masses of the people, is this not practicing generosity without being wasteful? If you choose those who are governable and command them, who will be resentful? If when you wish to attain humaneness you attain humaneness, what will there be to covet? The noble person does not care whether the people are many or few, whether the matter is great or small, he is never neglectful. Is this not to be solemn but not proud? The noble person is tidy in his clothing and headwear, and looks at you directly, with a solemnity that causes people to be afraid—is this not what it means to be awe-inspiring but not terrifying?"

Zizhang asked, "What are the four wicked actions?"

Confucius said, "To kill without educating is called cruelty; to fail to give warning but suddenly look for the results is called brutality; to start out in a leisurely fashion then suddenly enforce a deadline is called harming people; to be niggardly when it comes time to pay someone is called unwise frugality."

Comments: The last term, *you si* 有司 ("unwise frugality"), has always been considered difficult to interpret and some suggest there may be a wrong character. This is a tentative translation. Many commentators believe that this passage belongs with the previous chapter, which was all about Zizhang. It is true that Zizhang's questions are always about government, in contrast to Zengzi or others. This is why we should distinguish these two tendencies among Confucius's disciples. The *Analects* apparently can also be divided into the two large topics of "asking about humaneness" and "asking about government," with the former being more concerned with individual self-cultivation and the latter more concerned with the duties and systems of government. Because these two topics were so interwoven at the time (in what I have spoken of in this book as the legacy of clan society), [the concepts of] self-cultivation, ordering one's family, governing the state, and bringing peace to the world (修齊治平 *xiu qi zhi ping*) were mixed and not clearly distinguished, in a way that would have both deep and lasting influence on later generations. One manifestation of this is how even today we still venerate going "from inner sageliness to outer kingship" (由內聖開外王 *you nei sheng kai wai wang*). In this book I have advocated for differentiating between inner sageliness and outer kingship today, so that individual self-cultivation (private religious morality) might be allowed to develop separately from political duty (public social morality). The former has a categorical function, as the "psychological substance" that influences the construction of the "instrumental substance," that is, what I have called the "new way of inner sageliness and outer kingship." In summary, the old "inner sageliness and outer kingship" was helpful in creating the trinity of ethics, religion, and government, and the unity between the ruler and the teacher. The new inner sageliness and outer kingship emphasizes the separation of ethics, religion, and government. Because the world grows closer together by the day, and the global village is shrinking, the "common denominator" among the various cultures is a "public social morality" that is commonly practiced and respected among "global citizens." This common public social morality is increasing in scope daily, and only when it is able to more or less free itself from the various cultural traditions and ancient origins will it be able to work.

This passage is speaking about the duties of government, while the next passage has to do with self-cultivation, so it is fitting that these two passages bring the entire *Analects* to a close.

20.3. 子曰：「不知命，無以為君子也。不知禮，無以立也。不知言，無以知人也。」

Confucius said, "If you don't understand fate, you cannot be a noble person. If you don't understand the ritual system, you cannot establish yourself. If you don't understand language, you cannot judge people."

Comments: In this final passage, we return to "fate." I have already discussed it many times, so here I will briefly repeat what I have said before: "Fate is what is, though you do not know why it is" 命也者，不知所以然而然者也[4]—in other words, things that human power cannot control; external forces, prospects, experiences, or results that are difficult to predict. Therefore we could say that "fate" refers to chance. "If you don't understand fate, you cannot be a noble person" means that if you do not recognize the ungraspable, chance nature (and importance) of these external forces, you are not worthy of the title "noble person." **From the perspective of human life as a whole, it is always being affected and arranged by chance, and modern social life is even more so. How to pay attention to chance, to understand it, recognize it, and take it seriously, how to struggle against it (including by using it or harnessing it, etc.), and thus out of chance to establish one's own "necessity"—this is what it means to "establish one's fate" or "create one's fate."** Thus it is not a matter of blindly or passively following, fearing, or even worshipping chance, but rather grasping hold of, understanding, and actively adapting to chance. This is what Mencius meant when he said:

> Whether he is going to die young or to live to a ripe old age makes no difference to his steadfastness of purpose. It is through awaiting whatever is to befall him with a perfected character that he stands firm on his proper destiny [establishes his fate]. . . . Though nothing happens that is not due to destiny [or fate], one accepts willingly only what is one's proper destiny. That is why he who understands destiny does not stand under a wall on the verge of collapse. He who dies after having done his best in following the Way dies according to his proper destiny. It is never anyone's proper destiny to die in fetters.[5] (VII.A.1, 2)

> 殀壽不貳，修身以俟之，所以立命也。 莫非命也，順受其正。是故知命者，不立乎巖牆之下。盡其道而死者，正命也。桎梏死者，非正命也。

People can "establish their fate," "correct their fate," or "create their fate"—only then can they be considered to "understand fate," and only this manifests the loftiness and greatness of human subjectivity. For in establishing one's own fate, there is always a fundamental principle at work, and that principle is not natural animal desire, but human religious morality. This is what Mencius was referring to when he said:

> The way the mouth is disposed towards tastes, the eye towards colours, the ear towards sounds, the nose towards smells, and the four limbs towards ease is human nature [meaning natural human nature or "qualitative nature" 氣質之性 (*qizhi zhi xing*)], yet therein also lies [fate]. That is why the gentleman does not describe it as nature. The way benevolence pertains to the relation between father and son, duty to the relation between prince and subject, the rites to the relation between guest and host, wisdom to the good and wise man, the sage to the way of Heaven, is [fate], but therein also lies human nature [meaning the just and rational nature (義理之性 *yili zhi xing*), i.e., human will and morality]. That is why the gentleman does not describe it as [fate].[6] (VII.B.24)

> 口之於味也，目之於色也，耳之於聲也，鼻之於臭也，四肢之於安佚也，性也，有命焉，君子不謂性也。仁之於父子也，義之於君臣也，禮之於賓主也，智之於賢者也，聖人之於天道也，命也，有性焉，君子不謂命也。

As to whether or not this natural human nature can be fulfilled or to what extent it can be fulfilled—in other words whether one becomes rich or poor, lives long or dies young—this is also fortuitous, but not in the sense of being a natural human nature determined from birth to be so (i.e., necessary or inevitable). On the contrary, this fortuitousness can be adapted to and transformed. The principle of this adaptation or transformation is humanity's ethical categories of "humaneness, righteousness, ritual, and wisdom." This is what it means to establish one's fate, create one's fate, correct one's fate, or understand fate. Actually, the Neo-Confucians also said, "The sage knows only righteousness, and fate is found within it. . . . Obtain it by means of righteousness, and you will have no need to speak of fate";[7] "Master Cheng's discussion of speaking about righteousness and not speaking about fate was of advantage to scholars, for it was something that the sages of old had not expressed";[8] and "The great person creates his fate."[9] Clearly, it is not at all a case of bowing servilely in obedience to fate; rather, one must oneself go and create one's fate. This is where the significance of "knowing fate"—that is, recognizing the role of chance—lies. This is where one grasps hold of and experiences one's own existence. However, if we confuse "fate" with "nature," taking the chanceness that one can create for the necessity that one cannot create but can only submit to—especially after later Confucians' twisted interpretation that "Heaven's fate is called nature"—then "understanding fate," "establishing one's fate," and correcting one's fate will become "being content with one's fate," "submitting to (or obeying) fate," or "resting in fate." If we once allow an external regulation or principle (whether the external "Heavenly Principle" or a supposedly inner "conscience") to govern, control, or command the self, these will often manifest themselves in the form of systems of cosmology (like traditional yinyang and Five Elements thought, or modern "historical necessity") or moral laws (like the traditional saying "Heavenly Principle and conscience!" [天理良心 *tian li liang xin*] or the modern slogan "Struggle against selfishness and criticize revisionism" [鬥私批修 *dou si pi xiu*]). [In this way] subjectivity is denied and dissolved. Therefore, it is only when we have deconstructed these systems and exposed their internal contradictions and polysemy **that we will awaken to and cherish "chance," and allow individual mastery and creation to be seen in terms of the warm generosity of one's own fate. I would like to allow this to be the conclusion of these twenty books and five hundred passages of the *Analects*.**

Afterword

This book is very crude, and was not originally intended to be brought before the world in this form. Based upon the encouragement and urging of my friends, [I concluded that] to refrain from reissuing it would seem as if it contained some evil curse that I feared to expose to others. Actually, it is just that I am personally dissatisfied and embarrassed about it. But for now it appears that I will not be able to improve upon it, so it seems best to put it before my readers to seek their input. I began this book in Beijing, and completed it abroad, where I cannot fail to acknowledge how I depended upon my wife, Wenjun, through many years of comfortable but lonely life, as she attended to our everyday life and took care of our daily needs as well as the work of copying and transcribing. This is the reason for this afterword for the book.

Fall 1996, Colorado Springs, Colorado

Recently I read Bruce and Taeko Brooks's *The Original Analects* (1998), and I truly feel that this book fills a major gap after the analytical work of people like Cui Shu 崔述 (1740–1816) and Arthur Waley, at a level that has rarely been seen in recent decades. It has been hailed as a "surprising achievement" that "destroys traditional arguments" and will cause a "rewriting" of ancient Chinese philosophy.

[The Brookses'] book translates each passage of the *Analects* and, making use of recent scholarship, adds their own commentary. The second half of the book explains, chapter by chapter, the concrete historical process by which the *Analects* has continually grown and increased, and describes Confucius's family, clan, disciples, and so on. The book argues that the first seventeen passages of Book 4 (with passage 15 being a later interpolation) were the earliest records after Confucius's death and closest to the original meaning, while the other chapters that are ordered accordingly (placing Book 1 after Book 15, Book 2 after Book 13, and Book 3 after Book 11) were continually expanded and added to by the disciples, their respective schools, and especially Confucius's clan in the state of Lu over a 230-year period (from 479 to 249 BCE) until the collection was finally completed after the fall of the state of Lu. Among them, every book and passage contains many variations and contradictions, not only according to the passage of time and changes in the world, such as the abolition of the feudal system, and so on, so that all kinds of newer and older concepts appear alongside each other; but there is also the interpolation of concepts of the Mohists, Daoists, Legalists, and those that opposed them, including the arguments among the various schools of Confucians themselves.

For example, the Brookses' book argues that 9.1 ("Confucius rarely discussed profit, he spoke of fate and commended humaneness"), which is often said to be difficult to explain, is an addition by a later Confucian school that venerated ritual in opposition to the original Confucians who emphasized humaneness. Another example is 17.11 ("Ah ritual! Ritual! Is it only presenting jade and offering silks? Ah music! Music! Is it only ringing bells and striking drums?"), which is usually attributed to Confucius, but which the Brookses believe is an argument of the Lu Confucians against Xunzi. And it goes on. The discussion is rich, and the arguments logical.

But according to this, if the words and actions of Confucius and his disciples are largely the creations of later people, then "Confucius" proper really does not exist, and although his birth and death and homeplace have been researched, "Confucius" is only an empty name. Therefore, are not the *Analects* as a "record of conversations with Confucius" just an essentialist fabrication? If this is so, then the present book is superfluous and laughable.

Not so. Of course, as acknowledged by traditional interpretations, the *Analects* is not a contemporaneous record but the product of the memories of the disciples, and particularly of those disciples who were transmitting the teachings. It is not lacking in later interpolations, expansions, and corrections, and many passages contain contradictions, omissions, additions, difficulties, and places that are impossible to understand. These are of course worth careful deliberation, comparison, and research; this undoubtedly is of benefit to understanding the formation of the *Analects* and classical Confucianism.

However, "Going too far is the same as not going far enough" (11.16). If the Brookses' book could really in one go hammer out and deduce two-hundred-plus years of exact dates, schools, editors, and the implications of every passage of every chapter, this would appear to be a convincing argument, but in fact the evidence is weak and I suspect quite arbitrary. If one passage is used to determine a particular chapter's editing or dates, or if many passages are said to be directed toward opposing the Mohists, Mencius, Xunzi, or Zhuangzi, and so on, then perhaps this is so. On the other hand, if one reads through the entire *Analects* without prejudice, even though it may not be difficult to discover quite a few contradictory passages within it, overall in terms of the thought, content, diction, style, atmosphere, or mood, there are more similarities than differences, and more unities than divisions. Apart from a very few passages, the book can be considered to cohere as a whole, and to reflect a near approximation of Confucius's words and actions, in great contrast with other works particularly of the Warring States period (where the Brookses' book actually places it). Therefore, it is still right to say (as I did in the introduction) that "we can do little other than acknowledge the difficulty or near impossibility of determining through the evidence available to us which passages, words, and actions were actually those of Confucius and which were not. (Again, perhaps future archaeological finds will be of some help here.) What is important is that the *Analects* and our notion of Confucius have been passed down to us today in this form beginning in the Han dynasty with the *Zhang hou lun* (*The Marquis Zhang "Analects"* 張候論)." This is the assumption of the present work.

Both this book and *The Original Analects* include translations, notes, and comments, and the two books share many points that are arrived at independently, such as both demonstrating how Confucius emphasized the importance of government service for scholars, how the *Analects* is not primarily for the study of "inner sageliness," the religious tendencies of Zengzi's school, and so on. But our differences are of course greater. For example, in my book I emphasize how Confucius uses "humaneness" to explicate "ritual," how "ritual" and "humaneness" are of equal importance, and how they are connected with "filiality." The Brookses emphasize that Confucius only discussed "humaneness," and "ritual" and "filiality" both arose later and were not part of Confucius's original intention, and so on. The biggest differences are that ***The Original Analects* emphasizes the concrete situational character of the passages, while my book emphasizes their universal significance;** the former distinguishes based upon reliability, the latter based upon philosophical interpretation; the former embraces new scholarly trends and a thoroughgoing deconstruction of the *Analects*, erasing the image of Confucius as a symbol of Chinese culture;[1] the latter for the most part follows the old ways in striving to create new interpretations for reconstruction. Truly their objectives differ, their methods diverge, and the direction they take is very far apart. Perhaps the two should be allowed to proceed in parallel without being mutually exclusive, but just how this would work is impossible to know. With the fashion of "postmodernism" just now at its height, it just may shatter the *Analects* into a thousand pieces. Will it? Or won't it? I would like to ask the reader to think on this question, which is the reason for this second afterword.

April 1998, Swarthmore College

Notes

Translator's Preface

1. The translation is based upon the 2018 revised Shijie tushuguan edition (Beijing).

2. Michael Nylan, "Editor's Introduction," in Confucius, *The Analects*, trans. Simon Leys (New York: W. W. Norton, 2014), xlviii–lv.

Author's Prefaces

1. This index has not been included in this English edition. The reader is directed to ctext.org/analects for a fully searchable digital version of the *Analects*.

2. This essay was translated into English by Andrew Lambert as "Reevaluating Confucius" in *A History of Chinese Thought* (his translation of *Zhongguo gudai sixiang shilun*) (New York: Routledge, 2020), 1–29, and as such does not appear in this English edition.

Introduction

1. The term translated here and elsewhere as "Confucian" or "Confucianism," is *rujia*, which is sometimes rendered "the Ruists," or "the Ru school." For simplicity's sake I adopt the traditional translation, without denying that the term Ruist more exactly replicates the Chinese term, which makes no direct reference to Confucius.

2. For an English translation of this work see Li Zehou, *A History of Classical Chinese Thought*, trans. Andrew Lambert (New York: Routledge, 2020).

3. Li Zehou distinguished between "subjectivity" (*zhuguanxing* 主觀性) and "subjectality" (*zhutixing* 主體性), a term he coined to avoid the association with subjectivism and to suggest a more material and communal human subject.

See Andrew Lambert, foreword to his translation of *A History of Classical Chinese Thought*, xv–xvi; and Jana S. Rosker, "Li Zehou's Notion of Subjectality as a New Conception of the Human Self," *Philosophy Compass*, 2018, https://doi.org/10.1111/phc3.12484. In this translation, for the sake of simplicity I have opted to retain "subjectivity" for *zhutixing* because on the few occasions Li Zehou uses it in this work, the context makes it clear that subjectivity and not subjectivism is meant.

4. What is difficult to understand is that Mou Zongsan elevates Confucius far above others, and so also regards him as superior to Kant, yet he discusses only one or two passages from the *Analects*. He never did any thoroughgoing exposition or study of the *Analects*, while he expended great energy explicating Kant. I do not know why this is the case. Of course, I have no complaint about this, since this is his personal prerogative; I simply find it strange. (LZH)

5. This concept comes from Dong Zhongshu's *Chunqiu fanlu*.

6. From the "Great Learning" of the *Book of Rites*, trans. Wm. Theodore DeBary and Irene Bloom, in *Sources of Chinese Tradition*, 2nd ed., vol. 1 (New York: Columbia University Press, 1999), 331.

7. This term refers to people who use Marxist-Leninist language to mask an underlying selfish individualism. It dates from Shen Rong's 1980 novella *At Middle Age* (人到中年), which features an older female authority figure with revolutionary credentials who constantly parrots party slogans but is in fact self-seeking.

8. This line comes from Li Yu's (937–978) *ci* poem to the tune "Wu ye ti" (or "Xiang jian huan"), my translation of which appears in Cai Zong-qi, *How to Read Chinese Poetry* (New York: Columbia University Press, 2008), 246–47.

9. Or in Burton Watson's translation, "The gentleman regards [ceremonies] as ornaments, but the common people regard them as supernatural." Burton Watson, trans., *Hsun Tzu* (New York: Columbia University Press, 1963/1964), 85. From the "Tian lun" chapter of the *Xunzi*, no. 13.

10. The Caigentan 菜根譚 is a Ming dynasty (ca. 1590) collection of aphorisms by Hong Zicheng 洪自誠 combining Confucian, Daoist, and Buddhist teachings.

11. Li Zehou, "Zhexue tanxun lu" 哲學探尋錄 ("Notes on Philosophical Pursuits"), *Minbao yuekan* nos. 7–10 (1994).

12. In this book Li Zehou creates a modern Chinese translation of the *Analects*, which is the translation he is referring to here. As I emphasize in the translator's preface, in my translation into English I focus on capturing and maintaining Li Zehou's rendering into modern Chinese, rather than on creating a new English translation of the text.

13. Cangjie was said to have been an official serving the Yellow Emperor.

14. I here translate Li Zehou's explanation of his treatment of these terms, and in the translation of the *Analects* have allowed these remarks to shape my English translations of the terms as the context allows.

15. From the "Wu yi" 無逸 chapter.

16. *Junzi* was commonly translated into English as "gentleman," which had the advantage of suggesting both a social position and a value judgment. I translate the terms *junzi* and *xiaoren* as "noble person" and "petty person," each of which can also carry both levels of meaning.

17. This term has traditionally been translated as humaneness, benevolence, or goodness. In the body of the text, *ren* will be rendered as "humaneness," which captures its etymological connection with the word for human (*ren* 人), but has the disadvantage of overemphasizing the connotation of caring and underemphasizing the dimension of moral goodness or character. For a discussion of the etymology and development of the term, see Edward Slingerland, *Confucius Analects* (Indianapolis: Hackett, 2003), 238.

18. This English translation includes only such notes as are particularly important to Li Zehou's interpretation or commentary, and especially those that he refers to explicitly in his Comments. For translations that include a number of early commentaries on the passages in English, see Edward Slingerland; Daniel K. Gardner, *Zhu Xi's Reading of the* Analects (New York: Columbia University Press, 2003); or Peimin Ni, *Understanding the* Analects *of Confucius: A New Translation of "Lunyu" with Annotations* (Albany: State University of New York Press, 2017).

19. See, for example, Cui Shu, *Cui Dongbi yi shu* (*Cui Dongbi [Shu]'s Posthumous Works*) (Shanghai: Shanghai guji, 1983). (LZH)

20. This is the text in which we find the twenty chapters of the present edition for the first time. See John Makeham, *Transmitters and Creators: Chinese Commentators and Commentaries on the "Analects"* (Cambridge, MA: Harvard University Asia Center, 2003), 368ff.

21. Zhonghua shuju edition (1990), 1:80.

22. Zhonghua shuju edition (1990), 4:1158; see also the Wanyou wenku edition of *Hanxue Shangdui*, p. 6, note. (LZH)

23. From "The Doctrine of the Mean," 28, in the *Book of Rites*.

24. *Kongzi yu "Lunyu"* (*Confucius and the "Analects"*) (Taipei: Lianjing, 1994), 23. (LZH)

25. *Kongzi yu "Lunyu,"* 198.

27. See Chen Yinke, "Feng Youlan 'Zhongguo zhexue shi' xia ce shencha baogao (A Review of Feng Youlan's *Zhongguo zhexue shi*, vol. 2). (LZH)

27. Emmanuel Kant, "The Architecture of Pure Reason," in A *Critique of Pure Reason*, trans. J. M. D. Meiklejohn (Internet Archive edition: https://archive.org/details/critique-of-pure-reason), 657.

28. This term, *legan wenhua*, has often been rendered "culture of optimism" or "optimistic culture." Michael Nylan translates it as "culture attuned to pleasure," and Andrew Lambert explains it as "a culture characterized by a sensitivity toward socially grounded pleasure or delight." See Michael Nylan, editor's introduction in *The Analects*, trans. Simon Leys (New York: Norton, 2014), lii; and

Andrew Lambert, foreword in *A History of Classical Chinese Thought*, Li Zehou, xvii.

29. This piece appeared in the periodical *Zhongguo*, 1986.10. For an English-language version, see Li Zehou, "A Dialog with Li Zehou—the Sensate, the Individual, My Choice," in *Journal of Chinese Philosophy* 25.4 (1994): 25–73.

Book 1

1. Zhao references Lu Deming's *Jingdian shi wen* (*The meaning and text of the classics*), *juan* 24, "*Lunyu* yin yi" (The pronunciation and meaning of the *Analects*).

2. See Zhao Jibin, *Lunyu xin lun dao yan* (*A New Guide to the Analects*), in *Zhongguo zhexue*, vol. 10 (Beijing: Sanlian, 1983).

3. Zhao Jibin, *Lunyu xin lun dao yan*.

4. Reading *yue* 悅 for the original 說 (here *yue*).

5. Three of the four poems of the set are quoted here.

6. Li Zehou and Jane Cauvel, *Four Essays on Aesthetics* (Lanham, MD: Lexington Books, 2006), 115.

7. "Qian," 1. *The "I-Ching" or Book of Changes*, trans. Richard Wilhelm, rendered into English by Cary F. Baynes, 3rd ed. (Princeton, NJ: Princeton University Press, 1967), 6.

8. *Zhuzi yulei*, quoting from Zhu's commentary on *Analects* 1.2.

9. Li Zehou, *Zhongguo jindai sixiang shi lun* 中國近代思想史論 (Taipei: Fengyun shidai chuban gongsi, 1990).

10. See my "Zhexue tanxun lu."

11. Liang Shuming, *Dong xi wenhua ji qi zhexue* 東西文化及其哲學 (*Eastern and Western culture and philosophy*) (Shanghai: Shanghai shudian, 1989).

12. Burton Watson, trans., *Mo Tzu, Hsün Tzu, and Han Fei Tzu* (New York: Columbia University Press, 1963/1964), 110.

13. Edward Slingerland, trans., *Confucius Analects, with Selections from Traditional Commentaries* (Indianapolis: Hackett, 2003), 5.

14. Stephen C. Angle translates these terms as "monistic ethical authority" (*dao tong*) and "narrow political legitimacy" (*zheng tong*), respectively. See "Confucian Justification of Limited Government: Comments on Joseph Chan's 'Confucian Perfectionism,'" in *Philosophy East and West* 67, no. 1 (January 2017): 17.

15. Duke Xiang of Lu, year 29.

16. *Liji*, "Zhong Yong," 28, James Legge's translation. Chinese text project, http://ctext.org.

17. *Mencius* 6A.4.

18. Eric L. Hutton, trans., *Xunzi: The Complete Text* (Princeton, NJ: Princeton University Press, 2014), 310–11.

19. Referring to the vow of the Ksitigarbha Boddhisattva.

20. *Hanfeizi*, "Wai chu shuo zuo xia."

21. Quoting from James Legge's translation of Mao no. 55, "Qi yu," 淇奥 in the Airs of Wei.

22. See Huang Kan 皇侃, *Lunyu yi shubu* 論語義疏补. This would render Confucius's first answer "poor but happy in the Way."

23. English translation by Stephen Owen, in *Anthology of Chinese Literature* (New York: Norton, 1996), 164.

Book 2

1. *Zuo Tradition, Zuozhuan: Commentary on the "Spring and Autumn Annals,"* vol. 1, trans. Stephen Durrant, Wai-yee Li, and David Schaberg (Seattle: University of Washington Press, 2016), 255.

2. Arthur Waley translates this line in Mao no. 297 as "O without slip," and other translators of the *Analects* here tend to follow the metaphor of a horse pulling a chariot: "Go vigorously without swerving" (Ames and Rosemont), or "Oh, they will not lead you astray" (Slingerland). The word *si* 思 is an exclamation, "O."

3. *Mencius* II.A.6. D. C. Lau translates *si duan* as the "four germs," the heart of compassion, the heart of shame, the heart of courtesy and modesty, and the heart of right and wrong. These are "potentialities" from which develop humaneness, dutifulness or righteousness, ritual, and wisdom. See D. C. Lau, trans., *Mencius* (London: Penguin, 1970), 82–83.

4. This last is from Fan Zhongyan's 范仲淹 (989–1052) *Yueyanglou ji* 岳陽樓記.

5. A line from Yan Shu's 晏殊 (991–1055) *ci* poem to the tune "Die lian hua" 蝶戀花 ("Butterflies Lingering over Flowers").

6. A reference to *Mencius* 2B.13, "It must be that Heaven does not as yet wish to bring peace to the Empire. If it did, who is there in the present time other than myself?" D. C. Lau's translation, in *Mencius*, 94.

7. Lau, *Mencius*, 182.

8. The *Liji* quote is taken from James Legge's translation of *The Book of Rites* (Beijing: Intercultural Press, 2013 repr.), 8.

9. A Yuan dynasty text usually attributed to Guo Jujing 郭居敬.

10. *Mencius* II.A.6, in D. C. Lau's trans., *Mencius*, 82.

11. Li Zehou, *Zhongguo jin dai sixiang shi lun* (Taipei: Sanmin shuju, 1996).

12. Or, "Thoughts without content are empty; intuitions without concepts are blind." Immanuel Kant, *Critique of Pure Reason*, trans. and ed. Paul Guyer and Allen W. Wood (Cambridge: Cambridge University Press, 1998), 193–94.

13. *Mencius* VI.A.3. Book 6 of *Mencius* begins with a famous argument between Mencius and Gaozi on human nature.

14. *Quan Tang wen*, *juan* 559.

15. Zhang Zai 張載 (1020–1077), "Western Inscription" (*Ximing* 西銘), trans. Wing-tsit Chan, collected in Wm. Theodore de Bary and Irene Bloom, eds., *Sources of Chinese Tradition*, 2nd ed., vol. 1 (New York: Columbia University Press, 1999), 683.

16. The "Three Cardinal Guides" refer to the guiding relationship of ruler to subject, father to son, and husband to wife. The "Three Obediences and Four Virtues" refer to the obedience of a woman first to her father, then to her husband, and finally to her son, and to the feminine virtues of morality, proper speech, modesty, and diligence.

17. 極高明而道中庸.

18. *Xunzi* 12.1. Trans. Eric L. Hutton, in *Xunzi: The Complete Text* (Princeton, NJ: Princeton University Press, 2014), 117. The context of the quote reads: "There are men who create order; there are no rules [or laws] creating order of themselves."

19. This is taken from Huang Zongxi's *Ming yi dai fang lu* 明夷待访录, from the "Reason for the Law" (原法) chapter.

20. A cache of Qin documents on bamboo slips discovered in Hunan in 1975, also known as the Shuihudi Qin bamboo slips.

21. *Zhongguo gudai sixiang shi lun*, 139.

22. The Three Ritual Texts, or *Sanli* 三禮, consisted of the *Liji* 禮記 (*Book of Rites*), *Yili* 儀禮 (*Ceremonies and Rites*), and *Zhouli* 周禮 (*Rites of Zhou*), which together formed the ritual section of the Five Classics.

23. King Tang being the first king of the Shang, who overthrew the Xia, and King Wu being the first king of the Zhou, who overthrew the Shang.

24. See my *Zhexue tanxun lu* [*A record of philosophical inquiry*], *Minbao yuekan*, nos. 1–4, 1994.

Book 3

1. *Wushi wenhua* (巫史文化) refers to the culture in which the role of *wu* (shaman or sorcerer) often intersected with the role of *shi* (historian or scribe, a role that included knowledge of astronomy, astrology, and the calendar). As such a more accurate translation might be the "culture of the shaman-scribe/shaman-historian." I have kept "shamanistic-historical culture" to align with the bulk of English translations of the term.

2. *Zuozhuan*, Duke of Cheng (成公), year 4.

3. By Lu Longqi 陸隴其 (1630–1692) of the Qing.

4. See *Analects* 17.13. "Village worthy" is Roger Ames and Henry Rosemont's translation of the term in *The Analects of Confucius: A Philosophical Translation* (New York: Ballantine, 1998), 207. Edward Slingerland also uses this

translation; see *Confucius Analects* (Indianapolis: Hackett, 2003), 205, where he discusses the commentary on this term in *Mencius* VIIB.37.

5. A chapter of the *Lun Heng* 論衡 (*Critical Essays*).

6. The first two lines of the poem excerpt here appear in the *Shijing*, Mao no. 57, "Shuo ren 碩人," but the third line does not.

7. *Xunzi* 19.23. Trans. Eric L. Hutton in *Xunzi: The Complete Text* (Princeton, NJ: Princeton University Press, 2014), 212.

8. Max Weber, *Economy and Society: An Outline of Interpretive Sociology*, eds. Guenther Roth and Klaus Wittich (Berkeley: University of California Press, 1978), chap. 6, "Religious Groups: The Sociology of Religion," 405.

9. *Liji*, "Ji tong," 1, trans. James Legge (Beijing: Intercultural Press, 2013 repr. ed.), 229.

10. *Xunzi* 19.24 ("A Discussion of Ritual" 禮論, 24), trans. Burton Watson, in *Basic Writings of Mo Tzu, Hsün Tzu, and Han Fei Tzu* (New York: Columbia University Press, 1963), *Hsün Tzu*, 105.

11. From Tertullian's *De Carne Christi*, usually translated "It is credible, because it is impossible," or "I believe, because it is absurd."

12. In the original Chinese the opposition is drawn between venerating the kitchen god or the "stove" (*zao* 竈) and the corner shrine (*ao* 奥), the site of veneration of ancestors.

13. *Xunzi* 13.2 (*Chen dao* 臣道 "The Way of the Minister").

14. *Mencius* VII.A.35.

15. A controversy over whether Emperor Yingzong should ritually honor his biological father or his adoptive father (Emperor Renzong).

16. Part of the Great Rites Controversy of the Ming, which started over whether the Jiajing emperor should be posthumously adopted by his uncle in order to maintain the proper imperial sacrifices or whether he should elevate his own late father to the post of emperor instead.

17. These lines are a reversal of two lines from Han Yu's "Ten *qin* etudes: Etude on arrest and imprisonment" 琴操十首·拘幽操. Han Yu's speaker takes on the persona of King Wen of Zhou, who has been imprisoned by King Zhou 紂 of Shang, who has been regarded as a negative exemplar of a wicked ruler.

18. *Mencius* I.B.8. D. C. Lau, trans., *Mencius* (London: Penguin, 1970), 68. The context indicates that Confucius believes that when a ruler acts badly, killing him is not regicide, as could be said for the case of the "punishment" of Zhou, the last ruler of the Shang dynasty.

19. Trans. Hutton, *Xunzi*, 326.

20. This expression is associated with the "Diary of Lei Feng," who was reportedly happy to serve as a "cog in the revolutionary machine."

21. This tale is found in the *Guoyu*, "Discourses of Jin." Chu Ni is sent to assassinate an official but finds himself so impressed with the official's virtue that he kills himself rather than carry out his task.

22. This and the following quote are taken from the "Record of Music" in the *Book of Rites*. *Li ji* 19.1/99/10.

23. *Li ji*, 19.26/104/7.

24. See my *Wo de zhexue tigang* [*An outline of my philosophy*] (Taipei: Fengyun shidai chuban gongsi, 1990).

Book 4

1. D. C. Lau, trans., *Mencius* (London: Penguin, 1970), 107.

2. Qian Mu, *Lunyu yao lue* (Taipei: Taiwan shangwu yinshuguan, 1965).

3. Liang Shuming, *Zhongguo wenhua yaoyi*.

4. This may refer to Mou Zongsan's work titled *Xinti yu xingti* 心體與性體 (*Substance of mind and substance of human nature*).

5. *Yi* has also been translated as "righteousness" or "duty." The intersection of these ideas with the "appropriateness" and "reasonableness" chosen here can be found in the concept of "what is right." What is good and right may be what is obligatory as one's duty, what is morally correct ("righteousness"), or what is ritually or socially appropriate in a given situation.

6. Li Zehou's original references the "first year of Duke Zhao" here.

7. Quoting Stephen Durrant, Wai-yee Li, and David Schaberg's translation of *Zuo Tradition: Zuo Zhuan*, vol. 3 (Seattle: University of Washington Press, 2016), 1403.

8. Trans. Burton Watson, in *Basic Writings of Mo Tzu, Hsün Tzu, and Han Fei Tzu* (New York: Columbia University Press, 1963), *Hsün Tzu*, 89.

9. Trans. Watson, *Hsün Tzu*, 45.

10. Trans. Eric Hutton, in *Xunzi: The Complete Text* (Princeton, NJ: Princeton University Press, 2014), 45.

11. A quote from the *Book of Changes* ("Xici" part 2 系辭下).

12. These two phrases are pseudo-etymological definitions, relying upon the elements of the characters of *shu* 恕 (*ru* 如 and *xin* 心) and *zhong* 忠 (*zhong* 中 and *xin* 心).

13. *Book of Changes*, 40 (Hexagram *Xie* 解, *Liuwu* 六五).

14. The *Mencius* passage reads, 無君子莫治野人, 無野人莫養君子.

15. Trans. Hutton, *Xunzi*, 9.

Book 5

1. Possibly referring to the materials for building a raft (see Roger T. Ames and Henry Rosemont Jr., trans., *The Analects of Confucius: A Philosophical Translation* [New York: Ballantine Books, 1998], 96).

2. English translation by Michael E. Workman, in *Sunflower Splendor: Three Thousand Years of Chinese Poetry*, eds. Wu-chi Liu and Irving Yucheng Lo (Bloomington: Indiana University Press, 1975), 351.

3. D. C. Lau, trans., *Mencius* (London: Penguin, 1970), 107.

4. Metaplexis japonica.

5. Ligusticum sinense Oliv, also known as gao ben or chuang xiong, a type of garden angelica.

6. Milfoil stalks and tortoise shells were both used in divination.

7. Eric Hutton, trans., *Xunzi: The Complete Text* (Princeton, NJ: Princeton University Press, 2014), 308 ("Da lue" chapter).

8. This inverts the common phrase *zhongti xiyong* (中體西用), adopted by Chinese modernizers to express the application of Western learning while retaining core Chinese values. In Li Zehou's inversion of the phrase, the "substance" (which could be "Western" or "modern") consists in the foundational needs of society for food, clothing, and shelter, rather than the "learning" or "subject matter" implied by the original phrase. See Li Zehou, *Shuo xiti zhongyong* 說西體中用 [*On Chinese Application of Western Substance*] (Shanghai: Shanghai yiwen chubanshe, 2012).

9. *Mencius* VII.A.4, quoting from D. C. Lau's trans., *Mencius*, 182.

10. The line from Mencius reads 盡其心者, 知其性也。知其性, 則知天矣. D. C. Lau translates it: "For a man to give full realization to his heart is for him to understand his won nature, and a man who knows his own nature will know Heaven." D. C. Lau, *Mencius*, 182.

Book 6

1. The passage literally says that Ran Yong can take the south-facing position.

2. *Zhuzi yulei*, *juan* 12.

3. *Zhuzi yulei*, *juan* 12. *Jing* is the word Li Zehou translates here as "solemn."

4. *Zhuzi yulei*, *juan* 12.

5. *Zhuzi yulei*, *juan* 23.

6. *Zhuzi wenji*, *juan* 25: "Jing zhai zhen."

7. *Zhuzi wenji*, *juan* 25.

8. "Xiao cangshan fang chidu" ("Letter from a little house on Mount Cang"), final *juan*.

9. Edward Slingerland notes, "Oxen that were mottled in color or otherwise considered unattractive were relegated to farm use, while oxen with solid red coats and pleasantly-formed horns were specially bred for sacrifice to the spirits. Early commentators believe this passage to be concerned metaphorically with Zhonggong's [Ran Yong's] family background." Edward Slingerland, trans.,

Confucius Analects with Selections from Traditional Commentaries (Indianapolis: Hackett, 2003), 54.

10. Trans. D. C. Lau in *Mencius* (New York: Penguin, 1970), 184.

11. Cf. the "Zhi yue" 至樂 ("Perfect Enjoyment") chapter of the *Zhuangzi*: 至樂無樂 (perfect enjoyment is no enjoyment).

12. *Xunzi*, "Tian lun" 17.11, trans. Eric Hutton in *Xunzi: The Complete Text* (Princeton, NJ: Princeton University Press, 2014), 178.

13. From one of the quatrains of Wang Wei 王維 (701–961), in his Wang Stream collection.

14. A line from "Zui mian" 醉眠 by the Song poet Tang Geng 唐庚 (1070–1120).

15. *Analects* 19.9.

16. Ian Johnston, trans., *The Mozi: A Complete Translation* (New York: Columbia University Press, 2010), 689.

17. *Beixi zi yi* 北溪字義.

18. Xu Fuguan, *Zhongguo renxinglun shi* [*A history of Chinese humanism*] (Taipei: Shangwu yinshuguan, 2003), 113.

Book 7

1. *Yijing*, "Xici zhuan," trans. Richard John Lynn, in *Sources of Chinese Tradition*, Theodore deBary, ed., vol. 1 (New York: Columbia University Press, 1999), 322.

2. Quoting from Edward L. Shaughnessy, trans., *I Ching: The Classic of Changes* (New York: Ballantine, 1996), 240–41. The passage is from the *Yao* [Essentials] section of the Mawangdui text. Note that Li Zehou's original has: 吾與巫史同歸而殊途也. I have revised the Chinese characters to match the Mawangdui text.

3. *Yijing*, "Xici zhuan" ("The Appended Changes"), part 1, in *The "I Ching" or Book of Changes*, trans. Richard Wilhelm, rendered into English by Cary F. Baynes, 3rd ed. (Princeton, NJ: Princeton University Press, 1967), 299. Shaughnessy translates this phrase as "daily renewing it is called sincere virtue," based upon the character 誠 *cheng* which appears in place of 盛 *sheng* in the Mawangdui manuscripts. *Chengde* could also be translated "complete virtue." See Edward L. Shaughnessy, *I Ching*, 192–93,327n29.

4. A line from one of Tao Qian's poems on "Reading the *Classic of Mountains and Seas*," that describes the mythical figure Xing Tian 刑天 who continued to battle after his head was cut off.

5. A line from the "Hegemon's Lament" 垓下歌 attributed to the Chu hegemon Xiang Yu 項羽.

6. See Li Zehou and Liu Gangji, *Zhongguo meixue shi* (*A History of Chinese Aesthetics*), vol. 1.

7. Meaning a gift offered by a would-be student to his teacher.

8. These lines are most of the first stanza of the song lyric to the tune "Jiang chengzi," trans. James Hightower, in *The Columbia Anthology of Traditional Chinese Literature*, ed. Victor Mair (New York: Columbia University Press, 1994), 324.

9. D. C. Lau, trans., *Mencius* (New York: Penguin, 1970), 184.

10. D. C. Lau, trans., 185, 60.

11. *Xicizhuan*, part 1, section 11. Edward L. Shaughnessy, trans., *I Ching: The Classic of Changes* (New York: Ballantine, 1996), 199; see also 330n83.

12. Li Zehou translates *yayan* 雅言 here as *wenyan* 文言, which could also be rendered cultured writings, or speech about culture. *Wenyan* is also the modern Chinese term for classical Chinese, but that is clearly not the sense here. Note that in an alternate reading, the last phrase could be rendered "All of these Confucius often spoke of."

13. The "Six categories" (*liushu* 六書) refer to the six types of characters, or six categories of character formation first mentioned in the *Zhouli*, and developed during the Han. The types include pictographic, ideographic, phono-semantic, and compound ideographic characters.

14. As opposed to "In the beginning was the Word."

15. The passage quoted is from the *Xici zhuan*, II.2.

16. This story is attributed to the *Shizi* in the Northern Song encyclopedia, the *Taiping yulan*.

17. *Mencius* II.A.2, trans. D. C. Lau, *Mencius*, 77.

18. Mou Zongsan, *Xinti yu xingti* 心體與性體 (*Substance of Mind and Substance of Human Nature*), vol. 1, 58. See N. Serina Chan, *The Thought of Mou Zongsan* (Leiden: Brill, 2011), 239.

19. A Qing dynasty text by Wang Yinzhi 王引之 (1766–1834).

20. Trans. D. C. Lau, *Mencius*, 79.

Book 8

1. *Yijing*, *Xicizhuan*, part 2.

2. *Shijing*, Minor Odes, "Xiao min." Legge's translation reads, "We should be apprehensive and careful, / As if we were on the brink of a deep gulf, / As if we were treading on thin ice" (https://ctext.org/book-of-poetry/xiao-min).

3. What Li Zehou has translated into modern Chinese as "etiquette" (*liyi* 禮儀).

4. Yang Zhiyi, trans., in "The Road to Lyric Martyrdom: Reading the Poetry of Wang Zhaoming (1883–1944)," *Chinese Literature: Essays, Articles, Reviews (CLEAR)* 37 (2015): 139. The line quoted is from Wang's poem, "Bei dai kou zhan" 被逮口占 ("On Being Captured").

5. The line quoted is from Wen's poem "Zheng qi ge" 正氣歌 ("Song of righteous *qi*"); "flood-like" refers to Mencius's notion of the *haoran zhi qi* 浩然之氣 ("flood-like *qi*").

6. *Huaxia meixue* 華夏美學. Li Zehou, *The Chinese Aesthetic Tradition*, trans. Maija Bell Samei (Honolulu: University of Hawaii Press, 2010), 49ff.

7. See James George Frazer, *The Golden Bough: A Study of Magic and Religion*, chap. 3 ("Sympathetic Magic").

8. See my *Zhexue gangyao* [*Outline of Philosophy*], and *Meixue sijiang* [*Four Lectures on Aesthetics*].

9. Presumably he has to interrupt his bath or his meal to receive visitors seeking to serve under him.

10. *Xunzi*, "Renxing e" ["Human nature is evil"] chapter. Paraphrasing Eric L. Hutton, trans., *Xunzi: The Complete Text* (Princeton, NJ: Princeton University Press, 2014), 251, line 116.

11. Li Zehou's original is more literally "worldviews of Heaven-human feedback."

12. *Mencius* VII.A.9, quoting D. C. Lau's translation in D. C. Lau, trans., *Mencius* (London: Penguin, 1970), 183.

13. A quotation from the *Doctrine of the Mean*, sect. 27.

Book 9

1. Or subjectality. See Introduction, note 3 and Book 14, note 6.

2. "Hence always rid yourself of desires in order to observe its secrets; / But always allow yourself to have desires in order to observe its manifestations" (*Laozi*, chap. 1, trans. D. C. Lau, reading 皦 *for* 徼). D. C. Lau, trans., *Lao Tzu: Tao Te Ching* (London: Penguin, 1963), 57.

3. *Mencius* VII.A.13; D. C. Lau, trans., *Mencius* (London: Penguin, 1970), 184.

4. *Yijing*, "Qian." Trans. Richard Wilhelm, rendered into English by Cary F. Baynes, *The I Ching* (Princeton, NJ: Princeton University Press, 1950), 6, 4.

5. William Wertz Jr., "A Reader's Guide to *Letters on the Aesthetical*," in *Fidelio*, vol. 14, nos. 1–2 (2005): 93.

6. From "Du Shanhaijing" 讀山海經 [Reading the *Classic of Mountains and Seas*] no. 1, lines 3–4. Trans. Stephen Owen, in *An Anthology of Chinese Literature: Beginnings to 1911* (New York: Norton, 1996), 318.

7. From Li Bo's "Touring Ancient Sites in Yue" 越中覽古.

8. From Xin Qiji's (1140–1207) "Mo Yu'er," trans. Irving Y. Lo, in *Sunflower Splendor*, eds. Wu-chi Liu and Irving Yucheng Lo (Bloomington: Indiana University Press, 1975), 395–96.

9. *Shijing*, no. 33, "Odes of Bei," "Xiong Zhi" 雄雉.

10. *Yijing*, "Qian." Wilhelm/Baynes, trans., *The I Ching*, 6.

11. From Wen Tianxiang's poem "Yidai ge" 衣帶歌 ("Sash song"). Wen Tianxiang was a southern Song scholar-official known for his refusal to capitulate to Mongol rule at the end of the dynasty.

12. The *Shenjian* is a political handbook attributed to Xun Yue 荀悅 of the Later Han period.

Book 10

1. Herbert Fingarette, *Confucius: The Secular as Sacred* (New York: Harper and Row, 1972), 9.

2. James Legge, trans., *The Book of Rites* (Beijing: Intercultural Press; repr. 2013), 5.

3. See Legge, 308–11.

4. See *Mencius* VII.A.45.

Book 11

1. *Garden of Stories*, compiled by Liu Xiang of the Western Han.

2. Mao no. 256, trans. Arthur Waley, *The Book of Songs* (New York: Grove Weidenfeld, 1960), 301.

3. *Mencius* VII.A.20. D. C. Lau, trans., *Mencius* (London: Penguin, 1970), 185.

4. 百代皆行秦政制 (some manuscripts have 治 or 法 in place of the final character). This is a line from a heptasyllabic regulated verse by Mao entitled, "On Reading 'Discussion of Feudalism,' presented to Guo [Moruo]."

5. Or subjectality. See Introduction, note 3 and Book 14, note 6.

6. See *Shijing* no. 267, "Wei tian zhi ming" 維天之命.

7. See 9.5. Ames and Rosemont summarize: "Confucius had left Wey and was on route to Chen when he passed through Kuang. The people of Kuang had recently been ravaged by Yang Huo, also from the state of Lu, and mistook Confucius for him." Roger Ames and Henry Rosemont Jr., trans., *The Analects of Confucius: A Philosophical Translation* (New York: Ballantine, 1998), 244n136.

Book 12

1. Daniel K. Gardner, trans., in *Zhu Xi's Reading of the* Analects: *Canon, Commentary, and the Classical Tradition* (New York: Columbia University Press, 2003), 80.

2. Clifford Geertz, *The Interpretation of Cultures: Selected Essays* (New York: Basic Books, 1973), chap. 2, 44.

3. Geertz, 52.

4. "Yu Gao Jianping de duitan" [A conversation with Gao Jianping].

5. See *Mencius* V.A.6: "When a thing is done though by no one, then it is the work of Heaven; when a thing comes about though no one brings it about, then it is decreed [命 *ming*]." D. C. Lau, trans., *Mencius* (London: Penguin, 1970), 145.

6. *Yijing*, "Qian" hexagram, Duan commentary.

7. From Zhang Zai's 張載 poem, "Western Inscription 西銘."

8. By Li Yong 李顒 (1627–1705) of the Qing.

9. Eric L. Hutton, trans., *Xunzi: The Complete Text* (Princeton, NJ: Princeton University Press, 2014), 76.

10. Chad Hansen, "Language in the Heart-Mind," in Robert E. Allinson, *Understanding the Chinese Mind: The Philosophical Roots* (Hong Kong: Oxford University Press, 1989).

11. This phrase comes from Yan Fu's 1895 essay "Lun shi bian zhi ji 論世變之亟 [On the speed of world change]."

12. *Mencius* II.B.2 lists "three things which are acknowledged by the world to be exalted: rank, age and virtue." D. C. Lau, trans, *Mencius*, 87.

134. Irene Bloom translates *da* as "universal." The five "universal ways" are the relations between ruler and minister, parent and child, husband and wife, older and younger brother, and friends. The three "universal virtues" are knowledge, humaneness, and courage. See Theodore DeBary, ed., *Sources of Chinese Tradition*, 2nd ed., vol. 1 (New York: Columbia University Press, 1999), 337.

14. Chen Maoyong 宦懋庸 (1842–1892)

15. That is, four of the traditional Five Relationships 五論, between ruler and minister, father and son, husband and wife, older brother and younger brother, and between friends.

Book 13

1. Translator's note: The term Li Zehou uses here is "status," or *mingfen* 名分 (literally, "status names" or "terms"); the term *zhengming* 正名 has usually been translated "rectification of names." My use of "status terms" attempts to incorporate the "rectification of names" along with Li Zehou's interpretation of "name" here to refer to "status."

2. See the discussion of this term in the introduction.

3. D. C. Lau, trans., *Mencius* (New York: Penguin, 1970), 58–59.

4. *Xici zhuan*, section 5, trans. Richard John Lynn, in *Sources of Chinese Tradition*, 2nd ed., vol. 1, eds. Theodore De Bary and Irene Bloom (New York: Columbia University Press, 1999), 322.

5. De Bary and Bloom, 323.

6. 遠者近之, 舊者新之. *Mozi*, "Geng Zhu," 10. Ian Johnston translates this as "becoming close to those who are distant and treating old friendships like

new ones." Ian Johnston, trans. and ed., *Mozi: A Complete Translation* (Hong Kong: Chinese University of Hong Kong, 2010), 649.

7. From "The Great Learning" in the *Liji.*

8. From Chairman Mao's *ci* poem "To the tune, 'Manjiang hong': in answer to Guo Moruo."

9. Eric L. Hutton's translation, in *Xunzi: The Complete Text* (Princeton, NJ: Princeton University Press, 2014), 336.

10. Found in the *Yijing*, hexagram 32, *heng.*

Book 14

1. A tilting doll like a Weeble that stands back up when knocked over.

2. Ziyu's title is elsewhere given as "foreign minister" (Slingerland), "diplomat" (Ames and Rosemont), "receiver of envoys" (Waley).

3. Commentators differ on the meaning of *san gui*; some say it means that Guanzi had homes in three locations, some that he took wives from three different clans.

4. The son of Confucius's disciple Zengzi. See *Mencius* II.A.1.

5. From the "Ru xing" chapter of the *Liji*, trans. James Legge, in *The Book of Rites* (Beijing: Intercultural Press, 2013), 297.

6. Again, the term translated "subjectivity" here is *zhutixing* 主體性, which Li Zehou would normally have translated into English with the term he coined, "subjectality," to distinguish it from *zhuguanxing* 主觀性. However, the use of "subjectivity" in the present context in English emphasizes precisely the individual agency that Li Zehou's use of *zhutixing* was meant to indicate, and I have retained "subjectivity" to avoid introducing a neologism that might be a distraction for the non-specialist reader. See Introduction, note 3.

7. The "testing of professors" incident occurred in 1973 following Zhang Tiesheng's protest, when Chairman Mao's nephew, Mao Yuanxin, required professors to sit for an examination themselves.

Book 15

1. Dr. Sun Yatsen's "Eight Virtues," as highlighted in his "Three Principles of the People" 三民主義.

2. *Laozi*, 38. Trans. D. C. Lau, in *Lao Tzu: Tao Te Ching* (London: Penguin, 1963), 99.

3. *Shuowen jiezi* entry for 悳 (a variant of 德).

4. Slingerland relates the story from the *Hanshi waizhuan* of how Shiyu on his deathbed "laments to his sons that during his life he has failed to rectify his lord by getting the virtuous Qu Boyu promoted and wicked Mi Zixia demoted,

and insists that they give him a humble burial because of this failure. The Duke of Wei comes to the funeral and notices the humble arrangements, and when told the reason for them feels so ashamed that he immediately promotes Qu Boyu and dismisses Mi Zixia." See Edward Slingerland, trans., *Confucius Analects, with Selections from Traditional Commentaries* (Indianapolis: Hackett, 2003), 177.

5. For a discussion of this term see D. C. Lau, *Mencius* (London: Penguin, 1970), 25.

6. From the *Hanshu*, "Wendi ji."

7. From the "Chunqiu fanlü," attributed to Dong Zhongshu.

8. This phrase originates with the *Haiguo tuzhi* 海國圖志 by Wei Yuan 魏源 (1794–1857) of the Qing.

9. The last line of "回車駕言邁," one of the Nineteen Old Poems of the Han. Burton Watson translates this line, "A shining name—let that be the prize!" See Burton Watson, trans. and ed., *The Columbia Book of Chinese Poetry: From Early Times to the Thirteenth Century* (New York: Columbia University Press, 1984), 101.

10. See the discussion of this gloss from the *Rites of Zhou* in 4.15.

11. *The "I Ching" or Book of Changes*, trans. Richard Wilhelm, rendered into English by Cary F. Baynes, 3rd ed. (Princeton, NJ: Princeton University Press, 1967), 4.

12. Wilhelm/Baynes, 6.

13. *Xicizhuan* II.1, Wilhelm/Baynes, 328.

14. *Xicizhuan* I.5, Wilhelm/Baynes, 299.

15. *Daodejing* 1 and 2; D. C. Lau, trans., *Lao Tzu*, 57, 58.

16. The term here translated "subjectivity" is *zhutixing* 主體性, for which Li Zehou coined the English term "subjectality" to distinguish it from *zhuguanxing* 主觀性. The sense of *zhutixing* here emphasizes the agency of the individual subject, and since that is well-captured by the term "subjectivity" in this context, I have retained that term here and in the bolded section of this paragraph.

17. Wilhelm/Baynes, 328.

18. Edward L. Shaughnessy, trans., *I Ching: The Classic of Changes* (New York: Ballantine, 1996), 203.

19. *Mencius* IV.B.11, D. C. Lau, trans., *Mencius*, 130.

20. "Yi zhuan" [Commentary on the Book of Changes], on "Qian" [the Creative]; trans. Wilhelm/Baynes, 380–81.

Book 16

1. Also known as the "well-field" 井田 system, this was a type of feudal system whereby land was divided into nine squares, the center square of which would be cultivated for the feudal lord by those who held each of the surrounding nine squares.

2. The 三綱五常, "Three Cardinal Bonds" (between father and son, ruler and minister, and husband and wife) and "Five Cardinal Virtues" (*ren yi li zhi xin* 仁義禮智信) (humaneness, justice, ritual propriety, wisdom, and trustworthiness).

3. The phrase in quotation marks is a quotation from the *Book of Songs*, Mao no. 188. For a translation of the poem, see Arthur Waley, trans., *The Book of Songs* (New York: Grove Weidenfeld, 1960), 98.

Book 17

1. *Yijing*, "Qian" hexagram; *The "I Ching" or Book of Changes*, trans. Richard Wilhelm, rendered into English by Cary F. Baynes, 3rd ed. (Princeton, NJ: Princeton University Press, 1967), 6.

2. This is a line from Mao Zedong's poem "Sending Off the God of the Plague, No. 2" 送瘟神其二.

3. See his *The Confucian Creation of Heaven* (Albany: State University of New York Press, 1990).

4. These two sections of the *Book of Songs* largely consist of songs having to do with the relations between men and women, husbands and wives.

5. "The commentator Ma Rong (79–166) cites the calendrics chapter of the *Zhoushu* 周書 which states, 'In spring we take fire from the elm and willow trees, in summer from the jujube and apricot, in late summer from the different kinds of mulberry bushes, in autumn from the oak and *you* tree, and in winter from the sophora and sandalwood.'" Roger T. Ames and Henry Rosemont Jr., trans., *The Analects of Confucius: A Philosophical Translation* (New York: Ballantine, 1998), 267n304.

6. Edward Slingerland notes that Zhu Xi's 蘇氏 ("Mr. Su") may sometimes also refer to Su Shi's brother Su Zhe (or Su Che) 蘇轍 (1039–1112), or to their father Su Xun 蘇洵 (1009–1066). See Edward Slingerland, trans., *Confucius: Analects* (Indianapolis: Hackett, 2003), 263–64.

Book 18

1. See the "Rang wang" chapter of the *Zhuangzi*: "My body is here beside these rivers and seas, but my mind is still back there beside the palace towers of Wei." Burton Watson, trans., *Chuang Tzu* (New York: Columbia University Press, 1968), 317.

2. Li Zehou uses the English term "family value" in the original text. Most likely his meaning is that keeping this distinction is a way of valuing the family.

3. Once again, I am retaining the English translation, "subjectivity," rather than rendering this with Li Zehou's neologism "subjectality," because in

this context subjectivity clearly refers to the agency of a subject rather than to a subjective (vs. objective) viewpoint (主觀性). See Introduction, note 3.

Book 19

1. See chapter 17, note 6.

2. The latter comes from Wang Yangming's evolutionary reading of the Gongyang Commentary on the *Spring and Autumn Annals*. See Wang Yangming, "The Three Ages," trans. Chester Tan, in *Sources of Chinese Tradition*, eds. Theodore DeBary and Richard Lufrano, vol. 2 (New York: Columbia University Press, 2000), 267–68.

3. In his chapter "Fei shi'er zi" ["Against the Twelve Masters"].

4. From the "Kongzi shijia" chapter of the *Shiji*.

5. Wu Qi (440–381) was a general and philosopher, and Li Ke (455–395) a thinker and statesman, both of the Warring States period.

Book 20

1. These words are traditionally attributed to King Wu.

2. From the "Doctrine of the Mean" in the *Liji*.

3. On this term, see Andrew Lambert, foreword to his translation of Li Zehou's *Zhongguo gudai sixiang shilun*, *A History of Classical Chinese Thought* (New York: Routledge, 2020), xiv. Lambert translates the term as "Western root with Chinese application," explaining, "Li's analysis of Chinese history appeals to theoretical frameworks and social analysis (including Marxism) that originate in the West (*xiti*) in order to derive conclusions about, and prescriptions for, Chinese society (*zhongyong*)."

4. From the "Li Ming" chapter of the *Liezi*.

5. D. C. Lau, trans., *Mencius* (London: Penguin, 1970), 182. Lau translates *ming* here as "destiny."

6. D. C. Lau, trans., *Mencius*, 198–99. Lau translates *ming* in this passage as "the Decree." Bracketed interpolations are Li Zehou's.

7. *Henan Cheng shi yi shu* 河南程氏遺書, *juan* 2.

8. *Zhuzi yulei*, *juan* 3, no. 16.

9. *Wang Xinzhai yulu* 王心齋語錄.

Afterword

1. The Brookses' book does not go so far as to put this into words, nor does it use words like "deconstruction" or "essentialism;" their methods are traditional rather than postmodern, suggesting that the authors are naturally

opposed to these theories. However, I believe that this is the concrete situation. This work reaches the same goal by different routes as the thoroughgoing deconstruction of Confucius in the postmodern work *Manufacturing Confucianism* by Lionel Jensen (1997), but it is far more important. (LZH)

Index

This is an index to Li Zehou's discussion, and does not include the original text of the Analects.

www.ingramcontent.com/pod-product-compliance
Ingram Content Group UK Ltd.
Pitfield, Milton Keynes, MK11 3LW, UK
UKHW041120041026
8980IPUK00031B/962

9 798855 802795